BASIC CORROSION AND OXIDATION

BASIC CORROSION AND OXIDATION

JOHN M. WEST, M.A., Ph.D., M.I.M., C.Eng., F.I.Corr.T.
Department of Metallurgy
University of Sheffield

ELLIS HORWOOD LIMITED
Publishers · Chichester

Halsted Press: a division of
JOHN WILEY & SONS
New York · Chichester · Brisbane · Toronto

First published in 1980 by

ELLIS HORWOOD LIMITED
Market Cross House, Cooper Street, Chichester, West Sussex, PO19 1EB, England

The publisher's colophon is reproduced from James Gillison's drawing of the ancient Market Cross, Chichester.

Distributors:

Australia, New Zealand, South-east Asia:
Jacaranda-Wiley Ltd., Jacaranda Press,
JOHN WILEY & SONS INC.,
G.P.O. Box 859, Brisbane, Queensland 40001, Australia

Canada:
JOHN WILEY & SONS CANADA LIMITED
22 Worcester Road, Rexdale, Ontario, Canada.

Europe, Africa:
JOHN WILEY & SONS LIMITED
Baffins Lane, Chichester, West Sussex, England.

North and South America and the rest of the world:
Halsted Press: a division of
JOHN WILEY & SONS
605 Third Avenue, New York, N.Y. 10016, U.S.A.

British Library Cataloguing in Publication Data
West, John Michael
Basic corrosion and oxidation.
1. Corrosion and anti-corrosives
I. Title
620.1'1223 TA462 80–41158

ISBN 0–85312–196–6 (Ellis Horwood Ltd., Publishers)
ISBN 0–470–27080–2 (Halsted Press)

Typeset in Press Roman by Ellis Horwood Ltd.
Printed in Great Britain by R. J. Acford Ltd., Chichester

Table of Contents

Preface

'Rust never sleeps . . . .'

Song by Neil Young & Crazy Horse

Corrosion kills people, wastes resources and costs money we can ill afford. In the industrialised countries of the west, for example, it has been variously estimated to require the expenditure of some 2–3% of the gross national product. Perhaps more significantly, the more general dissemination and wider application of well understood principles could save a quarter of this sum.

This book is intended as a basic introduction to the science underlying corrosion at both low and high temperatures. It lays the ground rules supporting the technology of corrosion prevention and so, like any other basic book, cannot be expected to give detailed guidance about specific systems. What it does attempt to do is show how the phenomena of corrosion, especially localised attack of various forms, can be understood in terms of electrochemistry and thermodynamics and how rates of corrosion can often be predicted from a limited knowledge of the appropriate kinetics. In the low temperature section, extensive use is made of the 'Evans diagram', the plot of voltage vs current first introduced half a century ago by U. R. Evans. Unlike some other textbooks which treat high temperature oxidation as a separate phenomenon, I have as far as possible attempted a unified treatment: for example, I relate the rate constants observed in oxidation to the rates of corrosion through room-temperature passive films.

I have employed the S.I. system of units throughout. More especially, I have become a late convert to using amperes per square metre (A/m^2) as the unit of current density because of the fortunate coincidence with corrosion penetration rate expressed in mm/yr. Students more familiar with the f.p.s. and c.g.s. systems should have little difficulty in adapting to this, but I have included a table of conversion factors to minimise the ambiguities.

The first chapter sets the scene by describing the many and varied ways in which corrosion is manifested. The next three chapters provide some basic ideas in thermodynamics and chemistry for readers lacking the necessary background. The wealth of symbols required for a rigorous treatment of electrochemistry may be found to be a little daunting. The reader is urged to persevere with these in order to gain a full understanding of this basic science. It is, of course, possible to talk about corrosion without recourse to such detail. Chapter 5 shows how metal wastage results from anodic polarisation, and Chapter 6 relates this polarisation to the rate of attack. Chapter 7 then describes the various techniques that may be used to measure corrosion in-situ and identify its cause. Chapters 8 and 9 discuss the phenomena of localised attack and passive film formation, both major factors in many instances of aqueous corrosion. Chapter 10 is an optional chapter, in the sense that it brings together a number of complicating factors whose relative importance will depend on the reader. It gives a brief consideration of how anions modify corrosion, including those produced by microbial action, and discusses the influence of such design variables as electrolyte flow and metal microstructure. Chapter 12 summarises our current understanding of how mechanical stress and electrochemistry interact to make metals break more easily. It might be thought that the weight given here to this subject is out of keeping with its practical importance – although corrosion fatigue is possibly the major source of component failure in engineering. The principal features of chapter 12 not normally found in a corrosion textbook are a treatment of fracture mechanics and an indication of how it is possible to predict component life on the basis of crack propagation data. Chapters 13 and 14 describe the mechanisms of high temperature oxidation and the importance of scale properties. Here I have used the Darken diagram as an elegant way of characterising complex atmospheres in which oxidation may be accompanied by carburisation or sulphidation. In Chapters 11 and 15 I review the methods available to ameliorate corrosion. Again, the reader should be warned that the space accorded to the various methods is not a reflection of their relative importance. Coatings, in particular, are many and diverse, and there are whole books devoted to their technology. In Chapter 11 I have devoted some space to a numerical treatment of cathodic protection, so as to indicate that quantitative approaches to this subject are becoming technically important. In the final chapter, I describe three case histories in which various methods of protection have been successfully and economically applied. The costs quoted are merely intended to give an idea of the sums of money involved: they are approximate only, and I have deliberately excluded any discussion of cash flow principles. The book concludes with 70 numerical problems and worked answers, thereby providing an opportunity for self-testing and reinforcement.

The book is written chiefly for undergraduate students in metallurgy, materials science, chemistry and chemical engineering. In a subject of such technological importance, however, I have not neglected the mechanical and civil engineer but have included information on techniques and codes of practice which should be of practical value. I hope that all who read this book may enjoy the intellectual challenge offered by this fascinating subject.

Finally, I gratefully acknowledge the help given me by Dr. Vic Ashworth of UMIST and Mr Ellis Horwood. Without the careful and inspired criticism of the one and the wise patience of the other, this book would have lacked such merit as it now possesses.

J. M. WEST,
Sheffield University, November 1979.

Symbols used

Sup = superscript, *Sub* = subscript

A	Anion
A_i	Interstitial anion in ionic lattice
a	Raoultian activity; crack length; *Sub*: anodic
b	Interatomic spacing, lattice parameter; *Sub*: breakdown, as E_b
C	*Sup*: concentration, as η^C
C_p	Heat capacity (specific heat) at constant pressure
c	Concentration; *Sub*: cathodic
D	Diffusivity
E	Single potential; Young's modulus
$\mathcal{E}$	Electromotive force, driving force
e	Electron
F	Faraday's constant (96 480 C/mol)
f	Henrian activity coefficient
$f_\pm$	Mean molal activity coefficient
f	Vibration frequency of activated complex
G	Gibbs free energy, chemical free energy, free enthalpy
$\mathcal{G}$	Energy release rate of a crack, crack extension force
g	(in parentheses) gaseous
H	Enthalpy, heat content
h	Henrian activity; positive hole
h	Planck's constant (6.6×10^{-34} J s)
I	Current
i	Current density (= I/area)
i_{crit}	Critical passivating current density
i_p	Anodic current density in the passive state
i_L	Limiting current density
i_0	exchange current density
K	Equilibrium constant; stress intensity factor
K_{Ic}	Fracture toughness in air or argon

K_{Iscc}	Fracture toughness in SCC environment
K_n	Stability constant of n-ligand complex
K_s	Solubility product
K_w	Ionic product of water
k	Rate constant
$\mathbf{k}$	Boltzmann's constant (1.4×10^{-23} J/K)
L	Avogadro's number (6.02×10^{23} per mol)
l	(in parentheses) liquid
M	Relative molecular mass (molecular weight); Metal
M_i	Interstitial cation in ionic lattice
m	Molality; *Sup*: unimolal standard state, as μ^m
n	Number of moles
p	Pressure; the operator 'minus logarithm', as pH
Q	Activation energy; flaw shape parameter
q	Heat
R	Gas constant (8.31 J/mol K); electrolytic resistance
Re	Reynolds number
r	Pilling-Bedworth ratio
r_y	Radius of plastic zone at crack tip
S	Entropy
Sc	Schmidt number
s	(in parentheses) solid
T	Temperature in kelvins, absolute temperature
t	Transport number
U	Internal energy
u	Flow rate; additional lattice energy, as u_{gb}
V	Volume
V_M	Cation vacancy
V_A	Anion vacancy
x	Mole fraction or atom fraction
y	Film or scale thickness; *Sub*: yield
z	Charge on an anion in proton units

Greek symbols

α	Alpha	Transmission coefficient
Γ	Capital gamma	Surface excess concentration
γ	Gamma	Raoultian activity coefficient
Δ	Capital delta	'Finite change in', as ΔG
${}^{M}\Delta^{S}$		Used with φ (${}^{M}\Delta^{S}\varphi$) to denote absolute value of single potential measured relative to soln.
δ	Delta	Diffusion layer thickness; groove width, COD; 'infinitesimal change in' nonextensive variable, as δq
ϵ	Epsilon	Strain

η	Eta	Overpotential
κ	Kappa	Electrical conductivity of film
μ	Mu	Chemical potential
μ		Electrochemical potential
ν	Nu	Kinematic viscosity; Poisson's ratio
φ	Phi	Lange inner potential
ψ	Psi	Single potential relative to corrosion potential
ρ	Rho	Density; radius at root of a notch
Σ	Capital sigma	'The sum of' as $\Sigma(\mu_i\nu_i)$
σ	Sigma	Stress
σ_y		Yield stress
τ	Tau (rhymes with 'law')	Repassivation time

Special symbols and abbreviations

aq	*Sub*: aqueous, hydrated; (in parentheses) in aqueous solution
COD	Crack opening displacement
comp	*Sub*: complexed
corr	*Sub*: corrosion, as i_{corr}
CT	*Sup*: charge transfer, as η^{CT}
eq	*Sub*: equilibrium value
gb	Grain boundary
crit	Critical value for passivation, as i_{crit}
HER	Hydrogen evolution reaction
pp	*Sub*: Peak passivation, as E_{pp}
SHE	Standard hydrogen electrode, or SHE scale of potential
$\ominus$	*Sup*: Standard rate (unspecified)
$\bullet$	*Sup*: Raoultian standard state
∞	*Sup*: Henrian standard state
‡	Activated complex; also as *Sup* and *Sub*
~	*Sup*: Electrochemical, as $\tilde{\mu}$

The symbols e and π have their normal mathematical meanings. A, J, m and V have their normal significance as units (see Appendix).

Chapter 1

What is Corrosion?

1.1 DEFINITION

Metallic corrosion is the surface wastage that occurs when metals are exposed to reactive environments. The chemical compounds that constitute the products of such wastage are close cousins of the metalliferous mineral rocks that we find in the earth's crust. In other words, corrosion reactions cause metals to revert to their original ores.

At temperatures above 200°C there is usually significant reaction of most metals in dry air, and the rate and extent of reaction progressively increase, either as the temperature is raised or the air is contaminated by other gases. In general, it may be said that the degree of wastage is largely governed by the ionic conducting properties of the corrosion product, when this is present as a solid scale, and by its mechanical strength and adherence to the underlying metal. The study of high temperature corrosion is, therefore, a study of semiconducting oxides, sulphides and so on, and the influences of temperature, pressure and ionic contaminants on their mechanical coherence, stability and permeability.

At temperatures where water is liquid, the predominating corrosion process is electrochemical: that is, metallic wastage occurs by anodic dissolution. Thus, even in moist air, where there is no bulk water present, a very thin film of water may develop, perhaps as a result of hydration of an initially chemically formed solid film of oxide, sulphide or carbonate: condensation will occur when the ambient water pressure exceeds the partial pressure (that is, activity) of the water of crystallisation in a salt, for example. It is this thin film of water that provides the solvent and connecting electrolyte needed for electrochemical corrosion. Whatever the origin of the water, whether a condensed film or a bulk phase, the basic corrosion mechanisms are similar. Metal first dissolves as ions, and solid products such as *rust* may or may not form by subsequent reaction.

At room temperature the progress of electrochemical corrosion is determined by a number of factors, foremost of which is the nature (aggressiveness, concentration) of any oxidising reactants present. However, in contrast to corrosion at elevated temperatures, the rate of corrosion is thereafter determined not only by the conducting properties of surface films formed by the process but also by kinetic factors, such as bulk diffusion and electron transfer reactions, all of which of course take place more slowly at lower temperatures. The study of low temperature corrosion is, therefore, a study of electrochemistry, heterogeneous electrode kinetics and the influences of temperature, pH, concentration and specimen geometry on metal dissolution and on the formation and properties of surface films.

Much effort has been expended in developing artificially contrived coatings that isolate the metal from its environment or else bring the corrosion rate down to acceptable proportions. Sometimes this desirable end can be accomplished by manipulating the environment – by adding to it soluble corrosion 'inhibitors' which encourage the spontaneous formation of a protective film – or else the judicious addition of alloying elements to the metal leads to the same result.

In what follows, attention will be concentrated on the detailed processes whereby a metal ion in the solid crystalline lattice of a metal may be induced to become a solvated cation, whether in water or in a high-temperature scale, or else persuaded to stay where it is.

1.2 FORMS OF CORROSION

Corrosion takes many forms, the simplest of which is *uniform attack.* It is perhaps the most common form encountered, being characterised by progressive and uniform thinning of the metallic component. Because of this uniformity, it is relatively easy for the design engineer to make a 'corrosion allowance' when deciding how thick to make a reactor lining or a pipe wall. Uniform corrosion is exploited in a variety of metal finishing processes where, by careful control, it is possible to stop the corrosion at the point where the metal surface is attractively etched or has acquired a desired film of corrosion product.

Difficulty arises when, by inappropriate material selection or because of geometrical and other factors, corrosion develops in a nonuniform manner. Most frequent of these complications is *crevice attack,* where corrosion becomes concentrated in holes, flange joints and bolt heads and, indeed, wherever there is some kind of geometrical discontinuity which affects the availability of corrodent, Fig. 1.1. 'Differential aeration' is responsible for the preferential sideways corrosion that afflicts motor cars at small breaks in the paint coating; for the corrosion that occurs under deposits of sand and dirt; and for the waterline attack that results in the 'crevice' formed at the meniscus.

Another example of nonuniform corrosion is that caused by the (often inadvertent) juxtaposition of two or more metals, Fig. 1.2. This *bimetallic corrosion,* otherwise called 'galvanic attack', is characterised by accelerated dissolution of the more reactive metal, such as steel bolts in gunmetal valve casings. Allowance can of course be made for this by increasing the 'corrosion allowance', as in the use of thicker steel tube-plates in a copper-tubed heat exchanger, or else its

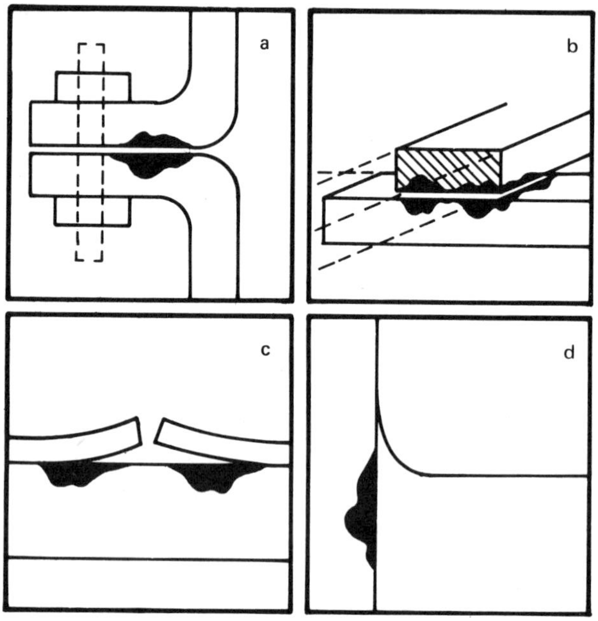

Fig. 1.1 Examples of crevice attack: (a) Flange, (b) Cross-members, (c) Breaks in surface coatings, (d) Waterline (meniscus)

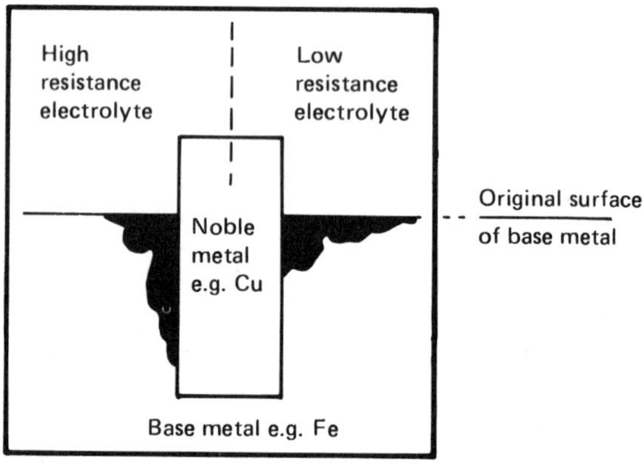

Fig. 1.2 Bimetallic corrosion.

effect limited by electrically insulating the two metals by means of nonconducting sleeves or filler pastes. The metallographer exploits the phenomenon when etching microstructures for microscopical examination. Here the local variations in chemical composition may take the form of chemical segregation at grain boundaries. What for the metallographer is a useful means of delineating grain structures is, however, disastrous if allowed to continue unchecked in an engineering component. Selective *grain boundary attack* can cause whole grains to fall out: this is especially dramatic when there is a strong rolled texture in the metal, for it produces *layer corrosion* (sometimes referred to as 'exfoliation' because of the leaf-like scale that results), Fig. 1.3. Again, the preferential dissolution of one component in an alloy, while useful for showing up small-scale variations in alloy composition such as cored structures in chill castings, is undesirable elsewhere. The leaching of zinc from α/β-brasses (and to a lesser extent from α-brasses also) is called *dezincification* (Note 1.1): the leaching of iron from flake-graphitic grey cast irons is misleadingly known as 'graphitisation', In either instance, the component retains its outward form but is converted internally to a porous husk.

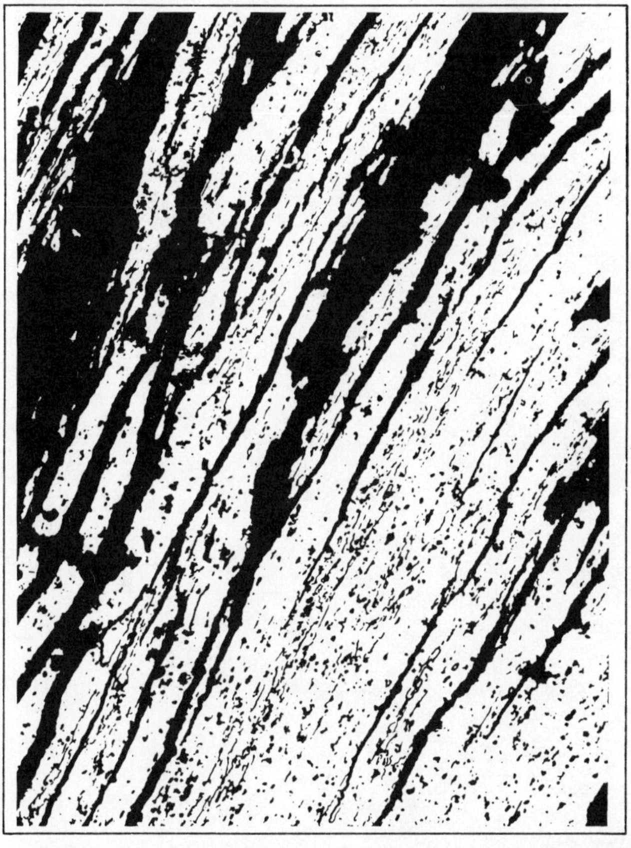

Fig. 1.3 Exfoliation of an aluminium alloy after exposure to a marine atmosphere. The intergranular attack is concentrated at the $CuAl_2$ precipitate (section 10.5). The leaf-like effect results from the severe flattening of the aluminium grains during rolling, so that the surface comes away in layers rather than rounded grains.

Other forms of nonuniform corrosion result from variations in reactivity brought about by surface films. The most important of these is *pitting attack*, Fig. 1.4. A pit is a hole that develops such that its width is comparable with, or less than, its depth. Usually it is extremely localised, that is, pits are widely separated as in the photograph, but they sometimes are so close together as to merge into a generally rough surface. Quite often the pitting takes place underneath a layer of corrosion product and is, indeed, sometimes actually initiated by a form of differential aeration attack underneath the layer. When it does occur, pitting can cause sudden failure in a component which is otherwise virtually immune to attack. It is, therefore, one of the most destructive forms of corrosion.

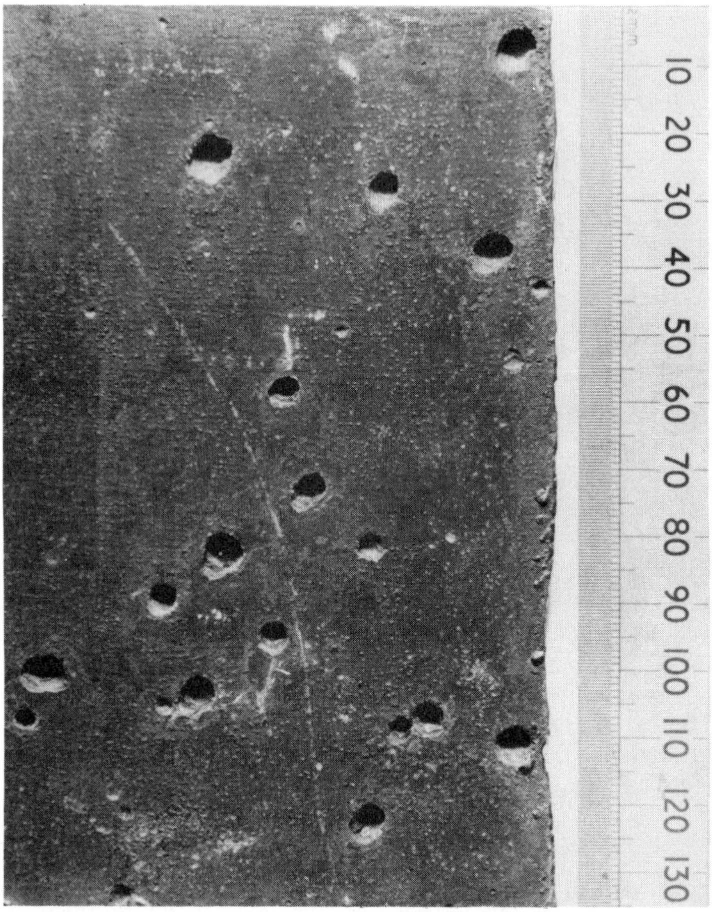

Fig. 1.4 Pitting corrosion of steel plate. Large diameter (ca. 3 mm) flat bottomed pits developed in a pig sterilising plant. The environment was essentially boiling water contaminated with chloride and various body fluids including blood.

Mechanical stress accentuates the damage. An otherwise protective surface film can be disrupted by tensile stress, by impact and by friction. The first of these, *stress-corrosion cracking* (Fig. 12.1), may be thought of as a special form of crevice attack, since the cracks that develop constitute a self-perpetuating region of localised attack. The second mode of film disruption is most commonly encountered in *impingement attack* (erosion corrosion), as a result of the impingement of entrained particles in a flowing corrodent or slurry; an alternative mechanism for breaking the surface film is cavitation caused by collapse of low-pressure bubbles in the liquid phase. Mechanical stress effects are also manifested in *hydrogen embrittlement* and in *corrosion fatigue.* Hydrogen embrittlement occurs in a variety of forms, but in every case is due to the interaction between an applied tensile stress and hydrogen dissolved in the metal lattice. Its most frequent manifestation is the cracking of weldments and other hardened steels when exposed to environments that generate hydrogen as a corrosion product. This can be especially frustrating when the hydrogen is inadvertently produced by cathodic protection systems intended to prolong the life of the structure.

In high temperature corrosion, uniform attack is the most frequent form encountered. This is largely because everything goes so much more rapidly that the subtle effects of geometry or variations in composition are less obvious.

1.3 A SELF-TEACH PLAN

It must be stressed from the outset that this book is intended chiefly to provide the scientific concepts which underlie corrosion phenomena. The practising engineer or metallurgist who wants merely to discover the design pitfalls that must be avoided, or the best procedure to follow to protect a particular structure at minimum cost, is advised to seek the detailed advice offered in the specifications and codes of practice listed in the *Appendix*. However, a preliminary guide to design considerations is provided in section 11.1, and further details and illustrations may be found in the bibliography to that chapter.

For the fortunate reader who is already a master of the basic skills of chemical thermodynamics and electrochemistry, the main chapters of this book should present little difficulty. Such readers will find that the science of corrosion is a straightforward matter, and that what makes corrosion complicated in practice is the important roles played by component geometry and composition and by climatic variables such as flow rate and intermittent wetting. For those readers who need first to master the science, I have provided Chapters 2 to 4 as an introduction to the basic ideas in physical chemistry.

I should expect that students in *chemical engineering* would need to follow the subject of corrosion in as much depth as possible, in view of its importance in determining plant life and efficiency. However, in very few degree courses is there more than a passing nod in the direction of corrosion and, in such circumstances, it may be felt appropriate to neglect the detailed mechanisms. Because chemical engineering students usually possess a good foundation in chemistry, they will perhaps consider that the basic ideas of low and high temperature corrosion are sufficient for their needs. These basic ideas may be gleaned from the following abbreviated plan:

Section 5.3 Corrosion potential
6.2 The Evans diagram
6.4 Corrosion in aerated water
Chapter 7 Measuring corrosion in-situ
Section 8.3 Crevice attack
8.4 Bimetallic corrosion
9.2 Surface films and polarisation
9.3 The Pourbaix diagram
10.4 Flowing environments
10.5 Metallurgical considerations
Chapter 11 Stopping low temperature corrosion
12 Stress and corrosion (omitting Sec. 12.4, 12.5)
Section 13.1 The driving force [in high temperature oxidation]
13.2 Parabolic oxidation
13.5 Oxidation in complex atmospheres
Chapter 15 Stopping high temperature oxidation
16 Some case histories

The chapters should be tackled more or less in sequence. The index should provide any linking ideas that may be missing.

Practising engineers also may wish to follow this plan although they will find the emphasis is on principles rather than detailed remedies and nostrums. I have not generally included tables of corrosion rates, principally because these depend so much on circumstances of detailed design and service conditions. However, the *Appendix* contains a list of a variety of standards and codes of practice, which form an essential part of the engineer's armoury.

The *metallurgy* or *materials science* student wishing to understand the subject should find that Chapters 5–12 offer a self-contained description of aqueous corrosion and its prevention, with Chapters 13–15 a rather abbreviated treatment of high temperature processes. An essential prerequisite of the low temperature section is Chapter 4, an area of physical chemistry not always adequately covered in pre-university courses; whilst a prerequisite of the high temperature section is Chapter 2, especially sections 2.4 and 2.5 on dissociation pressures and oxide stability.

The bibliography at the end of each chapter provides additional sources of information.

Note to Chapter 1

1.1 The dezincification process occurs by more than one mechanism. In some instances the copper redeposits to form a porous 'plug' after both components have initially dissolved. The loss of aluminium and tin from brasses is termed 'dealuminification' and 'destannification' respectively.

Chapter 2

Some Underlying Thermodynamics

2.1 DEFINITIONS

Thermodynamics is the study of heat in changing physical and chemical processes. That is, the heat generated or consumed as a result of changes that take place in natural systems is measured and, on the basis of such measurements, it is then possible to make deductions about the likelihood and extent of changes in related systems. Moreover, it is possible to deduce how much useful mechanical or electrical work might be extracted from such a system, together with the degree of efficiency with which the work is extracted following a given energy input. Because it is changes that are important, the absolute values are not normally relevant. Fundamental to such studies are certain concepts defined as follows:

A **SYSTEM** is a region of space containing matter of interest to us. It might, for example, contain the **working substance**, such as a fluid inside a cylinder fitted with a 'frictionless' piston; or else it might be the chemical contents of a reaction vessel. Our concern will primarily be with the contents of (often notional) reaction vessels and so with chemical thermodynamics, as against the more mechanical systems that are the concern of physicists and mechanical engineers. A system is almost always regarded as having a fixed mass, so that no material additions are made. It is normally considered to be thermally isolated from its surroundings (the rest of the universe) but, where appropriate, heat is allowed to pass into or out of the system. In any case, a system is free to do mechanical or electrical work on its surroundings.

EQUILIBRIUM in a system requires that there is no net transfer of heat or mass. For example, a system is in **thermal equilibrium** with its surroundings when, in the absence of any thermal insulation, no net heat flow occurs in either direction. Likewise, a system is in **chemical equilibrium** when, despite chemical reactions occurring between its constituents, there is no net change in the chemical composition: that is, the equilibrium is a dynamic one with each component decomposing exactly as fast as it is formed.

The **STANDARD STATE** of a constituent of a system is an arbitrarily defined state. It is usually taken to be the pure substance in its normal physical state at 1 atmosphere pressure (abbreviated to 1 atm = 101.3 kN/m^2) and at the temperature of interest. Alternative standard states are convenient in molten metals and aqueous solutions. All are indicated by a 'Saturn' superscript ($\ominus$).

2.2 THE LAWS OF THERMODYNAMICS

There are four laws of thermodynamics.

The **ZEROTH LAW** *is essentially a definition of 'temperature'. It states that, when any two systems are separately in thermal equilibrium with a third system (so that there is no net heat transfer), then they are in thermal equilibrium with one another.*

The **FIRST LAW** *is the law of energy conservation. It states that, in a system of constant mass, energy can neither be created nor destroyed, although it may be converted from one form to another.*

The **internal energy** U of a system depends only upon the amount of substance present in the system: it is therefore said to be a 'state' property since, for a given mass, its value is fixed for any appropriate combination of pressure and temperature. It is a consequence of the intermolecular and interatomic forces between the various components in the system. The first law states that any infinitesimal change $\mathrm{d}U$ in the internal energy of the system must balance the heat input δq and any work done $p\mathrm{d}V$ by the system, that is

$$\mathrm{d}U = \delta q - p\mathrm{d}V \tag{2.1}$$

where p and V are respectively pressure and volume. The negative sign before $p\mathrm{d}V$ indicates that the system loses energy when it does external work. Energy gains and losses are always measured with respect to the system.

Because work is done against the intermolecular forces when we compress or expand the system, the total heat energy or **enthalpy** H of the system is

$$\boxed{H = U + pV} \tag{2.2}$$

Enthalpy too is a state property and depends on the mass of substance; the total enthalpy of the system is the sum of the individual enthalpies of all the constituent substances. For an infinitesimal change of state at constant pressure,

$$\mathrm{d}H = \mathrm{d}U + p\mathrm{d}V \tag{2.3}$$

and the **heat capacity** C_p ('specific heat') at constant pressure is the rate of change of H with temperature:

$$C_p = (\mathrm{d}H/\mathrm{d}T)_p \tag{2.4}$$

When H is measured in J/mol, C_p is in J/mol K.

Finite changes in the system, represented by a Δ prefix,

$$\Delta X = X_{\mathrm{final}} - X_{\mathrm{initial}}$$

produce an enthalpy change

$$\Delta H = \Delta U + p\Delta V \tag{2.5}$$

and the application of the first law to a chemical reaction leads to the conclusion that *ΔH for any such reaction must be the same whether it is accomplished in one or several stages.* This is **Hess's Law.** As an example:

$$M + O_2 = MO_2 \quad ; \quad \Delta H_1 = H_{MO2} - H_M - H_{O2}$$

$$3MO_2 + O_2 = M_3O_8 \quad ; \quad \Delta H_2 = H_{M3O8} - 3H_{MO2} - H_{O2}$$

$$M_3O_8 + \tfrac{1}{2}O_2 = 3MO_3 \quad ; \quad \Delta H_3 = 3H_{MO3} - H_{M3O8} - \tfrac{1}{2}H_{O2}$$

so that, by simple addition, the enthalpy change for

$$3M + \tfrac{9}{2}O_2 = 3MO_3$$

is $3\Delta H_1 + \Delta H_2 + \Delta H_3$. The enthalpy change accompanying the formation of a compound from its elements *in their standard states* is called the **standard heat of formation** $\Delta H^{\ominus}$ of that compound. Thus, for the last reaction at 298 K,

$$M(s) + \tfrac{3}{2}O_2\ (g;\ \mathit{1\ atm}) = MO_3(s)\ ;\ \Delta H^{\ominus}\ (\mathit{298K})$$

usually measured in J/mol for the reaction as written. Typical values are listed in Table 2.1.

Table 2.1 Selected values of standard enthalpies, free energies and entropies at 298 K.

	Substance	$-\Delta H^\ominus$ kJ/mol	$-\Delta G^\ominus$ kJ/mol	$S^\ominus$ J/mol K
Metals and their compounds (all crystalline solids)	Al	0	0	28
	$AlCl_3$	704	629	111
	Al_2O_3	1676	1582	51
	Al_2S_3	724		
	Cu	0	0	33
	$CuCl_2$	220	176	108
	Cu_2O	167	146	101
	CuO	155	127	44
	Cu_2S	80	86	121
	Fe	0	0	27
	$FeCl_2$	342	302	118
	FeO	267	244	54
	Fe_3O_4	1118	1015	146
	Fe_2O_3	822	741	90
	FeS	100	100	60
	Ni	0	0	30
	$NiCl_2$	305	259	98
	NiO	244	216	39
	NiS	82	80	53
	Si	0	0	19
	SiO_2	911	857	42
	Ti	0	0	30
	TiO_2	912	853	50
	Zn	0	0	42
	$ZnCl_2$	415	369	111
	ZnO	348	318	44
	ZnS	203	198	58
Nonmetals	C(*s*)	0	0	6
	S(*s*)	0	0	32

Table 2.1 continued.

	Substance	$-\Delta H^{\ominus}$ kJ/mol	$-\Delta G^{\ominus}$ kJ/mol	$S^{\ominus}$ J/mol K
Gaseous reactants	Cl_2	0	0	223
	H_2	0	0	131
	N_2	0	0	192
	O_2	0	0	205
	CO	111	137	198
	CO_2	394	394	214
	CH_4	75	51	186
	H_2O	242	229	189
	H_2S	21	34	206
	NH_3	46	16	192
	S_2	128	79	228
	SO_2	297	300	248
Liquids	H_2O	285	237	70
	H_2O_2	188	120	109

Finally, because the heat capacities of substances are additive in the same way that enthalpies are, any chemical reaction has associated with it a net change of heat capacity

$$\Delta C_p = \mathrm{d}(\Delta H)/\mathrm{d}T \tag{2.6}$$

which upon integration gives the enthalpy change $\Delta H(T_2)$ at a temperature T_2 as a function of $\Delta H(T_1)$ at some lower temperature T_1 and of ΔC_p

$$\boxed{\Delta H(T_2) = \Delta H(T_1) + \int_{T_1}^{T_2} \Delta C_p \,\mathrm{d}T} \tag{2.7}$$

Heat capacities often approximate to simple linear functions of temperature ($a + bT$) so that integration is readily performed. Eqn (2.7) may be used to determine the heat of formation of a compound at some temperature other than 298 K. Some heat capacities are listed in Table 2.2 (Note 2.1).

Table 2.2 Some heat capacities expressed as functions of temperature.

$a + bT + cT^2 - d/T^2$ (J/mol K)

Substance	a	10^3b	10^6c	$10^{-6}d$
Al	20.0	13.5		
Al_2O_3	102.9	25.1		2.8
Cu	22.8	6.1		
Cu_2O	59.8	25.9		
Cu_2S	87.4			
Fe(γ)	31.8	4.8		
FeO	52.7	6.2		0.3
FeS(β)	50.6	11.4		
Ni(β)	24.7	8.6		
NiO	57.3	3.5		1.2
NiS	38.9	26.8		
Si	23.8	4.3		0.4
SiO_2	62.7	8.2		1.8
Zn	22.2	11.3		
ZnO	47.7	6.1		0.8
ZnS	53.5	4.0		0.8
C	37.9	−0.5		
S_2	32.6	3.7		
CO	27.1	6.6	−1.0	
CO_2	22.2	59.8	−3.5	
H_2	29.1	−1.9	4.0	
H_2O	32.2	1.9	1.1	
O_2	25.5	15.2	−7.2	

The **SECOND LAW** *may be expressed in various ways, but it is essentially a statement about the direction of spontaneous natural processes. One formulation is that, for any process to occur spontaneously, there must be an increase in 'entropy' of the universe; another is that it is impossible to construct a cyclical machine (heat engine) that extracts heat from a reservoir at constant temperature and converts it into mechanical work, without at the same time producing changes in the reservoir or its surroundings.*

Entropy S may be identified with the degree of disorder or randomness of the system. It is a state property and depends on the amount of substance. If an amount of heat δq is added to or removed from the system at a constant temperature T, then the entropy change is

$$\boxed{dS = \delta q/T} \tag{2.8}$$

It has the same units as heat capacity (J/mol K). The second law states that, although the total entropy of a system and its surroundings is constant if changes are infinitesimally small or carried out extremely slowly ('reversibly'), real processes occur sufficiently rapidly for 'irreversible' degradation of order to take place, so that $\Delta S > 0$: this criterion defines the direction of spontaneous change.

The entropy values of elements and compounds are calculated with the help of the third law of thermodynamics, standard values ($S^{\ominus}$) being listed for 1 atm and 298 K. It is therefore possible to calculate the net entropy change ΔS accompanying any chemical reaction. Again, from eqn (2.6) (2.8),

$$\Delta C_p/T = d(\Delta S)/dT \tag{2.9}$$

so that

$$\boxed{\Delta S(T_2) = \Delta S(T_1) + \int_{T_1}^{T_2} (\Delta C_p/T)\, dT} \tag{2.10}$$

and we may evaluate the entropy change for a chemical reaction at some temperature T_2 other than that ($T_1 = 298$ K) for which the entropy data are tabulated, Table 2.1. However, it must be emphasised that this evaluation corresponds to the change *within a closed system,* for which the second law offers no guide as to the direction for spontaneous change. (Thus, living organisms grow spontaneously and maintain themselves in a state of high order ($\Delta S_{\text{system}} < 0$) at the expense of their surroundings (total ΔS of the universe including the living 'system' > 0); simply examining the system in isolation reveals an apparent contradiction of the second law.) The criterion required is that, *for spontaneous change, the* **free energy** *G of the system must decrease* ($\Delta G < 0$). At equilibrium, $\Delta G = 0$.

Free energy is the recoverable energy from a system and represents the driving force effecting change

$$\boxed{G = H - TS} \tag{2.11}$$

Like H and S, G is a state property; it depends on the amount of substance and is additive. For any finite change in the energy of the system at constant temperature and pressure

$$\Delta G = \Delta H - T\Delta S \tag{2.12}$$

and Hess's law may be used to calculate ΔG for reactions that occur by several stages. The **standard free energy of formation** of a compound from its elements at 298 K is written $\Delta G^{\ominus}(298\text{ K})$ and is usually measured in J/mol, Table 2.1.

Because in practice the ΔC_p change in chemical reactions is small and the 'ΔC_p correction' in eqn (2.7) (2.10) is often less than the errors in measuring $\Delta H^{\ominus}$ and $\Delta S^{\ominus}$ at 298 K, eqn (2.12) may conveniently approximate to

$$\Delta G^{\ominus}(T) \approx \Delta H^{\ominus}(298\text{ K}) - T\Delta S^{\ominus}(298\text{ K}) \tag{2.13}$$

It may, however, still be necessary to take account of any phase changes which occur between 298 K and the temperature T of interest. Thus, suppose that there is a phase change in one of the constituents at T' (between 298 K and T) characterised by a latent heat L, then the enthalpy change for the overall reaction is augmented by $\pm L$: if the phase change is in one of the reaction *products* then the sign accorded to L is the same as that for the phase change itself, whereas the sign is reversed if the phase change occurs in one of the *reactants.* From the definition of entropy, eqn (2.8), the entropy change accompanying the phase change is L/T' and ΔS for the reaction is augmented by $\pm L/T'$. Hence, neglecting the ΔC_p correction,

$$\Delta G^{\ominus} \approx \Delta H^{\ominus}(298\text{ K}) - T\Delta S^{\ominus}(298\text{ K}) \pm L\{1-(T/T')\} \tag{2.14}$$

Some values of L are listed in Table 2.3, from which it may be seen that such phase-change corrections may normally be neglected unless they involve transformation to or from a gas (Note 2.2).

The **THIRD LAW** *offers the opportunity to determine the absolute value of the entropy of any substance. It states that the entropy of a system at absolute zero (0°K) is zero at thermodynamic equilibrium.*

Using eqn (2.10) and putting $T_1 = 0$, we have

$$\Delta S(T) = \Delta S(0^\circ\text{K}) + \int_0^T (\Delta C_p/T)\,\mathrm{d}T$$

$$= \int_0^T (\Delta C_p/T)\,\mathrm{d}T \tag{2.15}$$

provided that the substances in question are all in their lowest possible energy states, that is, pure and crystalline, at absolute zero. Unfortunately, heat capacities change rapidly at very low temperature and the integration is best effected using the Debye relationship

$$C_p = aT^3 \tag{2.16}$$

below about 15 K. Like eqn (2.13), eqn (2.15) needs also to take account of any phase changes. If, for example, there is such a change having a latent heat of transformation L at some temperature T', then the entropy of the substance is augmented by L/T', as in eqn (2.14).

Table 2.3 Some latent heats of transformation.

(m =melting, e = evaporation, s = sublimation)

Substance	Phase change	L kJ/mol	T' K	L/T' J/mol K
Al	m	11	933	12
Cu	m	13	1357	10
Fe	α–γ	4	1183	3
	γ–δ	1	1675	1
	m	16	1812	9
Ni	m	18	1725	10
Si	m	46	1710	27
Zn	m	7	693	10
Cu_2O	m	77	1800	43
FeO	m	31	1650	19
Fe_3O_4	m	138	1880	73
Cu_2S	m	23	1400	16
FeS	m	21	1463	14
NiS	m	24	1063	23
$AlCl_3$	s	120	455	264
$FeCl_2$	m	43	950	45
	e	126	1300	97
$NiCl_2$	s	202	1260	160
$ZnCl_2$	m	24	638	38
	e	119	1010	118

2.3 ACTIVITY AND ACTIVITY COEFFICIENT: CHEMICAL POTENTIAL

If we differentiate eqn (2.11), we obtain, using eqn (2.2)

$$dG = dH - d(TS)$$

$$= (dU + pdV + Vdp) - (TdS + SdT)$$

Now, from eqn (2.1) (2.8)

$$dU = \delta q - pdV = TdS - pdV$$

so that

$$dG = Vdp - SdT \qquad (2.17)$$

If 1 mole of ideal gas is our working substance at constant temperature ($dT = 0$),

$$dG = Vdp = (RT/p)dp = RT\, d(\ln p) \qquad (2.18)$$

which, on integration, gives

$$G = G^{\ominus} + RT \ln(p/p^{\ominus}) \qquad (2.19)$$

where $G^{\ominus}$ is the standard free energy in the standard state of unit pressure ($p^{\ominus}$ = 1 atm = 101.3 kN/m^2). To take account of the fact that real gases are not ideal ($pV \neq nRT$), the pressure ratio $p/p^{\ominus}$ is replaced by another dimensionless quantity called the **activity** a of the gas (Note 2.3)

$$\boxed{\begin{aligned} G &= G^{\ominus} + RT \ln a \\ a &= \exp\{(G - G^{\ominus})/RT\} \end{aligned}} \quad \text{for a pure substance} \qquad (2.20)$$

The departure from ideality is reflected in a numerical correction factor called the **activity coefficient** γ which varies with p

$$a = \gamma(p/p^{\ominus}) \qquad (2.21)$$

Obviously, the more closely behaviour approximates to ideal, the closer is γ to unity.

For mixtures of gases or for components in solution, the free energy contributed by each component i is

$$G_i = G_i^{\ominus} + RT \ln a_i \qquad (2.22)$$

where p in eqn (2.21) now represents the partial pressure of the component or else $p/p^{\ominus}$ is replaced by some more appropriate unit of concentration such as mole fraction.

If chemical reaction in a system results in an infinitesimal change $\mathrm{d}n_i$ in the number of moles of the ith component, the change in free energy of the total system (everything else being kept constant) is

$$\mathrm{d}G = (\partial G/\partial n_i)_{p,T,j\neq i} \times \mathrm{d}n_i \tag{2.23}$$

The partial differential is called the **chemical potential** ('partial molar free energy') of the component

$$\mu_i = (\partial G/\partial n_i)_{p,T,j\neq i} \tag{2.24}$$

so that, from eqn (2.18) (2.23) (2.24) for a mixture of ideal gases

$$\mathrm{d}\mu_i = RT\,\mathrm{d}(\ln p_i)$$

or, for a nonideal mixture or solution

$$\mathrm{d}\mu_i = RT\,\mathrm{d}(\ln a_i)$$

which, on integration, gives

$$\boxed{\begin{aligned}\mu_i &= \mu_i^{\ominus} + RT\ln a_i\\ a_i &= \exp\{(\mu_i - \mu_i^{\ominus})/RT\}\end{aligned}} \quad \text{for a mixture or solution} \tag{2.25}$$

This equation corresponds exactly to eqn (2.20) (2.22). Evidently the free energy (chemical potential) contributed by each component in a mixture is a simple function of the molar free energy in the standard state ($\mu_i^{\ominus} = G_i^{\ominus}$), the relative amount (concentration) being suitably adjusted for departures from ideality.

Because there is a variety of standard states which we may adopt, it is conventional to represent the free energy of pure substances by a solid • superscript, so that the 'pure substance' standard state (often referred to as the *Raoultian standard state*) is:

$$\mu_i^{\ominus} = G_i^{\ominus} = G_i^{\bullet} \tag{2.26}$$

For a component whose mole fraction x_i is close to unity, it is found that the activity and mole fraction are identical:

$$a_i = x_i \quad (x_i \to 1) \tag{2.27}$$

which is known as **Raoult's law.** At lower concentrations the (Raoultian) activity coefficient is no longer unity and the (Raoultian) activity becomes

$$a_i = \gamma_i x_i \tag{2.28}$$

The coefficient γ_i depends on x_i until the concentration becomes very small, whereupon it tends to a constant limiting value γ_i^∞, the *Raoultian activity coefficient at infinite dilution*

$$a_i = \gamma_i^\infty x_i \quad (x_i \to 0) \tag{2.29}$$

This proportionality is known as **Henry's law.** It is sometimes convenient to define a Henrian activity h_i

$$h_i = x_i = a_i/\gamma_i^\infty \tag{2.30}$$

for which $h_i = 1$ at $x_i = 1$, provided that we now define a new *Henrian standard state* corresponding to $x_i = 1$ and for which the standard chemical potential is

$$\mu_i^\infty = G_i^\bullet + RT \ln \gamma_i^\infty \quad (x_i = 1) \tag{2.31}$$

Since then

$$\mu_i = \mu_i^\infty + RT \ln h_i \tag{2.32}$$

$$= (G_i^\bullet + RT \ln \gamma_i^\infty) + RT \ln x_i$$

$$= G_i^\bullet + RT \ln a_i \quad \text{at } x_i \to 1 \tag{2.33}$$

The formal equivalence of eqn (2.32) (2.33) shows how the activity reflects the standard state adopted: the total chemical potential of i does not change, it is merely distributed differently between the 'standard' term and the 'activity' term. Figure 2.1 demonstrates this relationship graphically.

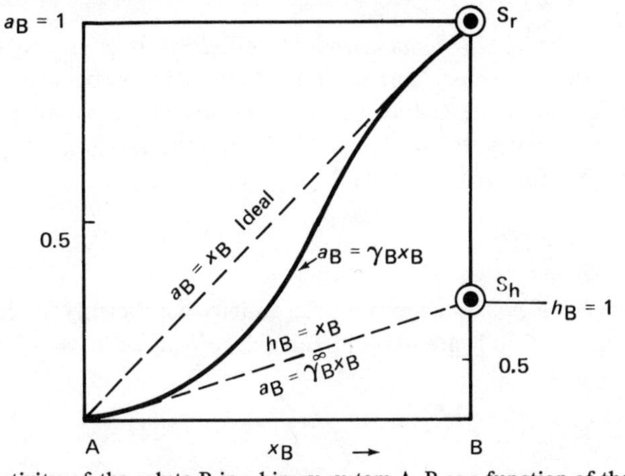

Fig. 2.1 Activity of the solute B in a binary system A–B as a function of the mole fraction x_B. The Raoultian activity scale is on the left and the Henrian on the right. S_r and S_h represent the Raoultian and Henrian standard states. The negative deviation from Raoult's law is a consequence of mutual attraction between A and B.

We can evidently adopt other standard states, for which there will be appropriate activities. In aqueous solutions it is normal practice to define a modified Henrian standard state corresponding to 1 mole of salt per kilogram of solvent water (the *unimolal standard state,* $m/m^{\ominus} = 1$) but in which 'infinite dilution' behaviour is manifested. We then write, for ideal Henrian behaviour,

$$\mu_i = \mu_i^m + RT \ln h_i \quad (h_i = m_i/m^{\ominus}) \tag{2.34}$$

where $m^{\ominus}$ denotes 1 mol/kg. This equation is similar in form to eqn (2.32). An activity coefficient f_i is introduced to allow for departures from 'infinite dilution' behaviour, that is, from Henrian ideality:

$$\mu_i = \mu_i^m + RT \ln f_i\,(m_i/m^{\ominus}) \tag{2.35}$$

To allow for the fact that salts ionise in solution (Note 2.4)

Salt $= n_+$ cations $+\, n_-$ anions

we may calculate the separate ionic activities as

$$\boxed{\begin{aligned} h_+ &= n_+ f_\pm\,(m_{\text{salt}}/m^{\ominus}) \\ h_- &= n_- f_\pm\,(m_{\text{salt}}/m^{\ominus}) \end{aligned}} \tag{2.36}$$

where $f_\pm$ is the *mean molal activity coefficient.* It is an averaged value that recognises that, because anions and cations cannot be dissolved separately, their absolute activities cannot be measured separately either. It may be shown that, for consistency between eqn (2.35) for the salt ($h_{\text{salt}} = f_{\text{salt}}\,(m_{\text{salt}}/m^{\ominus})$) and eqn (2.36) for the ions (Note 2.5),

$$f_\pm = f_{\text{salt}}^{1/n} \tag{2.37}$$

where $n = n_+ + n_-$. Some mean molal activity coefficients for common electrolytes in water at 298 K are listed in Table 2.4 (Note 2.6).

Table 2.4 Mean molal activity coefficients at 25°C

$m/m^{\ominus} =$	0.001	0.003	0.01	0.03	0.1	0.3	1	3	10
HNO_3	0.97	0.94	0.90	0.85	0.79	0.74	0.72	0.91	
$LiNO_3$	0.97	0.94	0.90	0.85	0.79	0.74	0.74	0.97	2.44
$AgNO_3$		0.94	0.90	0.84	0.73	0.61	0.43	0.25	0.11
$Cu(NO_3)_2$					0.51	0.44	0.46	0.90	
$Al(NO_3)_3$					0.20	0.15	0.19	1.02	
$LiOH$				0.83	0.76	0.67	0.55	0.49	
$NaOH$			0.91	0.85	0.77	0.71	0.68	0.78	3.23
HCl	0.97	0.94	0.90	0.84	0.80	0.76	0.81	1.32	10.4
$LiCl$	0.96	0.94	0.90	0.84	0.79	0.74	0.80	1.34	9.40
NH_4Cl		0.94	0.90	0.83	0.77	0.69	0.60	0.56	
$NaCl$	0.97	0.94	0.90	0.85	0.78	0.71	0.66	0.71	
KCl	0.97	0.94	0.90	0.85	0.77	0.69	0.60	0.57	
$MgCl_2$					0.53	0.48	0.57	2.32	
$CuCl_2$		0.82	0.72	0.62	0.51	0.43	0.42	0.52	
$ZnCl_2$		0.81	0.71	0.62	0.52	0.43	0.34	0.29	0.90
$FeCl_2$					0.52	0.45	0.51		
$NiCl_2$					0.52	0.46	0.54	1.69	
$AlCl_3$				0.53	0.34	0.30	0.54		
H_2SO_4	0.83	0.61	0.54	0.40	0.27	0.18	0.13	0.14	0.56
Li_2SO_4					0.47	0.36	0.28	0.29	
Na_2SO_4	0.89	0.82	0.71	0.59	0.45	0.32	0.20	0.14	
K_2SO_4	0.89	0.81	0.71	0.59	0.44	0.32			
$MgSO_4$					0.15	0.09	0.05	0.05	
$CuSO_4$	0.74	0.63	0.44	0.25	0.15	0.08	0.04		
$ZnSO_4$	0.70	0.54	0.39	0.24	0.15	0.08	0.04	0.04	
$NiSO_4$					0.15	0.08	0.04	0.04	
$Al_2(SO_4)_3$					0.04	0.02	0.02		

The chemical potentials of ions in aqueous solutions are given by a combination of eqn (2.35) (2.36)

$$\boxed{\begin{aligned} \mu_+ &= \mu_+^m + RT \ln \{n_+ f_\pm (m_{\text{salt}}/m^{\ominus})\} \\ \mu_- &= \mu_-^m + RT \ln \{n_- f_\pm (m_{\text{salt}}/m^{\ominus})\} \end{aligned}} \qquad (2.38)$$

The standard chemical potentials μ^m for the ions cannot be separately determined from that of the salt and it is necessary to have some fixed reference level. *Conventionally, we assume that μ^m for aquated hydrogen ions is zero at all temperatures.* This enables us to measure μ^m_{ion} by difference: by, for example, measuring the emf of an electrochemical cell containing hydrogen ions at unit activity ($\mu_{H+} = \mu^m_{H+} + RT \ln h_{H+} \equiv 0$), as may be seen later, Section 4.3. Some values of μ^m for various common ions in water at 298 K are listed in Table 2.5.

Table 2.5 Standard chemical potentials (kJ/mol) of ions in aqueous solution at 25°C relative to the hydrogen ion

Cation	μ^m	Anion	μ^m
Ag(I)	+77.1	Br^-	−102.8
Al(III)	−483.1	Cl^-	−131.1
Au(III)	+410.8	F^-	−274.8
Ca(II)	−555.1	I^-	−51.6
Cd(II)	−77.6	OH^-	−157.2
Cr(II)	−164.6	S^{2-}	+98.0
(III)	−205.0	HS^-	+12.3
Cu(I)	+50.4	CN^-	+163.7
(II)	+66.6	CO_3^{2-}	−528.7
Fe(II)	−84.9	ClO_4^-	−44.8
(III)	−10.6	CrO_4^-	−717.0
Hg(I) as Hg_2^{2+}	+162.5	MnO_4^-	−420.8
Mg(II)	−450.9	NO_2^-	−35.3
NH_4^+	−79.3	NO_3^-	−109.8
Na(I)	−261.8	PO_4^{3-}	−1008.0
Ni(II)	−48.2	SO_4^{2-}	−736.6
Pb(II)	−24.3		
(IV)	−824.1		
Pt(II)	+231.0		
Sn(II)	−26.3		
(IV)	+2.9		
Ti(II)	−157.0		
Zn(II)	−147.2		

2.4 EQUILIBRIUM: DISSOCIATION PARTIAL PRESSURE

For a spontaneous chemical reaction in solution

$$\Delta G = (\Sigma n_i \mu_i)_{\text{products}} - (\Sigma n_i \mu_i)_{\text{reactants}} < 0 \tag{2.39}$$

Expanding the chemical potentials using eqn (2.25)

$$\Delta G = \Sigma n_i \mu_i^{\ominus} + RT\, \Sigma n_i \ln a_i < 0 \qquad (2.40)$$

where the Σ terms include the differences between products and reactants. Thus, the second Σ term for a reaction

$$a\mathrm{A} + b\mathrm{B} = c\mathrm{C} + d\mathrm{D}$$

is

$$\begin{aligned} \Sigma n_i \ln a_i &= \ln \{(a_\mathrm{C}^c \times a_\mathrm{D}^d)/(a_\mathrm{A}^a \times a_\mathrm{B}^b)\} \\ &= \ln K \end{aligned} \qquad (2.41)$$

where K is the *equilibrium constant* when the system is in equilibrium. The first term

$$\begin{aligned} \Sigma n_i \mu_i^{\ominus} &= c\mu_\mathrm{C}^{\ominus} + d\mu_\mathrm{D}^{\ominus} - a\mu_\mathrm{A}^{\ominus} - b\mu_\mathrm{B}^{\ominus} \\ &= \Delta G^{\ominus}, \text{ the standard free energy change for the reaction} \end{aligned} \qquad (2.42)$$

Since at equilibrium $\Delta G = 0$, we have from eqn (2.40) to (2.42)

$$\Sigma n_i \mu_i^{\ominus} = -RT\Sigma n_i \ln a_i$$

or

$$\boxed{\Delta G^{\ominus} = -RT \ln K} \qquad (2.43)$$

An alternative form, sometimes more convenient, is

$$K = \prod a_i^{n_i} = \exp(-\Delta G^{\ominus}/RT) \qquad (2.44)$$

This result enables us to predict the equilibrium activities of the various constituents when the standard free energy change is known. It is variously called the *reaction isotherm* or the *van't Hoff isotherm.*

An important application of the reaction isotherm is the determination of the *dissociation partial pressures* of oxides, that is, the partial pressure of oxygen in equilibrium with each oxide and the metal from which it has formed. Consider, for example, cuprous oxide at 800 K:

$$2\mathrm{Cu(s)} + \tfrac{1}{2}\mathrm{O_2\,(g)} = \mathrm{Cu_2O(s)}\,; \;\; \Delta G^{\ominus}(800\,K) = -112.3 \text{ kJ}$$

$$K = a_{\mathrm{Cu_2O}}/a_{\mathrm{Cu}}^2 \cdot (p_{\mathrm{O_2}}/p^{\ominus})^{\frac{1}{2}} = \exp(-\Delta G^{\ominus}/RT)$$

If the copper and Cu_2O are pure, that is, in their Raoultian standard state, then $a_{Cu2O} = a_{Cu} = 1$ and we are left with

$$p_{O2}/p^{\ominus} = \exp 2\Delta G^{\ominus}/RT$$

$$= \exp(-224600/8.31 \times 800) = 2.2 \times 10^{-15}$$

whence the equilibrium oxygen pressure is 2×10^{-15} atm. Any partial pressure below this value will cause the oxide to decompose (dissociate). In other words, Cu_2O is unstable below this pressure and copper will not oxidise at 800 K under such conditions.

We may also deduce the manner in which equilibrium is affected by temperature. Differentiating eqn (2.43) at constant pressure,

$$R\frac{\partial(\ln K)}{\partial T} = \frac{\partial}{\partial T}\left(\frac{-\Delta G^{\ominus}}{T}\right) = \frac{\Delta G^{\ominus}}{T^2} - \frac{1}{T}\frac{\partial(\Delta G^{\ominus})}{\partial T}$$

$$= \frac{(\Delta H^{\ominus} - T\Delta S^{\ominus}) + T\Delta S^{\ominus}}{T^2}$$

whence

$$\boxed{\frac{\partial(\ln K)}{\partial T} = \frac{\Delta H^{\ominus}}{RT^2}} \qquad (2.45)$$

For example, in the ionisation of water, eqn (3.6), the ionic product (equilibrium constant) rises by a factor of some 500 times between 273 and 373 K. The standard enthalpy change, measured from the heat of neutralisation, is −57 kJ/mol. We might, therefore, expect that, if $\ln K$ changes linearly with temperature, so that T^2 can be taken as the square of the arithmetic mean temperature (323 K),

$$\frac{\Delta(\ln K_w)}{100} = \frac{-57\,000}{8.31 \times 323^2}$$

or $\Delta(\ln K_w) = 6.57$, a change of 700 times, in fair agreement since $\Delta H^{\ominus}$ in fact varies over the temperature range.

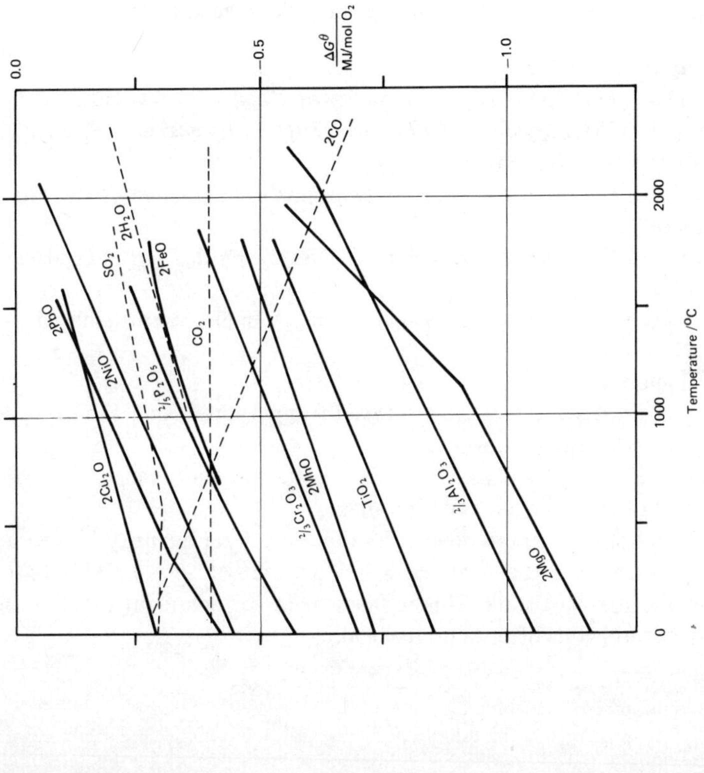

Fig. 2.2 The Ellingham diagram for common oxides

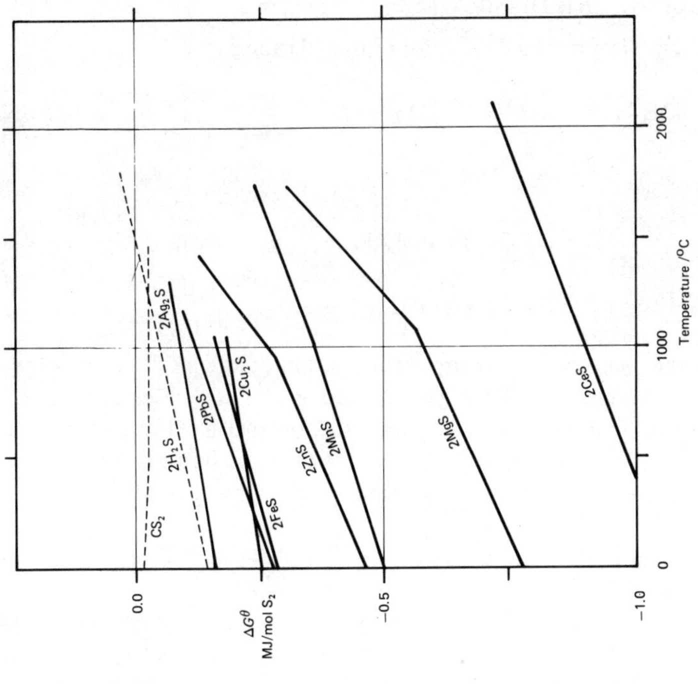

Fig. 2.3 The Ellingham diagram for common sulphides

2.5 THE ELLINGHAM DIAGRAM

The Ellingham diagram is a direct plot of the relationship

$$\Delta G^{\ominus}(T) = \Delta H^{\ominus}(T) - T\Delta S^{\ominus}(T) \tag{2.46}$$

for the reaction

$$(2x/y)\mathrm{M} + \mathrm{O_2(g)} = (2/y)\mathrm{M}_x\mathrm{O}_y$$

or

$$(2x/y)\mathrm{M} + \mathrm{S_2(g)} = (2/y)\mathrm{M}_x\mathrm{S}_y \tag{2.47}$$

that is, of the standard free energy of formation of the oxide or sulphide (etc) *per mole of oxygen or sulphur gas.* Plotted in this way, Figs 2.2 and 2.3, the thermodynamic data reveal at a glance the relative affinities of the various elements for oxygen or sulphur. Most of the lines can be seen to have a positive slope, which arises from the fact that, where $\Delta H^{\ominus}$ is invariant with temperature,

$$\mathrm{d}(\Delta G^{\ominus})/\mathrm{d}T = -\,\Delta S^{\ominus}(T) \tag{2.48}$$

and $\Delta S^{\ominus}$ is almost always negative in view of the fact that gaseous oxygen or sulphur (high entropy) is being consumed. A significant exception is carbon oxidation to CO(g) in Fig. 2.2, where there is a net entropy increase. The changes in slope result from phase changes in either reactants or products.

Bibliography to Chapter 2

Darken and Gurry (1953) *Physical Chemistry of Metals* McGraw-Hill.

Guggenheim (1970) *Elements of Chemical Thermodynamics,* 2nd edn. Royal Inst. Chemistry, London.

Kubachewski and Alcock (1979) *Metallurgical Thermochemistry,* 5th edn. Pergamon.

Upadhyaya and Dube (1977) *Problems in Metallurgical Thermodynamics and Kinetics* Pergamon.

Warn (1969) *Concise Chemical Thermodynamics* Van Nostrand Reinhold.

Notes to Chapter 2

2.1 Values in Tables 2.1 and 2.2 are taken from Aylward and Findlay (1974), *S.I. Chemical Data,* 2nd edn. Wiley.

2.2 Values in Table 2.3 are taken from Kubachewski and Evans (1951), *Metallurgical Thermochemistry,* 1st edn. Pergamon.

2.3 Many textbooks of thermodynamics replace p by a quantity known as the **fugacity** f and there is then defined a 'relative' activity $a = f/f^{\ominus}$, $f^{\ominus}$ being the fugacity in the standard state. This refinement in the argument is confusing for many students and adds little to understanding.

2.4 Positively charged ions are termed **cations** (because they move towards the cathode in an electrolysis cell), and negatively charged ions are termed **anions** (because they move towards the anode).

2.5 At equilibrium

$$\begin{aligned} \mu_{\text{salt}}^{\ominus} &= n_+\mu_+^{\ominus} + n_-\mu_-^{\ominus} \\ \mu_{\text{salt}} &= n_+\mu_+ + n_-\mu_- \end{aligned} \tag{2.49}$$

whence, by subtraction and dividing through by RT,

$$h_{\text{salt}} = h_+^{n_+} \times h_-^{n_-} = h_\pm^n \tag{2.50}$$

where (as in the text) $n = n_+ + n_-$ and $h_\pm$ is the geometric mean ionic activity. If we now define appropriate activity coefficients f_+, f_- and $f_\pm$,

$$f_\pm^n = f_+^{n_+} \times f_-^{n_-} \tag{2.51}$$

$$h_+ = f_+ n_+ (m_{\text{salt}}/m^{\ominus}); \qquad h_- = f_- n_- (m_{\text{salt}}/m^{\ominus}) \tag{2.52}$$

$$h_\pm = f_\pm N (m_{\text{salt}}/m^{\ominus}) \tag{2.53}$$

in which $N^n = n_+^{n_+} \times n_-^{n_-}$, then eqn (2.50) to (2.53) are self-consistent. However, we cannot separately determine h_+ and h_- experimentally nor can we determine the absolute values of f_+ and f_- on that account. We instead write eqn (2.52) in terms of $f_\pm$ to give 'working' values of the ionic activities

$$h_+ = f_\pm n_+ (m_{\text{salt}}/m^{\ominus}); \qquad h_- = f_\pm n_- (m_{\text{salt}}/m^{\ominus}) \tag{2.54}$$

which *can* be determined by experiment since the salt activity can be obtained by extrapolation of a suitable cell emf and, as in the main text, we have

$$f_\pm = (f_{\text{salt}})^{1/n} \tag{2.37}$$

For a 1:1 salt such as KCl this means

$$h_{K+} = h_{Cl-} = (h_{KCl})^{\frac{1}{2}} = f_\pm (m_{KCl}/m^{\ominus})$$

and

$$f_\pm = (f_{KCl})^{\frac{1}{2}}$$

whilst, for a 1:2 salt such as $MgCl_2$,

$$h_{Mg2+} = \tfrac{1}{2}h_{Cl-} = 0.63(h_{MgCl2})^{\frac{1}{3}}$$

and

$$f_{\pm} = (f_{MgCl2})^{\frac{1}{3}}$$

2.6 Values in Tables 2.4 and 2.5 are taken from Parsons (1959) *Handbook of Electrochemical Constants*, Butterworth.

2.7 Only the main outline is given here, without the refinements of direct estimation of equilibrium gas pressures, whether of oxygen, sulphur or H_2/H_2O, CO/CO_2, etc. The reader is referred to Richardson and Jeffes, (1948) *J. Iron Steel Inst.* **160** 261 for the original paper, also to Mackowiak (1966) *Physical Chemistry for Metallurgists*, Allen and Unwin.

Chapter 3

Some Underlying Chemistry

3.1 OXIDATION AND REDUCTION

When a substance combines with oxygen it is said to be oxidised; reduction takes place when oxygen is removed from a substance. There is, however, a more general sense in which we may use these terms. *Oxidation is, in fact, said to occur whenever there is an increase in valency state of the element concerned,* usually a metal:

$$Fe + \tfrac{1}{2}O_2 = FeO \quad ; \quad \text{increase from } Fe^0 \text{ to } Fe^{II}$$

$$2FeO + \tfrac{1}{2}O_2 = Fe_2O_3 \quad ; \quad \text{increase from } Fe^{II} \text{ to } Fe^{III}$$

$$Cu + \tfrac{1}{2}S_2 = CuS \quad ; \quad \text{increase from } Cu^0 \text{ to } Cu^{II}$$

$$Ag + \tfrac{1}{2}Cl_2 = AgCl \quad ; \quad \text{increase from } Ag^0 \text{ to } Ag^{I} \qquad (3.1)$$

In each case the oxidation state (valency state) of the metal has increased on passing from left to right. The reverse direction, corresponding to a decrease in valency of the metal, is called reduction.

We should also note that *the oxygen is itself reduced* whenever it accomplishes oxidation, for example, for FeO:

$$\tfrac{1}{2}O_2 + 2e \text{ (from Fe)} = O^{2-} \text{ (in FeO lattice)} \qquad (3.2)$$

where e represents an electron. This is because an even more general definition is that *reduction consumes electrons and, conversely, that oxidation liberates electrons.* Corresponding to eqn (3.2) is the oxidation process

$$Fe = Fe^{2+} \text{ (in FeO lattice)} + 2e \text{ (remaining in Fe)} \qquad (3.3)$$

and we may deduce that oxidation and reduction processes always complement one another. We can now rewrite the reactions in eqn (3.1) in the form of simultaneous ionic oxidations and reductions:

$$Fe = Fe^{2+} + \textcircled{2e}\,; \quad \tfrac{1}{2}O_2 + \textcircled{2e} = O^{2-}$$

$$Fe^{2+} = Fe^{3+} + \textcircled{e}\,; \quad \tfrac{1}{2}O_2 + \textcircled{2e} = O^{2-}$$

$$Cu = Cu^{2+} + \textcircled{2e}\,; \quad \tfrac{1}{2}S_2 + \textcircled{2e} = S^{2-}$$

$$Ag = Ag^{+} + \textcircled{e}\,; \quad \tfrac{1}{2}Cl_2 + \textcircled{e} = Cl^{-} \tag{3.4}$$

and we may, in fact, enlarge the example with three more:

$$2Fe + 3H_2O = Fe_2O_3 + 3H_2$$

(that is, $Fe = Fe^{3+} + \textcircled{3e}\ ;\ H_2O + \textcircled{2e} = H_2 + O^{2-}$)

$$Cu + \tfrac{1}{2}O_2 + H_2O = Cu(OH)_2$$

(that is, $Cu = Cu^{2+} + \textcircled{2e}\ ;\ \tfrac{1}{2}O_2 + H_2O + \textcircled{2e} = 2OH^{-}$)

$$Ni + 2HCl = NiCl_2 + H_2 \tag{3.5}$$

(that is, $Ni = Ni^{2+} + \textcircled{2e}\ ;\ H^{+} + \textcircled{e} = \tfrac{1}{2}H_2$, whilst Cl^{-} remains unaffected).

In every instance, when electrons appear on the right-hand side (RHS) of the equation there is oxidation taking place and, conversely, electrons on the LHS signify reduction. For emphasis the electrons have been ringed in eqn (3.4) and (3.5).

It is evident that a large class of molecular reactions may be seen as electron transfer processes, in which various atoms or molecules ionise or ions become discharged. The use of ionic equations enables us to represent corrosion processes as partial reactions and, as we shall see, these are often spatially separated, with electrons passing between regions of simultaneous oxidation and reduction.

3.2 ACIDITY AND *p*H

Water dissociates spontaneously into hydrogen ions and hydroxyl ions:

$$H_2O(1) = H^{+}(aq) + OH^{-}(aq) \tag{3.6}$$

The amount of dissociation is extremely small. If the ionic concentrations are expressed in *molality* units, that is, as the number of moles per kg of solvent water, we find that the equilibrium concentration of each ion lies in the region of 10^{-7} mol/kg (since 1 kg water = 55.5 mol H_2O, this means that roughly one water molecule in 500 million dissociates in this way at equilibrium). The product of the molalities of the ions, expressed as a number, is called the *ionic product of water* K_w

$$K_w = (m_{H+}/m^\ominus)\,(m_{OH-}/m^\ominus) \tag{3.7}$$

where $m^\ominus$ represents unit concentration of 1 mol/kg, eqn (2.34). At 298K K_w has the value 1.01×10^{-14}. It is, however, highly temperature sensitive, rising from 1.13×10^{-15} at 273 K to 5.6×10^{-13} at 373 K, as a result of a large enthalpy change of -57 kJ/mol associated with the ionisation (Note 3.1).

When various strong electrolytes such as HCl or NaOH are added to water they dissociate almost completely and so grossly unbalance the ratio of hydrogen ions to hydroxyl ions. When H^+ (aq) are in excess the solution is said to be acid; the solution is alkaline when OH^- (aq) are in excess. A useful measure of the degree of acidity or alkalinity is the *p*H scale. The symbol *p* is here used as a mathematical operator signifying 'take the negative logarithm to base 10 of . . .'; in this instance it means

$$\boxed{p\text{H} = -\log(m_{H+}/m^\ominus)} \tag{3.8}$$

In solutions of salts that are more concentrated than about 10^{-3} molal we find that there is an increasing departure from ideal (Henrian) behaviour, Table 2.4, that is, the various ions start interacting with one another and are no longer shielded from one another by their 'hydration sheaths' of water molecules. Accordingly, molality is replaced by activity, eqn (2.34). (The current internationally agreed definition of *p*H is based on instrumental measurement using an H^+ − sensitive electrode system and standard buffer solutions.) If, then, we write h_{H+} for $m_{H+}/m^\ominus$ and apply the operator *p* to h_{OH-} and K_w in eqn (3.7), we obtain

$$p\text{H} + p\text{OH} = pK_w \tag{3.9}$$

The range of *p*H covers approximately -2 to $+16$ at 298 K. The condition of neutrality corresponds to

$$m_{H+} = m_{OH-} = m^\ominus(K_w)^{\frac{1}{2}}$$

or, more strictly,

$$p\text{H} = p\text{OH} = pK_w/2 \tag{3.10}$$

That is,

$$(pH)_{neutral} = 7.47 \text{ at } 273 \text{ K}$$
$$7.00 \text{ at } 298 \text{ K}$$
$$6.13 \text{ at } 373 \text{ K}.$$

In what follows, we shall assume $pH = 7$ is approximately neutral.

3.3 SOLUBILITY PRODUCT

As the concentration of a salt in solution is increased, the disturbance to the structure of the solvent water becomes progressively greater: cations (positively charged) require freely oriented water molecules to form protective hydration sheaths around them, and anions (negatively charged) also disrupt the surrounding molecules as a result of their high surface charge density. Depending on ion size and charge density, the degree of disturbance at which oppositely-charged ions become significantly exposed to one another's electric fields varies from salt to salt. The resulting process of *ionic association* ('ion pair' formation) leads finally to the nucleation of undissociated crystalline salt particles, and at this point the solution is said to be 'saturated'.

Corresponding to the physical reality of disturbance/association, there is a progressive increase in activity coefficient $f_\pm$ (section 2.3). The ionic activity rises until, at saturation, the salt precipitates with the Raoultian salt activity $a_{salt} = 1$. For the equilibrium of a salt $A_{n+}B_{n-}$

$$A_{n+}B_{n-} = n_+A^{x+} + n\_B^{y-}$$

where $x/y = n_-/n_+$, we may write an equilibrium constant

$$K = (h_A^{n_+} \times h_B^{n_-})/a_{AB} \tag{3.11}$$

where h_A, h_B represent the Henrian activities of A^{x+} and B^{y-} and a_{AB} the Raoultian activity of the salt. At saturation, $a_{AB} = 1$ and we write the constant as K_s, the *solubility product*

$$K_s = h_A^{n+} . h_B^{n-} \tag{3.12}$$

Some typical solubility products are listed in Table 3.1 (Note 3.2). For example, silver(I) sulphide is Ag_2S, for which $pK_s = -\log K_s$ is 49, so that $h_{Ag+}^2 . h_{S2-} = 10^{-49}$: from this we may calculate the sulphide ion activity needed to precipitate silver from solution. If, say, we had 0.01 molal $AgNO_3$, Table 2.4 tells us that $h_{Ag+} = 0.9 \times 0.01 = 0.009$, so that the critical sulphide activity is $10^{-49}/(0.009)^2 = 1.2 \times 10^{-45}$. Such a calculation emphasises that sulphides are generally regarded as insoluble. Low solubilities are associated with large values of pK_s, and the table broadly confirms our expectation that higher charge density on either ion leads to lower solubility.

Table 3.1 Solubility products of some sulphides, hydroxides and chlorides in water at 298 K
The roman numeral in parentheses indicates the valence state of the metal in the compound. The negative values of pK_s (= $-\log K_s$) are approximate, corresponding to moderately soluble compounds.

		pK_s	
Metal	Sulphide	Hydroxide	Chloride
Hg	(II)52	(II)25	(I)18
Ag	(I)49	(I)8	(I)10
Cu	(I)48	(II)20	(I)7
Sn	(II)26	(IV)57 (II)26	(II)4
Pb	(II)29	(II)14	(II)5
Ni	(II)28	(II)17	(II)–5
Fe	(II)17	(III)39 (II)15	(II)–1
Cr	*	(III)30	(III)–1
Zn	(II)24	(II)16	(II)–6
Al	*	(III)32	(III)–4
Mg	*	(II)11	(II)–7

*Hydrolyses

3.4 REACTION KINETICS: ORDER OF REACTION

As one might predict, the rate of any chemical reaction depends on the relative amounts of reacting constituents. This means the concentration or partial pressure. If, say, the reaction is

$$A = X + Y$$

then the rate is given by

$$-\frac{dc_A}{dt} = k_1 c_A \quad (k_1 = \text{constant}) \tag{3.13}$$

where c_A is the concentration of A in the A-X-Y mixture at any time t. On integration this gives

$$c_A = (c_A)_0 \exp(-k_1 t) \tag{3.14}$$

where $(c_A)_0$ is the initial concentration at $t = 0$, so that we can see that the rate falls off exponentially. Such a reaction is said to be a *first order* reaction. Similarly, a *second order* reaction is of the type

$$A + B = X + Y$$

for which

$$-\,dc_A/dt = -\,dc_B/dt = k_2 c_A c_B \quad (k_2 = \text{constant}) \tag{3.15}$$

If A, B are the same constituent, so that the reaction is of the kind

$$2A = X + Y$$

then the rate is proportional to c_A^2.

It should be noted that the order of reaction (the number of constituents whose concentration determines the reaction velocity) is not necessarily the same as the *molecularity* (the number of atoms or molecules taking part in each act leading to chemical reaction). Thus, for example, the reaction of A and B may proceed in several steps in sequence, the slowest (that is, rate determining) step being

$$A + C = D$$

where C and D are intermediate compounds formed en route. Such a reaction is 'bimolecular', inasmuch as two molecules A + C are involved, but is nevertheless of first order, since the rate depends only on the concentration of A.

The rate constant k_1 or k_2 is found to depend upon temperature according to the **Arrhenius equation**

$$k = A \exp(-Q/RT) \tag{3.16}$$

where the pre-exponential constant A is called the **frequency factor** and Q is the **activation energy** of the reaction. Taking logarithms

$$\ln k = \ln A - (Q/RT) \tag{3.17}$$

so that $\ln k$ (or $\log k$) gives a straight line plotted vs. $1/T$ with a slope of $-Q/R$ (or $-Q/2.303R$), Fig. 3.1. R is the gas constant (8.31 J/mol K). Many *thermally activated* processes behave in this way, and an Arrhenius plot enables us to determine the activation energy Q. Such a result is empirical, and the next section provides a theoretical basis for this observation.

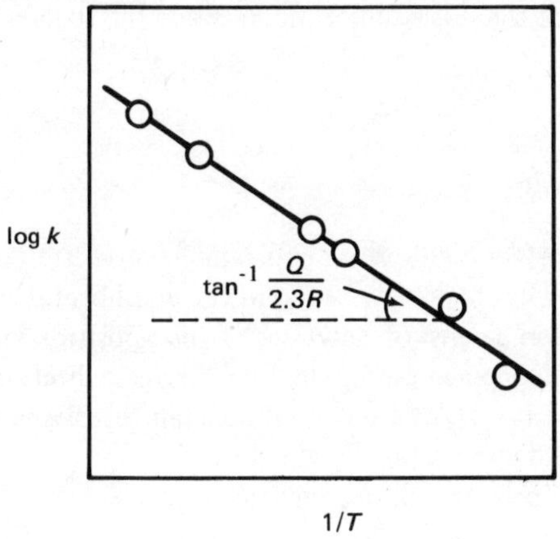

Fig. 3.1 Arrhenius plot of the reaction rate constant vs. reciprocal temperature. The slope d(log k)/d(1/T) is $-Q/2.303R$, where Q is the activation energy.

3.5 RATE PROCESS THEORY

The 'rate process' theory (perhaps more appropriately called the theory of process rates) postulates that each part of a chemical process is characterised by (a) molecular collision, (b) the formation of an intermediate complex of high energy and short life which is in equilibrium with the reactant molecules, and (c) the immediate decomposition of this complex to form products. An overall process may consist of several elementary steps in sequence, and we shall here concern ourselves only with the slowest of these steps, which determines the rate, Fig. 3.2. The intermediate or **activated complex** is represented by a double-dagger symbol ‡.

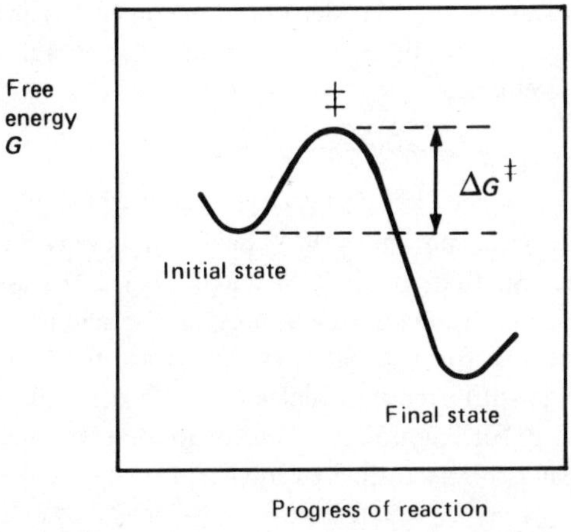

Fig. 3.2 The energy profile for the rate determining step.

We first assume that there is equilibrium between the species

$$A + B = \ddagger$$

so that

$$K^{\ddagger} = c_{\ddagger}/c_A c_B \qquad (3.18)$$

where $K^{\ddagger}$ is the appropriate equilibrium constant, here written in terms of concentrations; in the previous chapter we saw that the equilibrium constant is more accurately represented in terms of activities. Decomposition of the activated complex is assumed to take place during the first thermal vibration so that, if the vibration frequency is **f** (= **k**T/**h**, a universal constant involving the Boltzmann and Planck constants and approximately equal to $10^{12}\ s^{-1}$ at room temperature), the rate of formation of products of decomposition is

$$\text{Rate} = \mathbf{f}\, c_{\ddagger} = \mathbf{f}\, K^{\ddagger} c_A c_B \qquad (3.19)$$

From eqn (2.41), the equilibrium constant for any reaction is related to the standard free energy change accompanying the reaction so that, because here the change is $\Delta G^{\ddagger} = \mu_{\ddagger} - \mu_A - \mu_B$,

$$\Delta G^{\ddagger} = -RT \ln K^{\ddagger} \qquad (3.20)$$

whence, from eqn (3.19) (3.20)

$$\boxed{\text{Rate} = \mathbf{f}\, c_A c_B \exp(-\Delta G^{\ddagger}/RT)} \qquad (3.21)$$

The 'RT' in eqn (3.20) and (2.41) derives from eqn (2.18) and the gas laws. These in turn are based on the distribution of molecular energies described by the Maxwell-Boltzmann equation

$$n/N = \exp(-U/RT) \qquad (3.22)$$

which gives the proportion of molecules (n/N) having an energy U (J/mol) greater than the average value. So that, implicit in eqn (3.21) is the assumption that only those A, B molecules having a free energy $\Delta G^{\ddagger}$ greater than the average value are able to react and form ‡. Such energy is acquired by collision and thermal energy exchange with other molecules and with the walls of the reaction vessel. This critical energy for reaction is called the **free energy of activation** $\Delta G^{\ddagger}$. We can, of course, expand this according to eqn (2.11)

$$\Delta G^{\ddagger} = \Delta H^{\ddagger} - T\Delta S^{\ddagger} \qquad (3.23)$$

so that

$$\text{Rate} = \{\mathbf{f}\exp(\Delta S^{\ddagger}/R)\}\, c_A c_B \exp(-\Delta H^{\ddagger}/RT) \tag{3.24}$$

where the frequency factor in eqn (3.15) is seen to contain a **configurational entropy** term $\Delta S^{\ddagger}$ and the activation energy Q in that equation is now seen to be an activation *enthalpy* $\Delta H^{\ddagger}$. It should be noted that the frequency factor is slightly temperature-dependent (through **kT/h**) so that the Arrhenius plot is not exactly rectilinear: for this reason the value of $\Delta H^{\ddagger}$ obtained from Fig. 3.1 is sometimes referred to as the 'apparent' activation enthalpy.

Table 3.2 lists some typical activation enthalpies at 298 K. It may be seen that many electrolytic processes are characterised by an energy in the region of 40–50 kJ/mol.

Table 3.2 Some typical activation enthalpies at 298 K

Process	$\Delta H^{\ddagger}$ kJ/mol
Charge transfer on metals	30–70
Ionic diffusion in water	40–55
Gaseous reactions	
(homogeneous)	120–300
(heterogeneous)	60–180
Polymerisation	30–60
Surface diffusion	30–40
Interstitial diffusion in crystalline solids	40–80
Substitutional diffusion in crystalline solids	140–300
Diffusion in molten salts	200–300

Bibliography to Chapter 3

Eyring and Eyring (1963), *Modern Chemical Kinetics,* Reinhold.
Moore (1963), *Physical Chemistry,* Longmans.
Robbins (1972), *Ions in Solution,* Oxford University Press.
Robinson and Stokes (1959), *Electrolyte Solutions,* 2nd edn., Butterworths.
Sharpe (1969), *Principles of Oxidation and Reduction,* 2nd edn., Royal Inst. Chemistry, London.
Upadhyaya and Dube (1977), *Problems in Metallurgical Thermodynamics and Kinetics,* Pergamon.

Notes to Chapter 3

3.1 The ionic product is strictly an *activity* product and should therefore be $K_w = h_{H+} \times h_{OH-}$. It may therefore be seen to be the equilibrium constant for the water dissociation reaction, eqn (3.6), with $a_{H2O} = 1$. See section 2.4.

3.2 A word of caution: many published data refer to *ionic* products ($K_s = (m_A/m^{\ominus})^{n+} (m_B/m^{\ominus})^{n-}$) rather than activity products but are nevertheless of the right order of magnitude. The values in Table 3.1 are taken largely from Parsons (1959), *Handbook of Electrochemical Constants*, Butterworth, or else calculated from activity coefficient data close to saturation.

Chapter 4

Some Underlying Electrochemistry

4.1 ELECTROCHEMICAL POTENTIAL

In section 2.2 and eqn (2.11) it was claimed that the free energy change

$$\Delta G = \Sigma n_i \mu_i \text{ (final state)} - \Sigma n_i \mu_i \text{ (initial state)} \tag{4.1}$$

provides a measure of the driving force of a chemical reaction. Whilst this is generally valid, it is necessary to broaden the concept of free energy when electrically charged species are involved. Thus, the chemical potential μ_i of such species is augmented by the additional electrical energy $z_i F \varphi_i$ (J/mol) which it possesses by virtue of having a charge $z_i F$ (C/mol) and of being situated in a medium where the electrical potential is φ_i. That is, we may define an **electrochemical potential** (Note 4.1):

$$\boxed{\tilde{\mu}_i = \mu_i + z_i F \varphi_i} \tag{4.2}$$

such that the driving force is the change in electrochemical free energy (that is, the *total* free energy change of the system)

$$\Delta\tilde{G} = \Sigma n_i \tilde{\mu}_i \text{ (final state)} - \Sigma n_i \tilde{\mu}_i \text{ (initial state)} \tag{4.3}$$

At equilibrium $\Delta\tilde{G} = 0$. Similarly, the rate of reaction is governed by an electrochemical free energy of activation

$$\Delta\tilde{G}^\ddagger = \Delta H^\ddagger - T\Delta S^\ddagger + z_\ddagger F \Delta\varphi^\ddagger \tag{4.4}$$

where the activated complex possesses a charge $z_\ddagger F$ C/mol and exists at an electrical potential $\Delta\varphi^\ddagger$ V relative to that of the reactants. Eqn (3.25) becomes, for example,

$$\text{Rate} = \{f \exp(\Delta S^{\ddagger}/R\}\, c_A c_B \exp\{-(\Delta H^{\ddagger} + z_{\ddagger} F \Delta\varphi^{\ddagger})/RT\} \quad (4.5)$$

and an Arrhenius plot no longer provides an unequivocal indication of the activation enthalpy.

An example of the application of eqn (4.3) of immediate interest is the reduction reaction

$$Fe^{2+}(aq) + 2e(\text{in Fe}) = Fe(s) \quad (4.6)$$

which is the reverse of the copper and nickel oxidations portrayed in eqn (3.5). The electrochemical free energy change is

$$\begin{aligned}\Delta\tilde{G} &= \mu_{Fe} - \tilde{\mu}_{Fe2+} - 2\tilde{\mu}_e \\ &= (G^{\bullet}_{Fe} + RT\ \ln a_{Fe}) - (\mu^{m}_{Fe2+} + RT\ \ln h_{Fe2+} + 2F\varphi^{S}) \quad (4.7) \\ &\quad - 2(\mu^{\ominus}_e - F\varphi^{M})\end{aligned}$$

where eqn (2.25) (2.26) (2.34) have been used to expand the chemical potentials in terms of Raoultian and Henrian activities, and φ^S and φ^M respectively denote the electrical potentials in the aqueous solution at the reaction interface and within the metal itself. It should be noted that the charge on 1 mole of electrons is $-F$ coulombs. Collecting the various terms together, we obtain for equilibrium ($\Delta\tilde{G} = 0$)

$$2F(\varphi^M - \varphi^S) = (\mu^m_{Fe2+} - G^{\bullet}_{Fe} + 2\mu^{\ominus}_e) + RT\ \ln(h_{Fe2+}/a_{Fe}) \quad (4.8)$$

As we shall see in section 4.3, this is a form of the **Nernst equation** governing equilibrium at any electrode interface. It relates the potential differences across the interface to a standard free energy change and an activity term.

4.2 CELLS AND HALF-CELLS

An electrolytic or 'galvanic' cell invariably consists of two electronically conducting (for example, metal) electrodes in intimate physical contact with, or immersed in, an electrolyte which separates them. The electrolyte may be an aqueous solution or it may be an ionically conducting solid (ceramic or glass). On open circuit, each electrode is in electrical and chemical equilibrium with the electrolyte and any other solid or gaseous component which may be present. For example, in the cell

$$Pt(s), H_2(g; p=1\ \text{atm})\,|\,HCl(aq; \text{activity}\ h')\,|\,AgCl(s), Ag(s)$$

the platinum electrode is in equilibrium with hydrogen gas at a partial pressure of 1 atm and hydrogen ions at an activity $(h')^{\frac{1}{2}}$ (cf. end of note 2.4 in Chapter 2); whilst the silver electrode is in equilibrium with solid silver chloride – although not necessarily in direct contact with it – and chloride ions at an activity $(h')^{\frac{1}{2}}$. The convention used when writing such cells is that the various constituents are separated by commas and *the separate sources of potential difference* are represented by single vertical lines (Note 4.2). A double vertical line (see later) implies that any such potential differences normally present have been eliminated by suitable design of the cell. The emf of the cell is measured on open circuit, usually by means of a high-impedance voltmeter, in order to avoid passing currents which might upset the various electrode equilibria. The copper leads used between cell and voltmeter introduce (small) additional emf's at each metal/metal contact which cancel one another out.

By convention, electrolytic cells are always written so that, *if short-circuited externally,* they would spontaneously transfer a net positive charge from left to right through the electrolyte: electrons would flow from left to right through the external metallic connection, cations pass from left to right through the cell, and anions from right to left, Fig. 4.1. In short, *oxidation* would occur at the left-hand electrode, which is called the **anode**, and *reduction* at the right-hand electrode, which is called the **cathode**. It will be observed that there is a spontaneous tendency to generate electrons at the anode, which is at a negative potential φ_L with respect to that φ_R of the cathode, where there is a tendency to consume electrons.

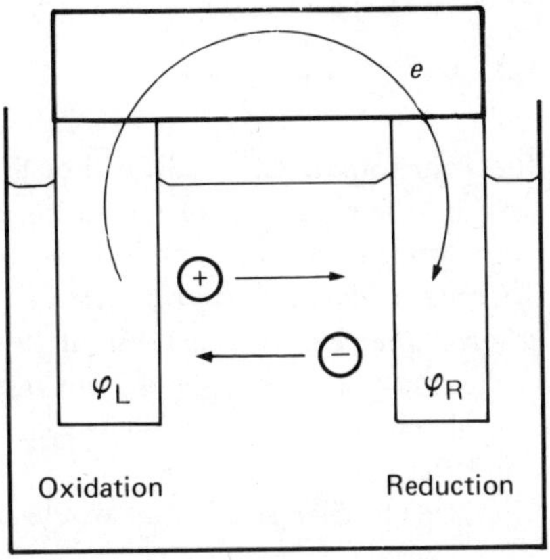

Fig. 4.1 Electrolytic cell convention. The anode (oxidation) is always written on the left-hand side, the cathode (reduction) on the right.
e represents the electron flow through the external short circuit.

The anode can always be identified as that electrode which has electrons leaving it, since that must be the site of oxidation. It is the nature of the process, that is, oxidation or reduction, which defines whether an electrode is an anode or a cathode. Thus, we should expect that the application of an external source of emf to the electrodes of a cell may change their polarity (so that $\varphi_L > \varphi_R$), but the anode will continue to be whichever electrode is the source of electrons.

The potential difference $\varphi_R - \varphi_L$ is likely to vary with the current passing through the cell. On open circuit the value of $\varphi_R - \varphi_L$ is the **electromotive force** (emf) of the cell, $\mathcal{E}$. It is a measure of the free energy change accompanying cell reaction if it were allowed to take place. Thus, for the cell already described, one mole of reaction would be

$$e(\text{Ag}) + \tfrac{1}{2}\text{H}_2(\text{g}) + \text{AgCl(s)} = \text{HCl(aq)} + \text{Ag(s)} + e(\text{Pt}) \tag{4.9}$$

for which the electrochemical free energy change is

$$\begin{aligned} \Delta\tilde{G} &= (\mu_{\text{HCl}} + \mu_{\text{Ag}} + \tilde{\mu}_{e(\text{Pt})}) - (\tfrac{1}{2}\mu_{\text{H2}} + \mu_{\text{AgCl}} + \tilde{\mu}_{e(\text{Ag})}) \\ &= (\mu^m_{\text{HCl}} + G^\bullet_{\text{Ag}} - \tfrac{1}{2}G^\bullet_{\text{H2}} - G^\bullet_{\text{AgCl}}) + (\mu^\ominus_{e(\text{Pt})} - \mu^\ominus_{e(\text{Ag})}) \\ &\qquad + RT\ln\{h'/(p/p^\ominus)^{\frac{1}{2}}\} - F(\varphi_L - \varphi_R). \\ &= 0 \end{aligned} \tag{4.10}$$

Now $G^\bullet_{\text{Ag}} = G^\bullet_{\text{H2}} = 0$ since these are pure elements, Table 2.1, and we further assume that electrons in both metals are in their standard state, so that $\mu^\ominus_{e(\text{Pt})} = \mu^\ominus_{e(\text{Ag})} = 0$. Moreover, $p/p^\ominus = 1$ and $\varphi_R - \varphi_L = \mathcal{E}$, whence

$$-F\mathcal{E} = (\mu^m_{\text{HCl}} - G^\bullet_{\text{AgCl}}) + RT\ln h' \tag{4.11}$$

which has precisely the same form as eqn (4.8). Although no actual cell reaction is allowed to take place, by the expedient of measuring $\mathcal{E}$ on open circuit, it is apparent that this arrangement allows equilibrium to be established. *The electrical potential difference is then a direct reflection of the chemical potential difference available to drive the cell.* To generalise, if spontaneous cell reaction were accompanied by the transport of nF C/mol from anode to cathode through the cell, then an electronic charge $-nF$ would pass externally from a potential φ_L to a potential φ_R and the energy released would be $-nF(\varphi_R - \varphi_L) = -nF\mathcal{E}$. This is the chemical free energy change ΔG that would be supplied by the cell reaction, so that

$$\boxed{\Delta G = -nF\mathcal{E}} \tag{4.12}$$

This equation applies when reaction is allowed to proceed, provided that no spurious potential drops result from the actual movement of charge, for example ohmic drops in the electrolyte or metal. Hence, although eqn (4.11) was derived on the assumption that reaction is prevented, eqn (4.12) still applies if we let the reaction take place infinitely slowly ('reversibly'), so that equilibrium is established at all times and the current passed is negligibly small.

Alternatively, we may treat the cell as being made up of two half-cells, each electrode now being regarded as the complete system: metal/electrolyte, for example

Anode Pt(s), H_2(g; $p = 1$ atm)| HCl(aq; $h = h'$)

Cathode HCl(aq; $h = h'$)| AgCl(s), Ag(s)

In each case, generalised in Fig. 4.2, it may be seen that the electrode contributes a potential difference ${}^{M}\Delta^{S}\varphi = \varphi^{M} - \varphi^{S}$ to the cell emf so that

$$\mathcal{E} = {}^{M}\Delta^{S}\varphi_{R} - {}^{M}\Delta^{S}\varphi_{L} \tag{4.13}$$

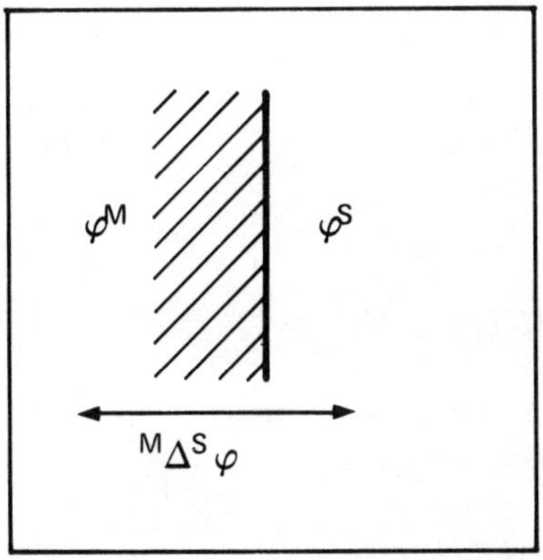

Fig. 4.2 Half cell (single electrode) consisting of a metal M immersed in an electrolyte S.

When the cell is open circuit there is no current flowing in the electrolyte, which is deemed to be homogeneous, and it possesses everywhere a potential φ^{S}. Then ${}^{M}\Delta^{S}\varphi_{R} = \varphi_{R} - \varphi^{S}$ and ${}^{M}\Delta^{S}\varphi_{L} = \varphi_{L} - \varphi^{S}$

so that $\mathcal{E} = \varphi_{R} - \varphi_{L}$

as before, being a measure of the electron energies in the two electrodes established as a result of the separate equilibria.

By analogy with eqn (4.8) (4.12), we anticipate that

$$nF\,{}^{\mathrm{M}}\Delta^{\mathrm{S}}\varphi_{\mathrm{R}} = -\,\Delta G_{\mathrm{R}}$$
$$nF\,{}^{\mathrm{M}}\Delta^{\mathrm{S}}\varphi_{\mathrm{L}} = -\,\Delta G_{\mathrm{L}} \tag{4.14}$$

where $\Delta G_{\mathrm{R}} - \Delta G_{\mathrm{L}} = \Delta G$, the free energy change for the cell as a whole. The anode reaction in our example is

$$\tfrac{1}{2}\mathrm{H_2(g)} = \mathrm{H^+(aq)} + e(\mathrm{Pt})$$

However, *for consistency in measuring the separate emf's, we must write all electrode reactions as reduction reactions* (as will appear more evident shortly), in this case

$$\mathrm{H^+(aq)} + e(\mathrm{Pt}) = \tfrac{1}{2}\mathrm{H_2(g)} \tag{4.15}$$

for which

$$\begin{aligned}\Delta G_{\mathrm{L}} &= \tfrac{1}{2}\mu_{\mathrm{H2}} - \mu_{\mathrm{H+}} - \mu_{e(\mathrm{Pt})}\\ &= \tfrac{1}{2}G^{\bullet}_{\mathrm{H2}} + (RT/2)\ln(p/p^{\ominus}) - \mu^{m}_{\mathrm{H+}} - (RT/2)\ln h'\\ &\qquad\qquad - \mu^{\ominus}_{e(\mathrm{Pt})}\\ &= -\,(RT/2)\ln h' \quad ;\end{aligned} \tag{4.16}$$

since μ^m for hydrogen ions is conventionally taken as zero, Table 2.5, $\mu^{\ominus}_e = G^{\bullet}_{\mathrm{H2}} = 0$ and $p/p^{\ominus} = 1$. Whereupon

$$F\,{}^{\mathrm{M}}\Delta^{\mathrm{S}}\varphi_{\mathrm{L}} = (RT/2)\ln h' \tag{4.17}$$

Similarly, for the cathode of our example,

$$\mathrm{AgCl(s)} + e(\mathrm{Ag}) = \mathrm{Ag(s)} + \mathrm{Cl^-(aq)} \tag{4.18}$$

and

$$\begin{aligned}\Delta G_{\mathrm{R}} &= \mu_{\mathrm{Ag}} + \mu_{\mathrm{Cl-}} - \mu_{\mathrm{AgCl}} - \mu_{e(\mathrm{Ag})}\\ &= G^{\bullet}_{\mathrm{Ag}} + \mu^{m}_{\mathrm{Cl-}} + (RT/2)\ln h' - G^{\bullet}_{\mathrm{AgCl}} - \mu^{\ominus}_{e(\mathrm{Ag})}\\ &= \mu^{m}_{\mathrm{Cl-}} + (RT/2)\ln h' - G^{\bullet}_{\mathrm{AgCl}}\end{aligned} \tag{4.19}$$

since $G^{\bullet}_{Ag} = \mu^{\ominus}_{e} = 0$; whence

$$F^{M}\Delta^{S}\varphi_{R} = -\mu^{m}_{Cl-} - (RT/2)\ln h' - G^{\bullet}_{AgCl} \quad (4.20)$$

Subtraction of eqn (4.17) (4.20), and adding $-\mu^{m}_{H+} = 0$ to the RHS, gives

$$F\mathcal{E} = F({}^{M}\Delta^{S}\varphi_{R} - {}^{M}\Delta^{S}\varphi_{L})$$

$$= -(\mu^{m}_{H+} + \mu^{m}_{Cl-}) + G^{\bullet}_{AgCl} - 2(RT/2)\ln h' \quad (4.21)$$

$$= -\mu^{m}_{HCl} + G^{\bullet}_{AgCl} - RT\ln h'$$

which is identical with eqn (4.11) derived for the complete cell.

4.3 SINGLE POTENTIAL: THE ELECTROCHEMICAL SERIES

The individual half-cell potential differences ${}^{M}\Delta^{S}\varphi$ are called the **single potentials**. We cannot measure these single potentials directly but their relative values can be separately determined with respect to a suitable reference half-cell. That most frequently employed is the *standard hydrogen electrode*, and potentials so measured are said to be on the standard hydrogen electrode (SHE) scale. The standard hydrogen electrode consists of a platinum sheet, suitably treated so as to have a large specific surface area, in contact with an acid solution containing hydrogen ions at unit activity (for example, 1.2 molal HCl has $h_{H+} = h_{HCl} = 1.000$) and in equilibrium with pure hydrogen gas at 1 atm pressure. For any electrode of interest, for example, a metal M in contact with a solution of its own ions at activity h_{Mz+}, the cell is written in the sense

$$Pt(s), H_2(g; p{=}1\ atm) | H^+(aq; h{=}1) \,||\, M^{z+}(aq; h{=}h_{Mz+}) | M(s)$$

where the double vertical lines imply that the liquid junction potential between the acid and metal-ion solutions is suitably eliminated (Note 4.3).

The emf of such a cell is clearly

$$\mathcal{E} = {}^{M}\Delta^{S}\varphi_{M} - {}^{M}\Delta^{S}\varphi_{SHE} = E_{M}$$

where ${}^{M}\Delta^{S}\varphi_{SHE}$ is the single potential of the standard hydrogen electrode and E_M represents *the single potential of the* $M^{z+}(aq) | M(s)$ *electrode on the SHE scale.*

The cell reaction for this cell requires oxidation to occur at the SHE and reduction to occur at M:

$$\tfrac{z}{2}\mathrm{H_2(g)} + \mathrm{M^{z+}(aq)} = z\mathrm{H^+(aq)} + \mathrm{M(s)} \tag{4.22}$$

$$\Delta G = G^{\bullet}_{\mathrm{M}} + z\mu^{m}_{\mathrm{H+}} - (\mu^{m}_{\mathrm{Mz+}} + RT\ln h_{\mathrm{Mz+}}) - \tfrac{z}{2}G^{\bullet}_{\mathrm{H2}}$$

$$= -(\mu^{m}_{\mathrm{Mz+}} + RT\ln h_{\mathrm{Mz+}})$$

and

$$E_{\mathrm{M}} = -\Delta G/zF$$

$$= (\mu^{m}_{\mathrm{Mz+}}/zF) + (RT/zF)\ln h_{\mathrm{Mz+}}$$

that is

$$\boxed{E_{\mathrm{M}} = E^{\ominus}_{\mathrm{M}} + (RT/zF)\ln h_{\mathrm{Mz+}}} \tag{4.23}$$

Eqn (4.23) is the more usual form of the *Nernst equation* which we encountered in eqn (4.8), and $E^{\ominus}_{\mathrm{M}}$ is the *standard single potential* on the SHE scale. A table of standard single potentials for the various metal electrodes is known as the **electrochemical series**, Table 4.1. Metals possessing large positive standard potentials are said to be 'noble', and the reactive metals at the opposite end of the series to be 'base'. The table obviously reflects the degree of reactivity implied in the reduction reaction

$$\mathrm{M^{z+}(aq)} + ze(\mathrm{M}) = \mathrm{M(s)} \tag{4.24}$$

with the sign of the standard single potential determined by the standard *chemical* potential of the ion relative to that of hydrogen ion, Table 2.4.

Table 4.1 The Electrochemical Series.
Standard single potentials (V, SHE) for metal-ion | metal equlibria at 25°C.

	Metal	$E^{\ominus}_{\mathrm{M}}$ (V, SHE)		Metal	$E^{\ominus}_{\mathrm{M}}$ (V, SHE)
Noble end	Au(III) | Au	1.50		Fe(II) | Fe	−0.44
	Pt(II) | Pt	1.2		Ga(III) | Ga	−0.56
	Ag(I) | Ag	0.80		Cr(III) | Cr	−0.74
	Hg(I) as			Zn(II) | Zn	−0.76
	Hg_2^{2+} | Hg	0.79		V(II) | V	−1.18
	Cu(II) | Cu	0.35		Mn(II) | Mn	−1.18
	Bi(III) as			Al(III) | Al	−1.66
	BiO^+ | Bi	0.32		Ti(III) | Ti	−1.8
	Ge(II) | Ge	0.23		U(III) | U	−1.80
	Pb(II) | Pb	−0.13		Be(II) | Be	−1.97
	Sn(II) | Sn	−0.14		Mg(II) | Mg	−2.36
	Ni(II) | Ni	−0.23		Na(I) | Na	−2.71
	Co(II) | Co	−0.28		Ca(II) | Ca	−2.87
	Tl(I) | Tl	−0.34		K(I) | K	−2.92
	Cd(II) | Cd	−0.40	Base end	Li(I) | Li	−3.04

4.4 REDOX EQUILIBRIA

The Nernst equation (4.23) may be extended to any process in which charge transfer, that is, oxidation and reduction (section 3.1), takes place. Thus, the single potential for the general reduction reaction

$$Ox^{n+}(aq) + ne(metal) = Red$$

may be measured in the cell

$$Pt(s), H_2(g; p=1\ atm) \mid H^+(aq; h=1) \parallel Ox^{n+}(aq) \mid Red, Metal$$

for which the overall cell reaction is

$$\tfrac{n}{2}H_2(g) + Ox^{n+}(aq) = nH^+(aq) + Red$$

and the emf is

$$\boxed{E = E^{\ominus} + (RT/nF)\ln(h_{Ox}/h_{Red})} \tag{4.26}$$

Here $E^{\ominus}$ may be calculated using an appropriate form of eqn (4.23) (Note 4.4):

$$E^{\ominus} = (\mu^m_{Ox} - \mu^m_{Red})/nF \tag{4.27}$$

Examples may be drawn from simple *homogeneous equilibria* such as

$$Fe^{3+}(aq) + e(Pt) = Fe^{2+}(aq) \tag{4.28}$$

and *reactions involving the formation of solid or gaseous compounds* such as

$$FeCl_2(s) + 2e(Fe) = Fe(s) + 2Cl^-(aq) \tag{4.29}$$

$$O_2(g) + 2H_2O(l) + 4e(Pt) = 4\ OH^-(aq) \tag{4.30}$$

Notice that, where a metallic conductor is not directly involved in the reaction (eqn (4.28) (4.30)), it is necessary to immerse a suitable inert metal such as platinum in the solution in order to measure the single potential, redox equilibrium being established between reactants adsorbed at the interface. We now apply the modified Nernst equation (4.26) to each of these examples, remembering that standard chemical potentials of elements are zero:

(I) $$E^{\ominus}_{Fe(3/2)} = (\mu^m_{Fe3+} - \mu^m_{Fe2+})/F$$

$$= (-10.6 + 84.9)/96.5 = +0.77\ V, SHE$$

using the data in Table 2.5 and working in kJ/mol

$$E_{Fe(3/2)} = E^{\ominus}_{Fe(3/2)} + (RT/F)\ln(h_{Fe3+}/h_{Fe2+}) \tag{4.28a}$$

$$= 0.77 + (2.303 \times 8.31 \times 0.298/96.5)\log(h_{Fe3+}/h_{Fe2+})$$

$$= 0.77 + 0.059\log(h_{Fe3+}/h_{Fe2+})\text{ V, SHE at }25°\text{C} \tag{4.28b}$$

(II) $$E^{\ominus}_{FeCl2} = (G^{\bullet}_{FeCl2} - 2\mu^{m}_{Cl-})/2F$$

$$= (-302.8 + 262.2)/193 = -0.21\text{ V, SHE}$$

$$E_{FeCl2} = E^{\ominus}_{FeCl2} + (RT/2F)\ln(a_{FeCl2}/a_{Fe} \times h^{2}_{Cl-}) \tag{4.29a}$$

$$= -0.21 + 0.030\log(a_{FeCl2}/a_{Fe} \times h^{2}_{Cl-}) \tag{4.29b}$$

(III) $$E^{\ominus}_{O2} = (2G^{\bullet}_{H2O} - 4\mu^{m}_{OH-})/4F$$

$$= (-474.4 + 628.8)/386 = +0.40\text{ V, SHE}$$

$$E_{O2} = E^{\ominus}_{O2} + (RT/4F)\ln(p_{O2}/p^{\ominus})/h^{4}_{OH-} \tag{4.30a}$$

$$= 0.40 + 0.015\log(p_{O2}/p^{\ominus}) - 0.059\log h_{OH-}$$

We now recall that $-\log h_{OH-} = pOH$

$$= pK_w - pH \tag{3.9}$$

$$= 14.0 - pH\text{ at }25°\text{C}$$

whence

$$E_{O2} = 0.40 + (14 \times 0.059) + 0.015\log(p_{O2}/p^{\ominus}) - 0.059\,pH$$

$$= 1.23 + 0.015\log(p_{O2}/p^{\ominus}) - 0.059\,pH\text{ V, SHE at }25°\text{C} \tag{4.30b}$$

A list of some typical standard redox potentials is given in Table 4.2. It may there be seen that the standard potentials for reactions (4.28) (4.30) are confirmed. Also included in the table are reactions involving oxy-anions such as $HCrO_4^-$ and SO_4^{2-}. These may be written out in full by judicious additions of H^+(aq) and/or H_2O, for example

$$HCrO_4^-(aq) + 7H^+(aq) + 3e(Pt) = Cr^{3+}(aq) + 4H_2O(l)$$

$$SO_4^{2-}(aq) + 5H^+(aq) + 4e(Pt) = \tfrac{1}{2}S_2O_3^{2-}(aq) + \tfrac{5}{2}H_2O(l) \quad (4.31)$$

It is therefore possible to calculate the single potential for any oxidation/reduction process for which the activities and appropriate standard chemical potentials are known. This enables one to predict the outcome of reactions where the electrode potential is maintained *at any arbitrary value,* either as the result of impressing a voltage from some external source of electric power or of having present a combination of several redox systems. Suppose, for example, we have the Fe(3/2) system, eqn (4.28), initially in equilibrium with a platinum electrode and with equal ionic activities $h_{Fe3+} = h_{Fe2+}$, so that

$$E_{Fe(3/2)} = 0.77 + 0.059\log(1.0) = 0.77 \text{ V, SHE}$$

We then add to the solution a reducing agent such as stannous ions Sn^{2+} (aq)

$$Sn^{4+}(aq) + 2e(Pt) = Sn^{2+}(aq) \quad (4.32)$$

for which, Table 4.2,

$$E_{Sn(4/2)} = 0.15 + 0.030\log(h_{Sn4+}/h_{Sn2+}) \quad (4.32a)$$

$$= 0.06 \text{ V, SHE at 25°C if the initial tin activity ratio is (say) } 10^{-3}: 1.$$

Evidently the platinum cannot adopt two single potentials simultaneously. In fact, it adopts a compromise **mixed potential** at some intermediate value between 0.77 and 0.06 V, SHE. The actual value is largely determined by kinetic factors (Chapter 6), so for convenience of calculation we shall assume that the mixed potential is here exactly half way between, at +0.415 V, SHE. If both electrode processes were at equilibrium, we should then have

$$E_{Fe(3/2)} = 0.415 = 0.77 + 0.059\log(h_{Fe3+}/h_{Fe2+})_{new}$$
$$\text{whence } (h_{Fe3+}/h_{Fe2+})_{new} = 10^{-6}$$

and

$$E_{Sn(4/2)} = 0.415 = 0.15 + 0.030\log(h_{Sn4+}/h_{Sn2+})_{new}$$
$$\text{whence } (h_{Sn4+}/h_{Sn2+})_{new} = 10^{9}.$$

Accordingly, the ferric/ferrous ion reaction is impelled towards a target ratio of ca. 10^{-6} which involves reduction, whilst the stannous/stannic ion reaction attempts to attain the ratio of 10^9 which involves oxidation. The overall reaction is

$$Sn^{2+}(aq) + 2Fe^{3+}(aq) = Sn^{4+}(aq) + 2Fe^{2+}(aq) \qquad (4.33)$$

This mutuality of oxidation and reduction further illustrates the principle stated in section 3.1. The mixed potential concept also explains why Sn^{2+}(aq) is a reducing agent and Fe^{3+}(aq) an oxidising agent in inorganic chemistry.

Table 4.2 Redox Equilibria Series.
Standard reduction potentials for common redox reactions at 25°C. As in Table 4.1, simple ions are represented in the form M(*Z*), for example Pb(IV) = Pb^{4+}(aq). Equations involving oxy-anions can be balanced by adding H^+ (aq) to the LHS and/or H_2O molecules to the RHS, as eqn (4.31).

Equilibrium Ox	Red	$E^{\ominus}$ V, SHE
Homogeneous reactions:		
Ag(II)	| Ag(I)	2.00
Pb(IV)	| Pb(II)	1.66
Ce(IV)	| Ce(III)	1.44
Au(III)	| Au(I)	1.41
Fe(III)	| Fe(II)	0.77
Cu(II)	| Cu(I)	0.17
Sn(IV)	| Sn(II)	0.15
Cr(III)	| Cr(II)	–0.41
MnO_4^-	| Mn(II)	1.51
$HCrO_4^-$	| Cr(III)	1.20
ClO_4^-	| ClO_3^-	1.19
NO_2^-	| $\frac{1}{2}N_2H_5^+$	0.28
SO_4^{2-}	| $\frac{1}{2}S_2O_3^{2-}$	0.24
H_3PO_2	| P	–0.51
Heterogeneous gas reactions:		
$\frac{1}{2}Cl_2(g)$	| Cl^-	1.36
HNO_3	| NO(*g*)	0.95
$\frac{1}{2}O_2(g)$	| 2 OH^-	0.40
H^+	| $\frac{1}{2}H_2(g)$	0.00

4.5 COMPLEXANTS

Water is not the only molecular entity that provides a solvation sheath for dissolved ions. Thus, although in nitrate solutions silver(I) and iron(II) ions exist as the hydrated cations $Ag(H_2O)_4^+$ and Fe $(H_2O)_6^{2+}$, alternative **ligands** are provided by NH_3, CN^-, OH^-, etc. These ligands denote their lone electron pairs (Note 4.5) to the positively charged cation and substitute for one or more water molecules in the solvation sheath, thereby forming a more stable entity, for example

$$Ag^+(aq) + 2CN^-(aq) = Ag(CN)_2^-(aq); \quad \Delta G^\ominus = -122 \text{ kJ/mol}$$

$$Fe^{2+}(aq) + 6CN^-(aq) = Fe(CN)_6^{4-}(aq); \quad \Delta G^\ominus = -139 \text{ kJ/mol}$$

The standard free energy change of reaction constitutes the 'stabilisation energy' of the complex in each case. Applying the reaction isotherm, eqn (2.43),

$$K_2 = h_{Ag(CN)2}/h_{Ag+} \times h^2_{CN-}$$

$$= \exp(-\Delta G^\ominus/RT)$$

$$= \exp(122/8.3 \times 0.298) = 10^{21.2} \text{ at } 25°C \qquad (4.34)$$

K_2 is the **stability constant** of the dicyano complex of Ag(I); the reciprocal is the 'instability' constant. In general, for a reaction

$$M^{z+}(aq) + nL^-(aq) = ML_n^{z-n}(aq) \qquad (4.35)$$

$$\boxed{K_n = h_{complex}/h_{Mz+} \times h^n_{L-}} \qquad (4.36)$$

Since the silver cyanide complex is highly stable, $K_2 = 10^{21.2}$, it follows that Ag(I) exists almost entirely in the complexed state provided that cyanide is present in excess. Thus, in a solution containing 0.1 molal $AgNO_3$ + 1.0 molal KCN and neglecting the activity coefficient (so that h is numerically equal to m),

$h_{complex} = 0.1$ since it derives from all the $AgNO_3$

$h_{CN-} = 1.0 - 2(0.1) = 0.8$ residual cyanide

$h_{Ag+} = 0.1/(0.8^2 \times 10^{21.2}) = 10^{-22.0}$ from eqn (4.35)

which gives the activity of residual hydrated silver cations. Again, for the general reaction eqn (4.34),

$$h_{Mz+} \approx (m_{salt}/m^\ominus)/K_n\, \{(m_{complexant}/m^\ominus) - n(m_{salt}/m^\ominus)\} \qquad (4.37)$$

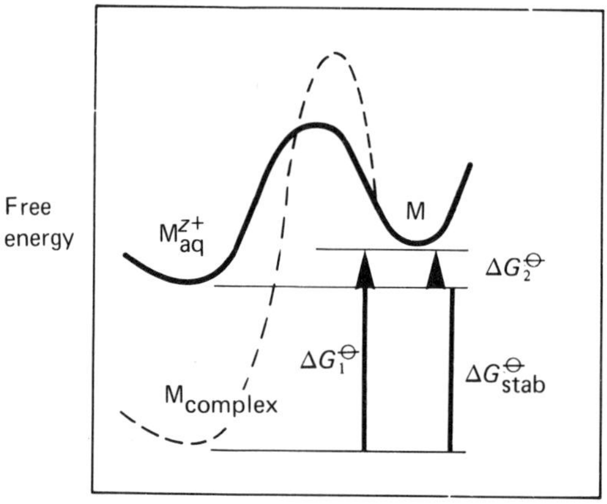

Fig. 4.3 Free energy profile for reduction of complex ion.

The lowering of the activity of 'free', that is, hydrated, cations by complexing has consequences in terms of their electrochemical potential and hence upon the single potential of any electrode in which they are involved, Fig. 4.3. That is, the reduction reaction

$$ML_n^{z-n}(aq) + ze(M) = M(s) + nL^-(aq)$$

$$\Delta G_1^{\ominus} = n\mu^m_{ligand} - \mu^m_{complex} \tag{4.38}$$

is accompanied by a more positive value of ΔG than is the reaction

$$M^{z+}(aq) + ze(M) = M(s); \Delta G_2^{\ominus} = -\mu^m_{ion} \tag{4.39}$$

and the complexing reaction (4.35) is accompanied by a stabilising free energy change

$$\Delta G^{\ominus}_{stab} = \mu^m_{complex} - \mu^m_{ion} - n\mu^m_{ligand}$$

$$= \Delta G_2^{\ominus} - \Delta G_1^{\ominus} \tag{4.40}$$

The standard single potentials for the complexed and simple hydrated ions are

$$E^{\ominus}_{complex} = -\Delta G_1^{\ominus}/zF \quad \text{and} \quad E^{\ominus}_{aq} = -\Delta G_2^{\ominus}/zF$$

whence

$$E^{\ominus}_{complex} - E^{\ominus}_{aq} = E^{\ominus}_{complex} - E^{\ominus}_{M}$$

$$= \Delta G^{\ominus}_{stab}/zF \tag{4.41}$$

Because $\Delta G^{\ominus}_{\text{stab}} < 0$ this means that $E^{\ominus}$ is lowered by an amount $\Delta G^{\ominus}_{\text{stab}}/zF$ or, because of the reaction isotherm eqn (2.41),

$$E^{\ominus}_{\text{complex}} - E^{\ominus}_{\text{M}} = -(RT/zF) \ln K_n$$

or

$$\boxed{\Delta E^{\ominus} = (2.303\, RT/zF)\, pK_n} \qquad (4.42)$$

Typical values of pK_n and $\Delta E^{\ominus}$ are listed in Table 4.3.

Table 4.3 Some ammine, hydroxylo and cyano complexes of metal ions at 25°C. Data from G. H. Aylward and T. J. V. Findlay, *S.I. Chemical Data* (New York: Wiley), 2nd edn. 1974

Ion	Ligand	n	$-pK_n$	$E^{\ominus}_{\text{complex}} - E^{\ominus}_{\text{aq}}$ Volts
Ag(I)	NH_3	2	7	–0.42
	CN^-	2	20	–1.18
Cd(II)	NH_3	4	7	–0.21
	OH^-	3	8	–0.24
	CN^-	4	18	–0.53
Co(II)	NH_3	6	5	–0.15
	OH^-	3	6	–0.17
Cu(I)	NH_3	2	11	–0.65
	CN^-	4	28	–1.66
Cu(II)	NH_3	4	13	–0.38
	OH^-	4	15	–0.44
Fe(II)	OH^-	3	8	–0.23
	CN^-	6	37	–1.09
Fe(III)	CN^-	6	44	–0.87
Ni(II)	NH_3	6	8	–0.25
	OH^-	3	12	–0.35
	CN^-	4	31	–0.92
Zn(II)	NH_3	4	9	–0.26
	OH^-	4	15	–0.46
	CN^-	4	20	–0.59

It is easy to show that the single potential obtained as a result of complexing is the same whether we derive it using

(a) $E^{\ominus}_{M}$ and the reduced activity of 'free' cations, or

(b) $E^{\ominus}_{complex}$ and the activity of complexed ions.

Taking silver(I) as in our previous example,

(a) $E^{\ominus}_{M} = 0.80$ V, SHE; $h_{Ag+} = 10^{-22.0}$
so the Nernst equation gives
$E = 0.80 + 0.059 \log(10^{-22}) = -0.50$ V, SHE

(b) $E^{\ominus}_{complex} = 0.80 - 1.18 = -0.38$ V, SHE
$h_{complex} \approx 0.1$; $h_{ligand} \approx 0.8$

$$E = E^{\ominus}_{complex} + (RT/zF) \ln (h_{complex}/h^{n}_{ligand}) \tag{4.43}$$

$$= -0.38 + 0.059 \log(0.1/0.8^2) = -0.50 \text{ V, SHE}$$

Q.E.D.

Bibliography to Chapter 4

Bockris and Reddy (1970), *Modern Electrochemistry,* 2 vols, MacDonald.
Davies (1967), *Electrochemistry,* Newnes.
Robbins (1972), *Ions in Solution,* Oxford Univ. Press.
West (1973), *Basic Electrochemistry,* Van Nostrand Reinhold.
A detailed treatment of electrode processes and their application to analytical techniques is given by Galus (1976) *Fundamentals of Electrochemical Analysis,* Ellis Horwood.

Notes to Chapter 4

4.1 The Spanish 'tilde' sign (~) may be read as such, for example 'mu tilde', but other writers sometimes replace the tilde by a bar superscript. For this reason I have adopted the practice of pronouncing it as 'mu squiggle', and the reader may wish to follow suit.

4.2 Some textbooks may still retain an earlier convention in which vertical lines were used to separate the *phases.*

4.3 Effected by interposing a solution saturated with anions and cations having roughly equal ionic mobilities, for example satd.KCl(aq). Such an arrangement is referred to as a 'salt bridge'.

4.4 The reader should beware of confusion here. Because eqn (4.23) (4.27) are written in the form $nFE^{\ominus} = +\mu^{m}_{ox} - \mu^{m}_{red}$ it might be supposed that we are really considering an *oxidation* reaction with $\Delta G^{\ominus} = \mu^{m}_{ox} - \mu^{m}_{red}$ and then equating $E^{\ominus}$ with $\Delta G^{\ominus}/nF$. Such an interpretation might justifiably be reinforced by (a) the plus signs in eqn (4.23) (4.26) and (b) the implication that the standard chemical potentials μ^{m} in Table 2.5 are really $\mu^{m}_{ion} - z\mu^{m}_{H+}$, which is the standard free energy change for the reaction (4.22) in reverse, that is, an oxidation. Whilst several earlier textbooks in corrosion and electrochemistry (among them my own *Electrodeposition and Corrosion Processes,* Van Nostrand 1965 first edn.) explicitly used this so-called 'European' sign convention: $E = +\,\Delta G^{\text{oxidation}}/nF$, I have here followed the 1954 Stockholm convention: $E = -\Delta G^{\text{reduction}}/nF$. That is, *the plus sign in eqn (4.23) (4.26) (4.27) originates from a double minus.* The implication (b) regarding the μ^{m} values in Table 2.5 is false. These energies of the ions in solution (relative to that of hydrogen ions) are merely a reflection of their relative abilities to do work in an appropriate electrochemical cell.

Finally, the system adopted here of writing reactions as half-cell reactions and ignoring the chemical potential of electrons leads to the same result as considering the complete cell reaction (where of course the electrons cancel out). In the determination of single potentials on the SHE scale this half-cell procedure is justified only because, on the SHE convention, the free energy change is zero for the reaction $\frac{1}{2}H_2$ (g; $p = 1$ atm) = H^+ (aq; $h = 1$) + e (Pt).

4.5 The 'lone pair' concept is part of the valence-bond model of the bonding in molecules, and the reader should consult, for example, Cartmell and Fowles, *Valency and Molecular Structure* (London: Butterworths) 1977. The oxygen atom in water has six electrons in its outer quantum shell, two of which are engaged in bond formation with the two hydrogen atoms that make up the water molecule. The remaining four electrons are spatially distributed in two vestigial 'lobes' resembling the two bonding orbitals. The result is that, on the side of the oxygen atom remote from the two hydrogens, there is a concentration of negative charge which is attracted to any (positively charged) cations in the vicinity. Similar lone pairs exist on other ligand groups.

Chapter 5

Why Corrosion Happens

5.1 ENERGETIC CONSIDERATIONS

When metals other than the 'noble' metals (gold and the platinum group of metals, Table 4.1) are exposed to water at room temperature, there is a tendency for them to dissolve. Thus, one might suppose that the reaction

$$M(s) + n\ H_2O(ads) = M^{z+}\cdot nH_2O(aq) + ze(M) \tag{5.1}$$

which includes the reorientation of water molecules, $H_2O(ads)$, close to the metal surface into an appropriate hydration sheath, must be accompanied by a negative change of free energy:

$$\Delta G^{ox} = \mu_{Mz+} + n\mu_e - \mu_M - n\mu_{H2O} < 0 \tag{5.2}$$

where, as in the previous chapter, μ_{Mz+} represents the chemical potential of the hydrated ion and μ_{H2O} here represents the chemical potential of adsorbed water. Why then don't metals spontaneously waste away?

The reason is that the oxidation reaction (5.1) occurs only to a limited extent for, as it does so, an adverse electrical potential gradient is set up, owing to the positive ions now in solution and the electrons left behind in the metal. This arrangement of charges at the interface constitutes an *electrical double layer* similar to a capacitor. By considering the overall energy change, including the electrical work done in moving charged particles through the double layer, we saw in eqn (4.8) (4.14) that at equilibrium

$$zF\,{}^{M}\Delta^{S}\varphi = -\,\Delta G_{eq}^{red} = +\,\Delta G_{eq}^{ox} \tag{5.3}$$

where $\Delta G_{eq}^{red} = -\,\Delta G_{eq}^{ox}$ is the equilibrium free energy change accompanying the reduction reaction of ion discharge, the reverse of eqn (5.1), and ${}^{M}\Delta^{S}\varphi$, the single potential, is the potential drop across the double layer. That is, net dissolution continues only up to the point where the electrical work done (J/mol) when ions cross this layer is balanced by the release of chemical free energy accompanying dissolution. Thereafter the rates of dissolution and deposition are equal and there is no net charge transfer.

From the foregoing argument, we can see why metals do not waste away spontaneously. But we now have to explain why in fact they often do! To understand this, we must consider what would happen if, by some suitable mechanism, we were to raise the electrical potential of the metal to some value

$$\varphi^{\mathrm{M}} = \varphi^{\mathrm{M}}_{\mathrm{eq}} + \eta \qquad (\eta > 0) \tag{5.4}$$

relative to its equilibrium value $\varphi^{\mathrm{M}}_{\mathrm{eq}}$, keeping $\varphi^{\mathrm{S}}_{\mathrm{eq}}$ in the solution the same. That is, we have increased the potential difference by an amount η, called the **over-potential.** Obviously, in such circumstances the anodic dissolution of 1 mole of metal by reaction (5.1) is now accompanied by a net electrochemical free energy change of

$$\Delta\tilde{G}^{\mathrm{ox}} = -zF\eta \tag{5.5}$$

For example, for a divalent metal at an overpotential of about 0.3 V, $\Delta\tilde{G}^{\mathrm{ox}} =$ −60 kJ/mol. Dissolution will, therefore, continue until either limited by the interposition of a suitable impenetrable barrier of corrosion product or until there is no metal left to waste away. The *rate* at which such corrosion occurs is determined by kinetic factors such as electron transfer across the double layer or mass transport (diffusion) in the solution.

The electrical potential of the metal can be raised in two ways: (a) by making it the positive pole in an electrolysis cell, which involves connecting it to an electron 'sink', or, as we saw in section 4.4, (b) by having present a suitable oxidising agent. The most common oxidising agent is dissolved oxygen, Fig. 5.1,

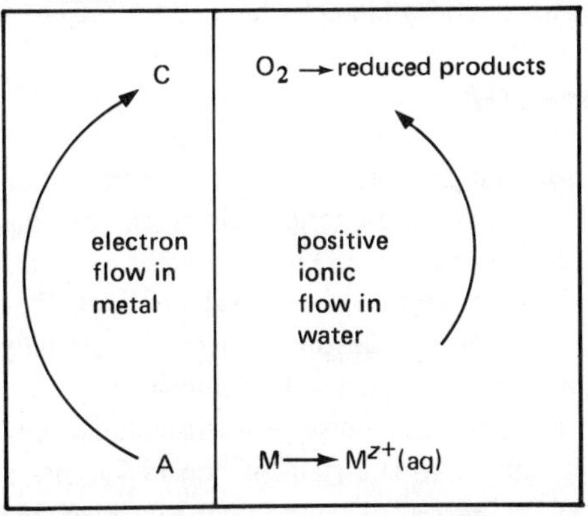

Fig. 5.1 Corrosion in aerated water. A and C denote anodic and cathodic areas, that is, the sites of oxidation and reduction respectively, in a corrosion cell. Such areas may be less than 1 mm apart or, in a differential aeration cell, separated by as much as several metres.

or else protons from acidified water itself. In the case (b) we should expect that the type of oxidant used will contribute to the rate of corrosion. It may also determine the nature of any surface films formed and, depending on its ready availability or otherwise, may also be expected to affect the distribution of corrosion over the metal surface.

5.2 GRAIN BOUNDARY ATTACK

Not all surface metal atoms are the same. Some are highly coordinated, as in a close-packed plane; some lie in grain boundaries; others may be associated with, or may themselves be, foreign solute atoms. So that we should recognise that ΔG_{eq}^{ox} of eqn (5.3) refers to some kind of statistically averaged 'norm'. In practice, it appears that the norm corresponds to more or less weakly coordinated atoms at the ends of atom rows, lying in 'kink' sites in the body of the exposed grains. Atoms in emergent grain boundaries or dislocations will therefore possess a higher energy than the norm, whereas atoms lying within a relatively perfect close-packed plane will possess a lower energy (Note 5.1). That is, if μ_M in eqn (5.2) represent the chemical potentials of 1 mole of 'normal' atoms, we may represent the chemical potentials of 'abnormal' atoms by, for example,

$$\text{Grain boundary: } \mu_{gb} = \mu_M + u_{gb} \; (u_{gb} > 0)$$

$$\text{Dislocation: } \mu_{\perp} = \mu_M + u_{\perp} \quad (u_{\perp} > 0) \tag{5.6}$$

$$\text{Close packed plane: } \mu_{pl} = \mu_M + u_{pl} \quad (u_{pl} < 0)$$

Dissolution at a grain boundary or dislocation is, therefore, accompanied by a greater release of free energy than elsewhere. Eqn (5.5) becomes, for example,

$$\Delta\tilde{G}^{ox} = -zF\eta - u_{gb} \tag{5.7}$$

per mole of grain boundary atoms dissolved. We must of course appreciate that not all grain boundary atoms are energetically identical: u_{gb} is here an averaged value for the extra lattice energy spread over a band of atoms some four or five spacings wide, say $5b$ (b = atomic spacing) (Note 5.2). This would indicate that grain boundaries ought to corrode preferentially, especially if u_{gb} is raised by piled-up dislocations or segregated solute. Even so, as a grain boundary corrodes it alters the surface morphology: a groove is formed. The extra interfacial energy introduced has to be added to the RHS of eqn (5.7). Since 1 mole corresponds to a volume Lb^3 (L = Avogadro's number), a groove $5b$ wide produces two surfaces each $Lb^2/5$ in area, Fig. 5.2. Writing γ for the specific interfacial energy,

$$\Delta\tilde{G}^{ox} = -zF\eta - u_{gb} + (2/5)Lb^2\gamma \tag{5.8}$$

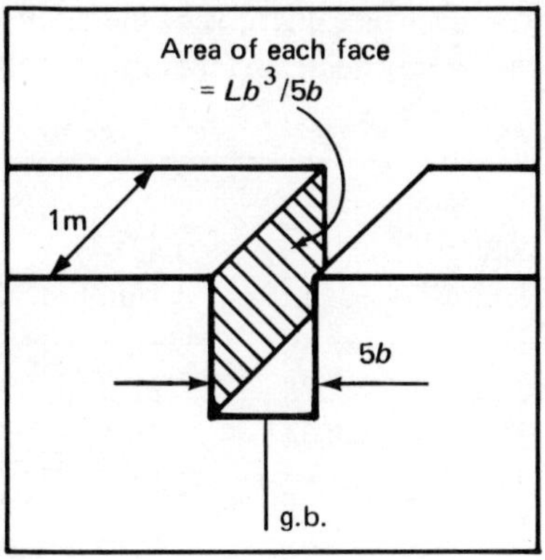

Fig. 5.2 Schematic groove formed by corrosion down a grain boundary.

This explains why grain boundaries do *not* always corrode preferentially, for there is no competitive advantage where $u_{gb} < 0.4Lb^2\gamma$. Table 5.1 indicates how the condition is generally fulfilled only when the grain boundary region is rendered sufficiently active by chemical or mechanical heterogeneity. Here, u_{gb} is the grain boundary energy for large-angle tilt boundaries in the pure solid, normally expressed in J/m^2 but now multiplied by $Lb^2/5$ to convert to J/mol. The value of u_{gb} in an 'activated' grain boundary, u^*_{gb}, is difficult to estimate but is here given as the sum of u_{gb} and an elastic energy term amounting to 10^{-7} times the elastic modulus (N/m^2), if we assume that 10% of the energy represented by the area under the Hooke's law curve is distributed uniformly over the total grain boundary volume (Note 5.3). The surface energy of a metal in water, γ, is given as the reported surface energy values in argon less 0.07 J/m^2 (the energy of the water/air interface) on the assumption that the metal is fully wetted, with a contact angle of zero. The last column indicates the sum of $-u_{gb}$ and $+0.4Lb^2\gamma$, both in kJ/mol (to compare with $\Delta\tilde{G}^{ox} = -60$ kJ/mol) and V (to compare with $\eta = 0.3$ V). The energetic advantage of 'activated' grain boundaries, with $\Delta\tilde{G}^{ox}$ becoming more negative by between 6 and 30 kJ/mol, contrasts with the relative increase in energy of some 20 kJ/mol for attack of 'normal' grain boundaries. Later, we shall see how surface films and mechanical stress can also play a part in localising attack.

We may also note, in passing, that highly coordinated metal atoms have a *lower* driving force for dissolution. This may explain why metallic glasses, formed by ultrarapid quenching from the molten state, often possess a relatively high corrosion resistance. There are no 'normal' atoms in their surface.

Table 5.1 Grain boundary and surface energies of metals in water at 25°C. The final column shows the energy decrease favouring dissolution of an 'activated' grain boundary.

Metal	u_{gb} kJ/mol	u^*_{gb} kJ/mol	γ J/m^2	$0.4Lb^2\gamma$ kJ/mol	Decrease in $\Delta\tilde{G}^{ox}$ kJ/mol	V
Gold	3.58	31.5	1.28	25.5	6.0	0.02
Copper	4.32	38.1	1.66	26.1	12	0.06
Tin	1.75	22.5	0.62	13.6	8.9	0.05
Nickel	5.18	57.7	1.28	19.2	38	0.20
Iron	5.76	60.0	1.85	27.3	33	0.17

5.3 THE CORROSION POTENTIAL

We have seen that metals normally adopt a characteristic electrical potential difference when immersed in aqueous solutions. This potential difference, which has to be measured on some arbitrary scale (usually the standard hydrogen scale, section 4.3), is given the symbol E_{eq} at equilibrium. Its absolute value is denoted by ${}^{M}\Delta^{S}\varphi_{eq} = \varphi^{M}_{eq} - \varphi^{S}$, where φ^{M}_{eq} and φ^{S} are respectively the electrical potentials of the metal and the aqueous solution. The value of ${}^{M}\Delta^{S}\varphi_{eq}$ (and hence E_{eq}) depends on the effective concentrations of the various species involved in the equilibrium. Values for the 'standard' equilibrium potentials $E^{\ominus}_{eq}$, corresponding to appropriately chosen unit concentrations, are listed in the Electrochemical Series, Table 4.1.

We have also seen that continued metal dissolution, that is, corrosion, will result if the potential of the metal is raised to some non-equilibrium value

$$\varphi^{M} = \varphi^{M}_{eq} + \eta \tag{5.4}$$

where η (eta, the so-called overpotential) > 0. Subtracting the potential of the solution φ^{S} from both sides and measuring the resultant single potential on some suitable scale, we get

$$E = E_{eq} + \eta \tag{5.9}$$

The spontaneous achievement of this nonequilibrium state is effected when the metal is simultaneously exposed to an oxidising agent. Thus, iron dissolves in acids because its equilibrium single potential lies below that of $H^{+}(aq)/\frac{1}{2}H_2(g)$, Tables 4.1 and 4.2. The iron conducts electrons so that its potential φ^{M} is the same all over its surface; the acid solution likewise, being ionically conducting, will have a potential φ^S which is substantially the same at all points close to the surface; so that the single potential ${}^M\Delta^S\varphi$ $(= \varphi^M - \varphi^S)$ is everywhere the same at the interface. This potential is the *mixed potential* adopted by the mutually oxidising/reducing electrodes, that is, it is the compromise value lying between the equilibrium single potentials of iron and hydrogen. The mixed potential E is more noble than the equilibrium value E_{eq} for iron and so satisfies eqn (5.9). Because here metal wastage is involved, it is usually called the **corrosion potential** and is represented by the symbol $E_{corrosion}$ (or, more briefly, E_{corr}). We should remember that it is a potential difference ${}^M\Delta^S\varphi$ and so can be measured in the same way as E_{eq}, that is, by means of a high-impedance voltmeter and a suitable reference electrode dipped into the acid, section 7.1.

In order that the corrosion potential should lie above E_{eq} for any particular metal, that is, for metal wastage to occur, the equilibrium single potential of the oxidising agent or *cathodic reactant* must be more positive than E_{eq}. Hence, relatively noble metals such as copper do not dissolve in mineral acids but do so in oxidising acids such as HNO_3 or aerated water: these gas reactions, included at the bottom of Table 4.2, are characterised by standard equilibrium potentials of +0.95 and +0.40 V, SHE respectively. From eqn (4.30a), however, we saw that +0.40 V, SHE corresponds to pOH = 0 (pH 14) and, if we correct for non-standard conditions, viz. air ($a_{O2} = p_{O2}/p^{\ominus} = 0.2$) in equilibrium with neutral water (pH 7), eqn (4.30b) becomes

$$E_{O2} = +1.23 + 0.015 \log(0.2) - 0.059\,(7.0)$$

$$= +0.80 \text{ V, SHE at } 25°\text{C},$$

and we see that oxygen is comparable with HNO_3 in its oxidising power. The Nernst equation (4.23) for copper at an initial trace concentration (= activity) of, say, $h_{Cu2+} = 10^{-6}$ becomes

$$E_{Cu} = +0.35 + 0.03 \log(10^{-6})$$

$$= +0.17 \text{ V, SHE at } 25°\text{C}.$$

Hence the copper will oxidise in aerated neutral water, the 'driving emf' of the corrosion cell being

$$\mathcal{E} = E_{O2} - E_{Cu} = 0.80 - 0.17 = 0.63 \text{ V}.$$

Equation (4.13) was derived for the emf of any electrochemical cell, expressed in terms of single potentials of the anode and cathode. We should therefore anticipate that

$$\boxed{\mathcal{E} = -\Delta G_{\text{corrosion}}/nF} \tag{5.10}$$

refers to the free energy change accompanying the corrosion reaction

$$Cu(s) + \tfrac{1}{2}O_2(g) + H_2O(1) = Cu^{2+}(aq) + 2\ OH^-(aq) \tag{5.11}$$

where, by inspection, it can be seen that 1 mol of reaction leads to the transfer of $2F$ coulombs of electrons from copper to oxygen. Substituting $n = 2$, $\Delta G_{\text{corrosion}}$ here equals

$$-(0.63 \times 2 \times 96.5) = -122 \text{ kJ/mol},$$

confirming that there is a decrease in free energy of the system.

Bibliography to Chapter 5

Electrical double layer theory is well covered by Bockris and Reddy (1970), *Modern Electrochemistry,* MacDonald. Books relating to corrosion principles are listed in the bibliography to Chapter 11.

Notes to Chapter 5

5.1 The fact that atoms in the grain boundary are in energetic equilibrium with those of the grain matrix would indicate that, in the bulk, chemical potentials are equal. However, in a free surface this is not the case, as may be seen from 'thermal grooving' that results from preferential evaporation from the boundary at high temperatures.

5.2 The width of a grain boundary depends on the angle of tilt or twist. From field ion microscopy it appears commonly to be nearer to $3b$ than $5b$.

5.3 This argument is speculative but has been advanced here to account for the observation than grain boundaries are preferentially attacked electrochemically, often to the extent of whole grains falling out of the surface (Lacombe and Yannaquis, *Rev. Met.* 1948 **45** 68; Wyon and Marchin, *Phil. Mag.* 1955 **46** 1119; Dix, *Trans. Amer. Inst. Mining & Met. Engrs.* 1940 **137** 11; Bakish and Robertson, *Acta Met.* 1955 **3** 513 and *J. Electrochem. Soc.* 1956 **103** 320; Graf, *Werkstoffe u.Korr.* 1957 **8** 261). If ϵ_y is the yield strain and E the elastic modulus, then 10% of the energy represented by the area under the elastic part of the stress/strain curve is $E\epsilon_y^2/20$ J/m^3, which is presumed to be distributed in a grain boundary volume of approximately $10b/d^3$ m^3, where d is the average grain diameter. Since 1 mole occupies Lb^3 m^3, we find that the extra elastic energy stored in the boundary varies between $10^{-6}E$ and $10^{-7}E$, for grain diameters in the region of 50 to 100 μm.

Chapter 6

How Fast?

6.1 CHARGE TRANSFER OVERPOTENTIAL: THE TAFEL EQUATION

It is one thing knowing that corrosion is able to happen, with an accompanying free energy change of (say) −122 kJ/mol. What is of greater interest to the corrosion engineer is how fast the attack takes place. To know that, we need to know how rates of reaction vary with overpotential. We shall first examine the kinetics of charge-transfer reactions because in many cases of corrosion it is this type of reaction that is rate determining.

The rate of dissolution may be expressed as a current density (A/m^2). At the equilibrium single potential E_{eq} this flux of charge through the double layer is the same in both directions and we call this the **exchange current density** i_o. Its value in the 'dissolution' direction will obviously be governed by a rate constant k_a, where the 'a' subscript indicates that anodic oxidation is taking place in this direction. The species taking part in the formation of the activated complex are the 'kink site' metal atoms in the surface and, usually (and a little surprisingly), one or more hydroxyl ions in the double layer rather than water molecules. Whence the rate in $mol/m^2\,s$ is

$$i_o/zF = k_a \, a_{kink} \, h^n_{OH^-} \tag{6.1}$$

The rate constant is of course simply

$$k_a = \mathrm{f} \exp(-\Delta\tilde{G}^{\ddagger}/RT) \tag{6.2}$$

where f is the vibration frequency of the activated complex and $\Delta\tilde{G}^{\ddagger}$ replaces $\Delta G^{\ddagger}$ in eqn (3.19) because charged species are involved. From eqn (6.1) (6.2)

$$i_o = zF \, \mathrm{f} \, a_{kink} \, h^n_{OH^-} \exp(-\tilde{G}^{\ddagger}/RT) \tag{6.3}$$

The assumption is then made that the potential gradient in the charge transfer part of the double layer is uniform. The activated complex is deemed to be situated a fraction α ($\approx \frac{1}{2}$) of the double layer thickness from the metal surface, and hence $(1 - \alpha)$ from the solution side of the interface: α is the **symmetry factor** (or otherwise the *transmission coefficient*). It follows that, if the electrochemical free energy of ions in the metal surface is raised by $zF\eta$ (J/mol) relative to the equilibrium value, then that of ions in the transition state is raised by $(1 - \alpha)zF\eta$, Fig. 6.1. The activation energy now becomes $\{\Delta\tilde{G}^{\ddagger} + (1 - \alpha)zF\eta\} - zF\eta = \Delta\tilde{G}^{\ddagger} - \alpha zF\eta$, so that the rate of charge transfer across the double layer is the anodic current density

$$\begin{aligned} i_a &= zF\,\mathrm{f}\,a_{\text{kink}}\,h^n_{\text{OH}^-}\exp\{-(\Delta\tilde{G}^{\ddagger} - \alpha zF\eta)/RT\} \\ &= i_o \exp(\alpha zF\eta/RT) \end{aligned} \tag{6.4}$$

Rearranging and inserting 'CT' (=charge transfer) superscript for the overpotential,

$$\boxed{\eta^{\text{CT}} = (2.303RT/\alpha zF)\log(i_a/i_o)} \tag{6.5}$$

which is the *Tafel equation.*

By a similar argument it may be seen that the activation energy for deposition is raised to $\Delta\tilde{G}^{\ddagger} + (1 - \alpha)\,zF\eta$ and the cathodic current density is

$$i_c = i_o \exp\{-(1 - \alpha)zF\eta/RT\} \tag{6.6}$$

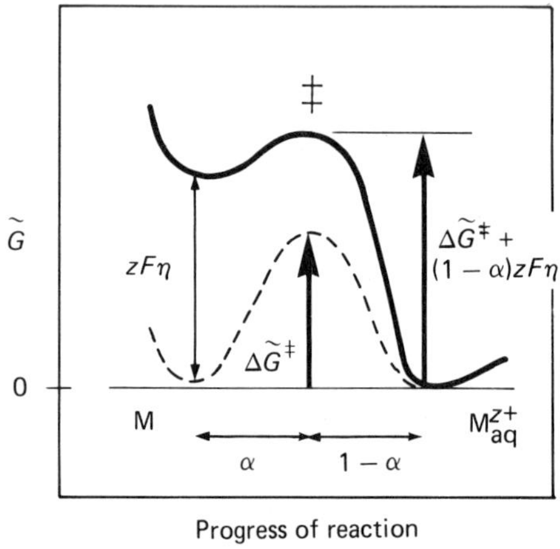

Fig. 6.1 Electrochemical free energy change for metal dissolution when the metal is anodically polarised. η = charge transfer overpotential; α = symmetry factor.

For $\eta >$ about 0.03 V, $i_a \gg i_c$ since the anodic process is enhanced and the cathodic one supressed. There is, therefore, a log-linear relationship between the net flow of anodic current and the overpotential of an electrode, Fig. 6.2.

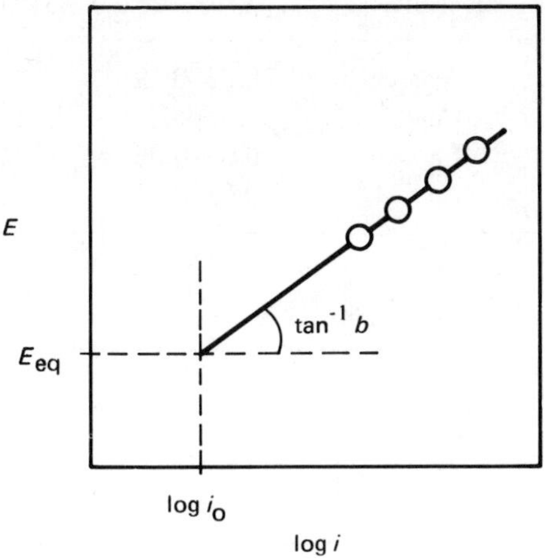

Fig. 6.2 Tafel plot of anodic polarisation.

The relationship may be simplified to

$$\eta^{CT} = b_a \log(i_a/i_o) \tag{6.7}$$

in which b_a is the anodic *Tafel coefficient.* This coefficient is the slope $d\eta/d(\log i_a)$ of the curve in Fig. 6.2

$$b_a = 2.303RT/\alpha zF \tag{6.8}$$

Some typical values of i_o and b are given Table 6.1 (Note 6.1). Tafel coefficients have the units 'volts per tenfold change in current density', that is, V/decade or, more briefly, V.

When a battery or dry cell is connected to an electrical load, the larger the current that flows the smaller the residual emf available to push it around the circuit. This phenomenon is commonly attributed to a (nonlinear) 'internal resistance' of the cell but is, in fact, mainly due to 'polarisation' of the two electrodes that constitute the cell. That is, overpotential at the electrodes increases as the current drawn from the cell. The two terms are synonymous: Fig. 6.2 may equally well be taken to represent the *polarisation curve* for the oxidising electrode.

Table 6.1 Some Tafel coefficients and exchange current densities in non-complexing aqueous solutions at 25°C

System	Metal substrate	b V/decade	i_o A/m²
$Ag^+ \mid Ag$	Ag	0.03–0.12	10^4
$Cu^{2+} \mid Cu$	Cu	ca. 0.06	1 – 10
$Fe^{2+} \mid Fe$	Fe	0.05–0.08	10^{-5} to 10^{-4}
$Zn^{2+} \mid Zn$	Zn	0.03–0.06	10^{-3} to 10^{-1}
$Fe^{3+} \mid Fe^{2+}$	Pt	ca. 0.12	5 – 50
$HNO_3 \mid NO$	Pt		ca. 1
$H^+ \mid H_2$	Pt	ca. 0.12	10^2
	Fe, Cu		10^{-3} to 10^{-2}
	Zn		10^{-7}
	Pb		10^{-9}
$O_2 \mid OH^-$	Pt	0.10–0.15	10^{-6}
	Fe	>0.12	ca. 10^{-10}

Polarisation occurs for both positive and negative values of η^{CT}. When $\eta^{CT} > 0$, then the Tafel relationship describes how charge transfer controls the rate of anodic dissolution, eqn (6.7). When, however, instead of raising φ^M we lower it to some value

$$\varphi^M = \varphi^M_{eq} + \eta^{CT} \qquad (\eta^{CT} < 0) \tag{6.9}$$

while keeping φ^S the same, the dissolution reaction is accompanied by an *increase* in free energy, eqn (6.4). The cathodic deposition (reduction) reaction

$$M^{z+}.nH_2O(aq) + ze(M) = M(s) + n\ H_2O(l) \tag{6.10}$$

now takes place much faster than the dissolution reaction and, for η more negative than about −0.03 V, the net charge flux across the double layer becomes i_c. The cathodic polarisation curve is represented by

$$\eta^{CT} = b_c \log(i_c/i_o) \tag{6.11}$$

in which

$$b_c = -2.303RT/(1 - \alpha)zF \tag{6.12}$$

The Tafel slope b_c is now negative and, for $\alpha = 0.5$, has the same magnitude as b_a for the anodic reaction.

6.2 THE EVANS DIAGRAM

The previous section has shown us that there is an energy penalty that has to be paid every time we force an electrode to depart from its equilibrium state. This is a direct consequence of the ionic flux that has to pass through the metal/electrolyte interface. The charge-transfer overpotential η^{CT} (>0) that is required to make a metal dissolve anodically, for example, arises from the energy barrier that exists within the electrical double layer at the interface. As we have seen, η^{CT} and the ionic flux (= current density) are simply related by the Tafel equation (6.7).

We can now attempt to evaluate corrosion rate in terms of charge transfer overpotential. For the corrosion of copper, for example, the corrosion potential adopted lies above E_{eq} for copper and below E_{eq} for oxygen, so that these electrodes in the corrosion cell are respectively anodically and cathodically polarised, Fig. 6.3. Here, the Tafel relationships are plotted on the left and a simplified linear plot is given on the right. The algebraic sign of i_c is disregarded. The linear diagram on the right is called an **Evans diagram**, after its originator, Ulick Evans in 1929. It indicates clearly how the rate of corrosion, here represented by the **corrosion current density** $i_{corrosion}$ at the point of intersection of the polarisation curves, depends on the driving emf $\mathcal{E}$ (= 0.63 V in this instance) and the slopes of the two relevant polarisation curves.

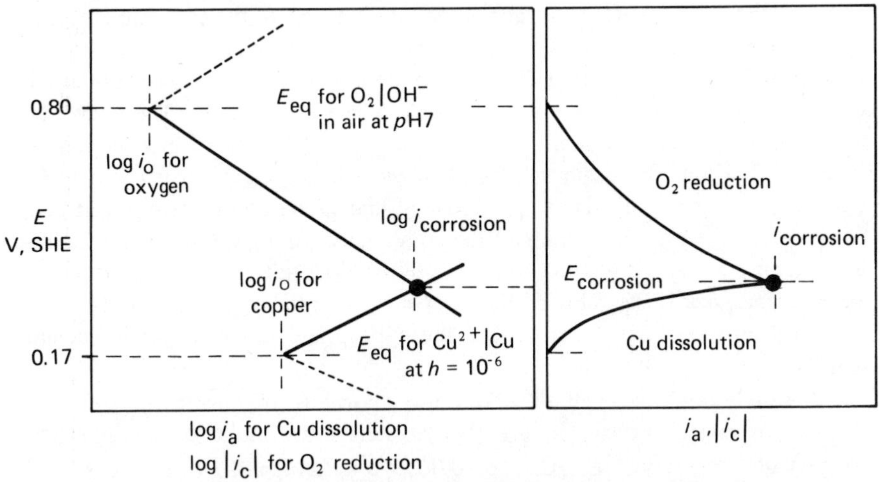

Fig. 6.3 Evans diagram for a corrosion cell in which anodic and cathodic areas are equal and electrolyte resistance is neglected. The intersection of the anodic and cathodic curves in the RH diagram gives the corrosion rate (current density) and corrosion potential. When the anodic and cathodic areas are different, Fig. 8.1, the abscissa is replaced by total current I. In this particular example, it has been incorrectly assumed that only charge transfer contributes to the cathodic polarisation of oxygen.

To summarise, the Evans diagram is a linear plot of potential *vs.* current or current density. (Whether current or current density is more appropriate will be discussed below.) On it are plotted the cathodic polarisation curve for the reduction process, that is, the oxidising agent responsible for the corrosion, and the anodic polarisation curve for the metal dissolution process. *The rate of attack, measured in amperes or A/m^2 depending on the abscissa, is given by the point of intersection of these two curves.* This is so whatever the shapes of the two polarisation curves, and it is therefore valid even when charge-transfer is not rate-determining. The Evans diagram therefore offers a valuable demonstration of how the corrosion rate depends on the distance apart of the equilibrium single potentials, that is, $\mathcal{E}$, and the average slopes of the two curves. The steeper they are, the smaller the amount of corrosion will be, measured in terms of current or current density.

At the point of intersection in the Evans diagram, it is obvious that the total number of electrons generated by metal dissolution must exactly balance the number of electrons being consumed by the cathodic reduction process. That is, the anodic and cathodic *currents* must be equal at the corrosion potential $E_{corrosion}$. It is for this reason that the Evans diagram is most universally drawn with current as abscissa, as in Fig. 8.1. As we shall see later, this allows us to take account of complicated situations, where the anodic and cathodic areas are not the same or where there is a multiplicity of anodic and cathodic processes. In simple situations, however, where the anodic and cathodic areas are both equal to the nominal area that the component presents to the environment, that is, *in cases of uniform corrosion* (and only in these circumstances), the anodic and cathodic *current densities* ($i = I$/area) are equal at the corrosion potential. E *vs.* i diagrams are therefore a special case of E *vs.* I diagrams. They have the advantage of yielding a current density $i_{corrosion}$ at the point of intersection, as in Fig. 6.3. From the engineer's point of view it is $i_{corrosion}$ that needs to be known, for this is directly proportional to the intensity of corrosion attack, expressed as the rate of thinning of the component. An E *vs.* I diagram, which is used when corrosion is nonuniform (Chapter 8), does not yield $i_{corrosion}$ directly. What it does give is the value of the corrosion potential $E_{corrosion}$, and it is then necessary to use $E_{corrosion}$ to deduce the appropriate value of anodic current density.

A simple application of Faraday's laws allows us to convert $i_{corrosion}$ into the rate of metal wastage. Taking M_{Cu} as the relative molar mass (equivalent weight) of copper, that is, $\frac{1}{2}Cu^{2+}$ or 0.0635/2 kg/mol, and ρ as the density of copper, that is 9800 kg/m^3, the wastage rate in m/s is

$$r = (M_{Cu}/\rho F) \times i_{corrosion}$$

$$= 3.4 \times 10^{-11} \, (i_{corrosion})$$

And, since $i_{corrosion}$ for copper in aerated neutral water is only about 10^{-2} A/m^2, it follows that $r \approx 3.4 \times 10^{-13}$ m/s. This number seems unimaginably small, and it is much more practical to express this in 'engineering' units of millimetres per year (mm/yr) by multiplying by 3.2×10^{10}. We then have

$$\frac{r}{\text{mm/yr}} = 3.2 \times 10^{10} \, (M_{\text{Cu}}/\rho F) \frac{i_{\text{corrosion}}}{\text{A/m}^2}\,, \tag{6.13}$$

and the copper wastage rate is seen to be *ca.* 10^{-2} mm/yr. The fortuitous numerical agreement between current density in A/m^2 and corrosion rate in mm/yr is worth committing to memory, for the ratio M/ρ for many metals of engineering interest is roughly constant (*ca.* 3×10^{-6} m^3/mol):

$$\boxed{\text{A/m}^2 = \text{mm/yr}} \tag{6.14}$$

A second illustration of the Evans diagram is the acid dissolution of metals. Here the cathodic reactant is hydrogen ions, whose reduction is characterised by an exchange current density that is highly dependent upon the nature of the metal substrate, Table 6.2 (Note 6.2). Hence a *linear* plot of the cathodic polarisation curve for hydrogen will display progressively higher mean slopes as i_o decreases, Fig. 6.4. In this figure, the dissolution curve M is here representing anodic polarisation of (say) iron, cadmium and lead, whose ionic concentrations have all been adjusted to give the same value of E_{eq} via the Nernst equation (4.23); but for simplicity I have ignored differences in the slopes of the anodic polarisation curves arising from differences in i_o for the M^{2+}/M equilibrium.

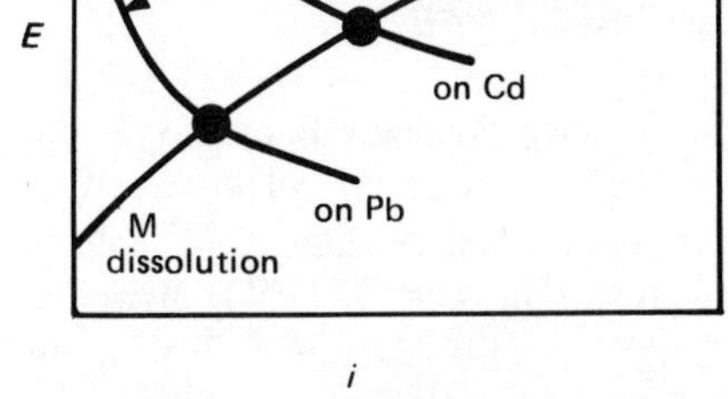

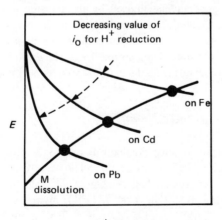

Fig. 6.4 Acid corrosion of metals. This Evans diagram shows how the corrosion rate is influenced by differences in exchange current density for the hydrogen electrode.

Granted this assumption of a common anodic curve, so that we may concentrate on the effect of *cathodic* polarisation, it may be seen that iron dissolves most rapidly in acids and lead least so. The reduced rate of corrosion of cadmium is exploited in the protective coatings used on high-strength steels exposed to moist air. The cadmium not only affords a small measure of cathodic protection (section 11.3) but, by making hydrogen ion reduction more difficult, reduces the amount of hydrogen gas produced and so lessens the likelihood of embrittlement of the steel (Note 6.3).

Table 6.2 Exchange current densities for the $H^+ \mid \frac{1}{2}H_2$ equilibrium on various metal surfaces in sulphuric acid at 25°C

Metal substrate	i_o (A/m^2)
Pt, Rh	3 – 10
Fe, Ni	10^{-2} to 10^{-1}
Ti	6.10^{-5}
Cd	2.10^{-7}
Pb	10^{-8}
Hg	5.10^{-9}

6.3 CONCENTRATION POLARISATION

When the reactants at an electrode are in short supply, the rate controlling step for the reaction will generally be limited by mass transport processes such as diffusion. Thus, for sufficiently rapid oxidation or reduction of a redox process, for cathodic deposition of a metal or for cathodic reduction of oxygen, there exists a limiting diffusion rate. On a simple Fick's Law model, that is, a linear activity gradient across a diffusion layer of thickness δ, the ionic flux to the cathode is (Note 6.4)

$$i_c/zF = -D_{Mz+}(h_{Mz+}^{surface} - h_{Mz+}^{bulk})/\delta \qquad (6.15)$$

where D_{Mz+}, the proportionality constant between the flux and the activity gradient, is the 'diffusivity' of the metal ions. (The negative sign reflects the fact that the diffusion is down the gradient.) When $h_{Mz+}^{surface}$ falls to zero, the chemical potential difference (that is, $RT \ln (h_{Mz+}^{bulk}/h_{Mz+}^{surface})$) driving the diffusion process reaches a maximum (infinity!) and the diffusional flux attains a limiting value

$$i_L/zF = D.\,h_{Mz+}^{bulk}/\delta$$

that is

$$\boxed{i_L = zFDh_{Mz+}/\delta} \tag{6.16}$$

Commonly D_{Mz+} is in units of m^2/s and the bulk ionic activity is then replaced by the *concentration in mol/m³*, that is, for consistency

$$[A/m^2] = [Coulombs/mol]\ [m^2/s]\ [mol/m^3]/[m]$$

As a result of the diffusion limitation, the activity of ions $h^{surface}_{Mz+}$ in the interface falls to $\{1 - (i_c/i_L)\}\ h^{bulk}_{Mz+}$. From the Nernst equation the equilibrium single potential therefore falls to

$$E' = E^{\ominus} + (RT/zF) \ln \{1 - (i_c/i_L)\}\ h^{bulk}_{Mz+}\ , \tag{6.17}$$

whence the concentration overpotential is

$$\boxed{\eta^C = E' - E_{eq} = (RT/zF) \ln \{1 - (i_c/i_L)\}} \tag{6.18}$$

If we write $i_c = i_L - \Delta i$, rearrangement of eqn (6.18) gives

$$\Delta i = i_L \exp(zF\,\eta^C/RT) \tag{6.19}$$

which is similar in form to the Tafel equation. Concentration and charge-transfer overpotentials are additive, that is,

$$\text{Total } \eta = \eta^{CT} + \eta^C \tag{6.20}$$

If diffusion were the only contributing factor to polarisation, the overpotential would be given by eqn (6.18) (6.19) and the slope of the polarisation curve would be

$$\begin{aligned} dE/di\ (\Omega m^2) &= -RT/zF\,\Delta i \\ &= -(RT/zFi_L) \exp(-zF\,\eta^C/RT) \end{aligned} \tag{6.21}$$

or, if plotted on a log-linear basis,

$$\begin{aligned} dE/d(\log i)\ (V) &= -(2.303RT/zF)\,(i/i_L) \exp(-zF\,\eta^C/RT) \\ &= (2.303RT/zF)\,\{1 - \exp(-zF\,\eta^C/RT)\} \end{aligned} \tag{6.22}$$

This second slope defines a 'quasi Tafel' coefficient whose value may be compared with that given by the Tafel eqn (6.12). It clearly depends on i_L and, in Table 6.3, a limiting current density of 0.5 A/m² has been assumed. When η^C is small, $dE/d(\log i) = 2.303\eta^C$ whereas, when η^C is large, the 'quasi Tafel' slope is $-(2.303RT/zF)(i_L/\Delta i)$ so that the slope becomes large also. Polarisation slopes are additive, just as the overpotentials themselves are. Thus, for cathodic polarisation involving simultaneous charge-transfer and concentration effects,

Total $dE/d(\log i) = b_c$ + Quasi-Tafel coefficient

$$= \frac{-2.303RT}{zF}\left\{\frac{\log(i_c/i_o)}{1-\alpha} - 1 + \exp(-zF\eta^C/RT)\right\} \tag{6.23}$$

Concentration polarisation therefore leads to anomalously high Tafel slopes, as the following example illustrates.

Table 6.3 'Quasi-Tafel slope' arising from concentration polarisation and its relation to overpotential and linear slope at 25°C
Linear slopes calculated assuming $i_L = 0.5$ A/m²

$-\eta^C$ mV	$\frac{\Delta_i}{i_L}$	$-\frac{dE}{d(\log i)}$ V	$-\frac{dE}{di}$ Ωm^2
1	0.93	0.001	0.028
3	0.81	0.003	0.032
7	0.56	0.01	0.046
15	0.30	0.03	0.086
28	0.11	0.1	0.23
41	0.041	0.3	0.63
56	0.013	1	2.0
70	0.004	3	6.0
85	0.001	10	20
100	<0.001	30	60

6.4 CORROSION IN AERATED WATER

Oxygen is relatively insoluble in water at room temperature. For example, pure water saturated with air ($p_{O_2} = 0.2$ atm) contains some 40 ppm oxygen at 20°C, and this concentration falls to 10 ppm (approximately 0.3 mol/m³) at 5°C in seawater. This low solubility in turn means that there is a small limiting current density for the cathodic reduction of oxygen. Using eqn (6.16) and assuming δ is typically some 100 μm,

$$i_L = zFDc/\delta \qquad (c = \text{concentration})$$

$$= 2 \times 96500 \times 10^{-9} \times 0.3 \div 10^{-4}$$

$$= 0.6 \text{ A/m}^2$$

in which z, the number of unit charges transported per ion in the diffusion process, is assumed equal to 2 (on the basis of an observed charge-transfer Tafel slope for oxygen reduction on gold of −0.06 V and using eqn (6.12)); and the diffusivity of oxygen in water is taken as 10^{-9} m²/s. Such a small limiting current means that, unless aeration is dramatically increased, as occurs in the 'splash zone' at wave level, or unless the temperature is raised, the rate of corrosion of metals is effectively limited to about 0.5 mm/yr, no matter how large the emf $\mathscr{E}$.

Thus, various metals corroding in seawater at potentials between −0.4 and −0.9 V, SHE exhibit cathodic polarisation curves for oxygen reduction with very large slopes, Fig. 6.5. Corrosion is said to be 'under *cathodic control*' and, as may be seen, $i_{\text{corrosion}} \approx i_L$. This is an important result of concentration polarisation. It is further considered in section 10.4 on the effect of electrolyte flow upon corrosion rate. Typically the Tafel coefficient $dE/d(\log i)$ in aerated water is around −1 to −3 V, whereas eqn (6.12) would predict −0.06 V ($= 2.303RT/F$) as for gold in the previous paragraph. Table 6.3 indicates that a quasi-Tafel slope of the order of −2 V reflects a value of i_c very close to i_L ($\Delta i/i_L \sim 0.01$). The concentration overpotential lies between −60 and −70 mV.

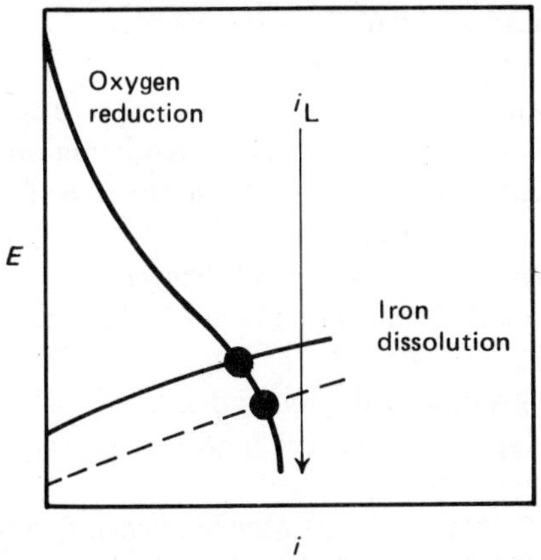

Fig. 6.5 Corrosion in aerated water. This Evans diagram shows that the corrosion rate is limited by the slow diffusion of oxygen in water, irrespective of the driving emf of the corrosion cell. That is, $i_{\text{corrosion}} \approx i_L$.

Knowing the concentration overpotential, we can also calculate the charge transfer overpotential for oxygen reduction at 0.5 A/m². We first calculate the corrosion potential. Iron in seawater exhibits an equilibrium potential around −0.44 V (Table 4.1), the effective concentration of iron ions is around 10^{-6} mol/kg. (This is the basic assumption made whenever we are dealing with an electrolyte containing nominally zero concentration of the ions of interest, see section 7.1 and 9.3.) The Nernst equation gives

$$E_{Fe} = -0.44 + 0.0295 \log(10^{-6}) = -0.61 \text{ V, SHE}$$

Because the iron dissolution reaction is under charge transfer control, we may write, using data from Table 6.1,

$$\eta^{CT} = E_{corr} - (-0.61) = b_a \log(i_{corr}/i_o)$$

$$\approx 0.06 \log(0.5/3.10^{-5})$$

$$\approx 0.25 \text{ V}$$

so $E_{corr} \approx -0.36$ V, SHE. We already know from section 5.3 that the equilibrium potential for oxygen in air-saturated water at pH 7 is +0.80 V, SHE, so that the *total* overpotential for the oxygen process is (−0.36) − (+0.80) = −1.16 V. Some −0.06 V of this is contributed by concentration polarisation, as we have already deduced from Table 6.3, leaving −1.10 V as charge transfer overpotential.

This in turn allows us to calculate the Tafel slope for the reduction of oxygen on iron. Thus, since i_o for oxygen on iron is ca. 10^{-10} A/m²,

$$-1.10 = b_c \log(0.5/10^{-10})$$

and $b_c = -0.113$ V, which is in fact very close to 2 × (2.3RT/F). Evidently this value conflicts with that observed for oxygen reduction on gold. The factor of two almost certainly arises because of the surface films formed on iron at the high pH that develops, section 9.2.

Although our example has been iron in seawater, it is quite typical of the corrosion of metals in aerated waters of all kinds. What emerges is that

(a) The corrosion rate is limited to around 0.5 A/m²;
(b) The quasi-Tafel slope at the corrosion potential is very high. (This is important in cathodic protection);
(c) Most of the overpotential at the cathode areas is due to charge transfer (in this example 1.10/1.16 = 95%) but the actual *rate* of corrosion is due to diffusion limitation;
(d) The true Tafel slope is anomalously high because of surface films.

Bibliography to Chapter 6

Bockris (1954), *Modern Aspects of Electrochemistry, No. 1,* Butterworth.
Bockris and Reddy (1970), *Modern Electrochemistry,* MacDonald.
West (1973), *Basic Electrochemistry,* Van Nostrand Reinhold.
Van Rysselberghe (1966), *Modern Aspects of Electrochemistry, No. 4,* ed. Bockris, Butterworth.

Notes to Chapter 6

6.1 Exchange current densities mainly from West, *Electrodeposition and Corrosion Processes,* 2nd edn. (Van Nostrand Reinhold, 1971).

6.2 Bockris and Reddy, *Modern Electrochemistry* (MacDonald, 1970).

6.3 Cadmium coatings are frequently electrodeposited, as are many other kinds of metallic coatings such as nickel-chromium. The electroplating process itself commonly introduces hydrogen into the metal substrate. To avoid embrittlement it is then necessary to 'bake out' this dissolved hydrogen by raising the temperature sufficiently to allow escape through the coating, which otherwise traps it inside the metal. A typical baking treatment is 12 or 24h at 150°C.

6.4 It is sometimes asserted that the role of oxygen in solution is to 'depolarise' hydrogen ion reduction, by removing adsorbed hydrogen atoms from the surface:

$$2H(ads) + \tfrac{1}{2}O_2(g) = H_2O(l)$$

and so allowing access of fresh protons to the surface. There is no evidence for this.

Chapter 7

Measuring Corrosion In-situ

7.1 ELECTROCHEMICAL METHODS

Corrosion rates may need to be measured for a variety of purposes of which the two most important are (a) to help us to choose the most appropriate material of construction at the design stage and (b) to enable us to monitor metal wastage during service. Because the exact simulation of service conditions is often difficult to achieve, the assessment of a material's susceptibility to corrosion is often best carried out by using small samples or 'coupons', which are exposed at an appropriate place or places inside the chemical plant or on a raft in the harbour, etc. Once a material has been chosen and the structure is complete, it is usually necessary to inspect it at intervals. Inside a chemical plant or pipeline this can only be done at shutdown periods. Nevertheless, it is sometimes possible to make use of the fact that corrosion in aqueous environments is electrochemical in nature, for this enables us to monitor progress in-situ. It is this kind of assessment that will be examined in this chapter.

When corrosion occurs uniformly over a metal surface (that is, general attack) anodes and cathodes are constantly moving around, even interchanging, as kink sites and other surface irregularities are revealed by the wastage. The effective anodic area is, therefore, coincident with the effective cathodic area and both are equal to the nominal area presented to the corrosive environment. As we saw in the last chapter, that is why the Evans diagrams of Figs 6.3–6.5 are drawn with current density as abscissa: when corrosion is general, so too are the current densities equal. The corrosion rate, as we saw from eqn (6.14), may be expressed either as a current density (A/m^2) or as an average penetration rate (mm/yr).

The first method of measuring this rate is to determine the *corrosion potential*. As we learned in the last two chapters, corrosion occurs at a mixed potential, $E_{corrosion}$, and we should expect the corrosion rate to depend on the anodic overpotential, that is, on how far $E_{corrosion}$ lies above the equilibrium single potential of the metal. Knowledge of the appropriate Tafel slope and, where relevant, the effects of concentration change, should provide us with a way of deducing the corrosion rate simply from a measurement of $E_{corrosion}$.

This was done in reverse at the end of section 6.4, where $E_{\text{corrosion}}$ for iron in seawater was calculated from a knowledge of the corrosion rate. For example, from eqn (6.7),

$$E_{\text{corrosion}} = E_{\text{eq}} + b_a \log(i_{\text{corrosion}}/i_o) \tag{7.1}$$

whence

$$i_{\text{corrosion}} = i_o \exp\{2.303(E_{\text{corrosion}} - E_{\text{eq}})/b_a\} \tag{7.2}$$

Where the quantities i_o, b_a and E_{eq} are not known precisely, a reasonable estimate can usually still be arrived at on the assumptions that:

(a) i_o exhibits an activation enthalpy of *ca.* 50 kJ/mol;
(b) b_a is given by $4.606RT/zF$; and
(c) the ionic concentration (= activity) affecting E_{eq} is in the region of 10^{-6} mol/kg.

Complications arise only when surface films are present or when corrosion is nonuniform, of which more later.

The measurement of $E_{\text{corrosion}}$ is made by means of a high-impedance voltmeter connected to the metal and to a convenient reference electrode dipping into the electrolyte, Fig. 7.1. Measurement directly on the SHE scale can of course be effected by using a standard hydrogen electrode as the reference, but such electrodes are temperamental and require a supply of purified hydrogen gas. Instead, more convenient secondary standards are used as reference electrodes, the most common being the saturated calomel electrode (SCE) and the saturated copper sulphate electrode (SCSE), which are included in Table 7.1.

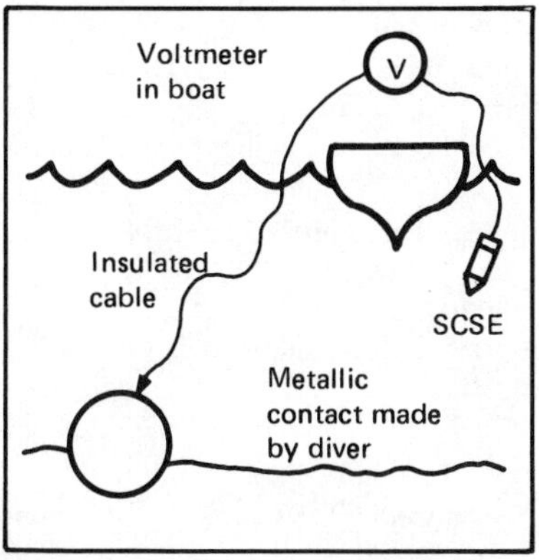

Fig. 7.1 Measuring the corrosion potential of a submarine pipeline. To survey the potential along the line, contact is made at selected points. If electric currents are flowing in the seawater, as may occur if the line is cathodically protected, *IR* drops are minimised by bringing the SCSE close to the contact point.

Table 7.1 Some common reference electrodes. The calomel (Hg_2Cl_2) and silver chloride electrodes provide a single potential that depends on the activity of the chloride anion, whilst the constancy of the copper sulphate electrode potential is provided by the fixed Cu(II) activity in saturated solution. All are temperature dependent.

Electrode	V, SHE at 25°C
Hg,Hg_2Cl_2(s)/Cl^-(aq, satd. KCl)	+ 0.25
Cu/Cu^{2+}(aq, satd. $CuSO_4$)	+ 0.32
Ag,AgCl(s)/Cl^-(aq, 1 mol/kg KCl)	+ 0.29
Ag,AgCl(s)/Cl^-(aq, seawater)	+ 0.25

The second method of determining corrosion rate is to measure the **polarisation conductance**, which is essentially the reciprocal of the linear slope dE/di of the polarisation curves close to the corrosion potential. This 'linear polarisation' method was developed by Stern (Note 7.2) on the assumption, eqn (7.1), that corrosion is frequently controlled by activation overpotential. As it has subsequently turned out, the method may be used even when concentration polarisation is rate determining, provided that calibration is possible. A small potential increment $\pm\Delta E$, between 1 and 6 mV is applied to the freely-corroding component, and the current through the external circuit used to apply the potential thereby increases from zero (at $E_{\text{corrosion}}$) to $\pm\Delta I$ (at $E_{\text{corrosion}}$ $\pm\Delta E$). Divided by the nominal surface area of the component, this gives the corresponding change in corrosion current density $\Delta i = \Delta I/\text{area}$ (Note 7.3). From Fig. 7.2 we can see that

$$\Delta i = \text{AB} = \text{AD} + \text{DB}$$

$$= \frac{\beta_a + |\beta_c|}{\beta_a|\beta_c|} \cdot \Delta E \qquad (7.3)$$

where $\beta = dE/di$ at $E_{\text{corrosion}}$. Differentiating eqn (7.2),

$$\frac{di_{\text{corrosion}}}{dE} = \frac{2.303}{b_a} \cdot i_{\text{corrosion}} = 1/\beta_a \qquad (7.4)$$

so that

$$\beta_a = b_a/2.303 i_{\text{corrosion}} \text{ and } \beta_c = b_c/2.303 i_{\text{corrosion}} \qquad (7.5)$$

Substitution of eqn (7.5) in eqn (7.3) gives

$$i_{\text{corrosion}} = (1/2.303)\,\{b_a|b_c|/(b_a + |b_c|)\}\,\frac{\Delta_i}{\Delta E} \qquad (7.6)$$

The quantity $\Delta i/\Delta E$ is the polarisation conductance K_{corr}. Since b_a and $|b_c|$ generally lie between 0.03 and 0.25 V/decade, $i_{corrosion}$ lies between 0.01 and 0.03 times K_{corr}. Concentration polarisation may increase the linear slope dE/di of the cathodic polarisation curve to, say, $5\Omega m^2$ (Table 6.3 for $\Delta i/i_L \sim 0.01$) rather than the 0.1 to 1 Ωm^2 one might expect for simple charge transfer control and for $i_{corrosion} \sim 10^{-2}$ to 1 A/m^2. This means that $|\beta_c| \gg \beta_a$ and eqn (7.6) approximates to

$$i_{corrosion} = b_a K_{corr}/2.303 \tag{7.7}$$

and the proportionality between rate and K_{corr} depends only on the anodic Tafel slope.

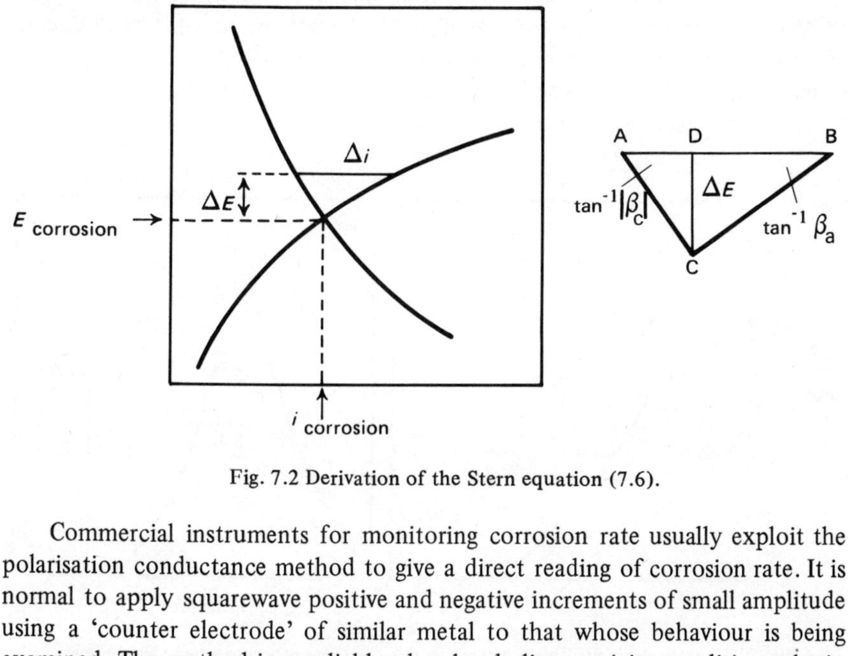

Fig. 7.2 Derivation of the Stern equation (7.6).

Commercial instruments for monitoring corrosion rate usually exploit the polarisation conductance method to give a direct reading of corrosion rate. It is normal to apply squarewave positive and negative increments of small amplitude using a 'counter electrode' of similar metal to that whose behaviour is being examined. The method is unreliable when borderline passivity conditions obtain (Chapter 9) or where corrosion is nonuniform. Neither electrochemical method can be used where the component is exposed to gaseous environments or where it is only partly or intermittently wetted.

7.2 PHYSICAL METHODS

Visual inspection is the first and most obvious way of assessing the course of corrosion. To quantify the observation usually involves subjecting small 'coupons' of the metal to the service environment and measuring the weight loss after a given time. Laboratory determinations of a similar kind may be conducted, but difficulty may be encountered in simulating the service environment sufficiently accurately.

A problem arises when corrosion is nonuniform, as in crevice corrosion, pitting, and stress-corrosion cracking. By and large the problem resolves itself according to the use to which the component is to be put. For example, if visual appearance rather than mechanical strength is required, crevice and pitting attack need to be judged in terms of the *incidence* (frequency) of pits or else the localised deterioration of any surface coatings (as may be vouched for by motorists the world over!). And the pitting incidence may be readily evaluated by counting the number of pits in representative areas of the surface. One may then draw a distribution profile such as that in Fig. 7.3(a), judging the progress of corrosion by changes in (a) the largest pit diameter (1), (ii) the most frequent pit diameter (2), or (iii) the total number of pits per unit area (3), according to personal preference. Alternatively, where mechanical strength or containment is of importance, it is the *depth* of pits and, more especially, the depth of the deepest pit that is our concern, Fig. 7.3(b).

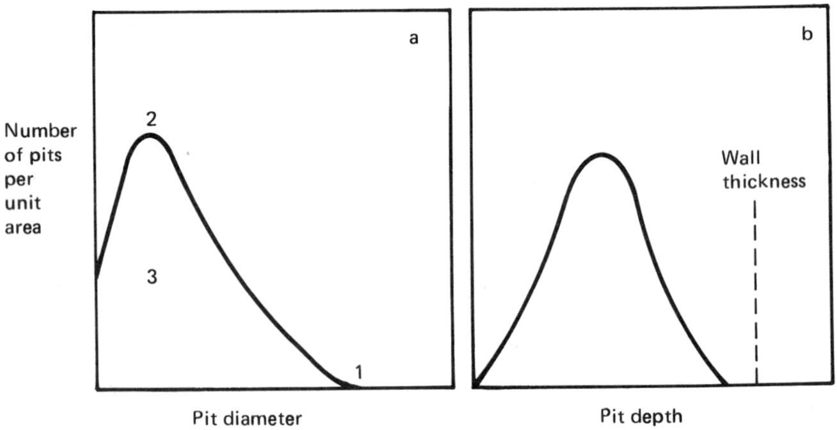

Fig. 7.3 Distribution profile of pitting attack. (a) Area affected when visual appearance is paramount; (b) Depth of penetration when containment is paramount.

The measurement of pit depth is relatively easy when pits are shallow. Feeler gauges, or even ultrasonics, can accomplish this readily enough. When the pits are small and isolated it is possible to measure depth by use of a microscope having a high-power objective. This exploits the fact that visible-light microscopes have a very limited depth of focus, so that the stage movement required in focusing successively on the pit bottom and on the external surface corresponds to the pit depth. Longer pits, especially those which progress sideways or which are very narrow, can only be measured by metallographic section. This of course means that the component must be destroyed or replaced, and such a method is normally resorted to only after failure has taken place (Note 7.4).

The in-situ measurement of the corrosion inside a reactor or container vessel wall is best effected by means of ultrasonics. Two shaped transducers are used externally, one to transmit the ultrasonic signal pulse (usually 500 kHz or more) and the other to receive it. A cathode ray display may be used to show the time interval and hence the depth of the reflecting surface, or else a microprocessor may be used to read this directly. By using frequencies in the region of 1 MHz it is possible to achieve sensitivities of less than 1 mm, but care is needed, both in making the measurement and in interpreting the result. In skilled hands the method yields information on roughness, pitting and (with luck) cracks.

7.3 ANALYSIS OF CORROSION PRODUCTS (Note 7.1)

Corrosion products are always closely related to the chemistry of the *corrodent* (that is, the corrosive medium) and, whenever possible, a representative sample of this should be taken. It is then possible to determine, for example, *p*H and oxygen content as well as such 'aggressive' ions as sulphide and chloride; microbial investigation of a soil or electrolyte may also be appropriate (Chapter 10). In high-temperature gaseous environments it is not always possible to gain accurate and full analyses, even when process records are kept, but it is desirable to establish what one can in order to assess, for example, the likely oxygen partial presssure at the service temperature. By the same token, such information needs to be treated with healthy scepticism: so-called 'representative' samples are always post-hoc and may bear little relation to the corrodent conditions which actually caused the observed corrosion.

Corrosion products are usually solid or else constitute a sludge at the bottom of a container vessel, for example. In-situ examination is often essential because colours may change during transmission to the analytical laboratory (for example, black sulphides oxidise to white sulphates and green hydrated magnetite – Fe_3O_4 – converts to the black form as it dries out) or smells disperse (for example, the H_2S associated with sulphate-reducing bacteria). Usually, however, the purpose of the analysis is to determine why the attack took place at all, and this can be accomplished by *x-ray fluorescence analysis* of the solid sample to identify the elements present (Note 7.5). For example, an unexpected tarnishing of Nichrome tubular-encased heaters was traced to the existence of a contaminated water supply. This had been used in making up the magnesia/borax paste that formed a 'bed' for the spiral heater wire, filled the interstices and prevented the wire from touching the tubular casing. XRF analysis identified chlorine in the magnesia paste surrounding the tarnished elements but this contaminant was entirely absent from the original magnesia supply. XRF results are normally only semiquantitative because of difficulties of calibration, for example standards are rare or there is insufficient time to prepare them. Moreover, *the technique fails to detect oxygen and elements of lower atomic number,* making it impossible to distinguish sulphide from sulphate or detect nitrates and borates.

Table 7.2 Line densities for some iron compounds. The 'contaminated rust' sample was extracted from the interface between a paint coating and the underlying rusted steel. The data are consistent with its being a decomposed millscale ($FeO \rightarrow Fe_3O_4 + Fe$) containing some α—$Fe_2O_3.H_2O$ rust.

Lattice spacing *d* picometres*	Contaminated rust sample	JCPDS standard data			
		Fe_3O_4	Hydrated α—Fe_2O_3	Hydrated γ—Fe_2O_3	$FeSO_4$
485	m	w	w		
420	m		vs		
365					s
330	w		w	vs	m
295	m	m			
270	vw		s		vs
250	vs	vs	vw	s	
240	m		m	w	m
225	w		w		
210	m	m	vvw		m
190	w		vw	m	
180	w		w	vw	m
170	m	m		m	m
160	s	s	w		
156	w		w		
151	w		w	m	
147	s	s		w	
142	vw		vvw		s
138	vw		vw	vw	
132	w		w	vw	
127	m	vw	vw		
120	w	w	vw		
117	vw		vw	vvw	
109	s	m	vw		
105	m	w			
97	m	w			
94	m	w			

*1 pm = 10^{-3} nm = 0.01 Å. Errors in *d* are ±1 or 2% on each spacing. JCPDS = Joint Committee on Powder Diffraction Standards, incorporating the previous ASTM index. s = strong, m = medium, w, = weak, v = very . . .

A back-up analytical facility is *x-ray structural analysis* (Note 7.6) to identify the specific chemical compounds present. It is here that visual information and chemical intuition combine to help the hapless technician, for it is nearly always essential to have some idea of what is being sought. The JCPDA index of line densities makes it possible to identify many pure compounds and not a few mixed ones. But it is unfortunate that many corrosion products are strongly contaminated and give anomalous line densities. Table 7.2 compares the diffraction pattern obtained for a sulphate-contaminated rust with that of (JCPDS standard) ferric oxide, magnetite and ferrous sulphate.

Notes to Chapter 7

7.1 Laboratory investigation of corrosion mechanisms is excluded from this discussion. The reader is referred to a detailed exposition by Ailor, *loc. cit.*

7.2 Stern and Geary, *J. Electrochem. Soc.* 1957 **104** 56.

7.3 The assumption is made here that corrosion is uniform. If the surface is heterogeneous and corrosion non-uniform, Fig. 7.2 is drawn instead as E *vs.* I, and the polarisation conductance dI/dE then yields $I_{corrosion}$ rather than the corrosion current density. This information is less valuable but it at least offers a means of monitoring changes in the corrosivity of the system.

7.4 Post-hoc examination nearly always entails metallographic section to determine the extent of corrosion. The microscope enables us to discover the mode of attack related to microstructural features such as grain boundaries, inclusions and second-phase particles. Only rarely does 'stereoscan' electron microscopy give additional information in this context. Examination of surface layers of corrosion product is made possible by impregnating them under vacuum with a thermosetting resin. Thin coatings or pitted surfaces can be prepared by chemically depositing (electroless plating) about 2 μm of nickel prior to mounting and sectioning.

7.5 X-ray fluorescence spectroscopy involves illuminating the sample, whether liquid or solid, with 'white' x-rays. The characteristic fluorescent x-radiation that is then emitted by the excited atoms is diffracted by a crystal spectrometer and this spatial discrimination of the various wavelengths allows quantitative estimates to be made of the elements in the sample. The lighter elements, most notably oxygen, cannot be detected by this technique.

7.6 X-ray structural analysis usually involves monochromatic x-rays and these are diffracted from the sample in a suitable 'powder' camera. The sample is rotated or oscillated and the diffracted beam forms a series of lines on a photographic film. The line spacing and density yield information on the crystal lattice structure(s) of the sample which is then compared with published data (the Joint Committee on Powder Diffraction Standards).

Bibliography to Chapter 7

Ailor (1971), *Handbook on corrosion testing and evaluation,* Wiley.
Champion (1964), *Corrosion testing procedures,* Chapman and Hall.

Chapter 8

Localised Attack

8.1 NONUNIFORM CORROSION

Nature is rarely so obliging as to offer environments that attack metal structures uniformly. Instead, either the environment or the metal is heterogeneous, and so corrosion becomes localised. If, for example, the oxidising agent (cathodic reactant) is air whose availability is limited in some places, Fig. 1.1, we get *differential aeration corrosion.* Attack becomes largely confined to the anaerobic areas and may well result in pitting, which in turn accentuates the differential effect still further. Or again, the metal structure may be made up of several alloys (or separate microstructural phases) whose chemical composition is such that one alloy or phase is more susceptible than the others and so corrodes preferentially. Such *bimetallic corrosion* is one of the principal causes of avoidable damage in engineering structures. Both examples of localised attack make the reporting of a single current density relatively meaningless: as pointed out in Chapter 7, we need to know the degree of localisation and how much the structure is weakened by pitting. For example, pits may constitute stress-raising notches which initiate catastrophic failure (Chapter 12) or else may cause slow leakage of dangerous or radioactive chemicals from an otherwise satisfactory container.

In such circumstances, it is the *total* anodic and cathodic *currents,* not current densities, that determine the corrosion potential, Fig. 8.1. The corrosion intensities for the various areas of the surface may then in turn be inferred from the corrosion potential because it is the current *density* that depends on potential, for example eqn (6.7) (7.2). Imagine, for example, a structure made up of two areas X and Y which differ (say) in chemical composition or oxygen availability. The total area is represented by $A_X + A_Y$. For any particular potential there will exist anodic current densities i_X, i_Y on these areas, and the total anodic current at this potential will be $I = i_X A_X + i_Y A_Y$. The effective total anodic polarisation curve is therefore a *composite* curve made up by adding the abscissae of the anodic curves for X and Y, each suitably weighted in proportion to its area. A composite cathodic curve may be obtained by a similar weighted summation for the cathodic process(es) appropriate to X and Y. The intersection of the two composite curves gives the corrosion potential $E_{corrosion}$, as shown in the left-hand diagram. On the right of the diagram is the anodic polarisation curve, plotted as E *vs.* current *density,* for area X, whence it may be seen that the corrosion rate of X is given by the abscissa corresponding to $E_{corrosion}$.

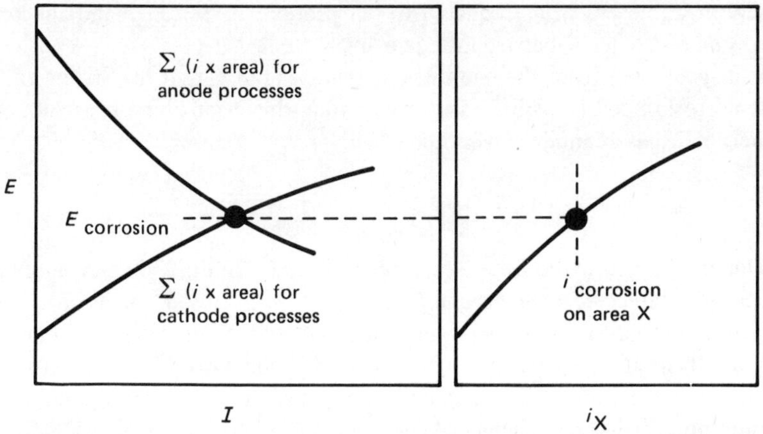

Fig. 8.1 Evans diagram for nonuniform corrosion, neglecting electrolytic resistance. Anodic and cathodic polarisation curves are composite curves taking account of the relative surface areas of X and Y. Their intersection in the Evans diagram on the left gives the total corrosion current. The corrosion rate of area X is given by the value of the anodic current density i_X at the corrosion potential.

A further complication arises when the electrolyte contributes an appreciable resistance to the corrosion cell, either because of high resistivity or because anodes and cathodes are widely separated. The Evans diagram is then further modified, Fig. 8.2. Although the metal is electronically conducting so that its

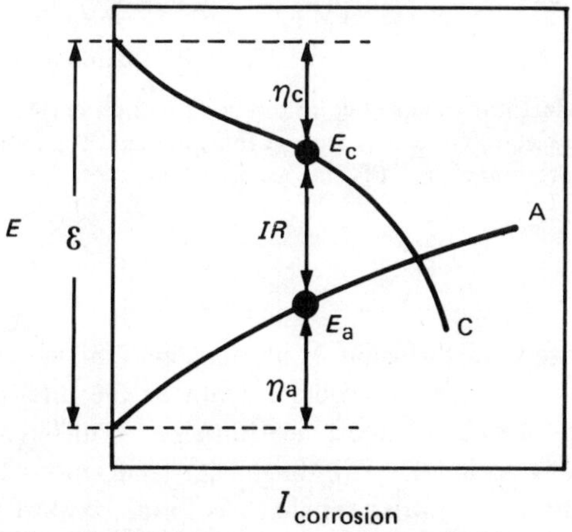

Fig. 8.2 Evans diagram when there is electrolytic resistance. Anode and cathode potentials are now different.

potential is everywhere close to φ^M, the electrolyte offers a resistance to the passage of ions and so will exhibit potentials of φ_a^S and φ_c^S ($\varphi_a^S > \varphi_c^S$) at anode and cathode areas respectively. When the corrosion cell is established, therefore, the single potentials E_c ($= \varphi^M - \varphi_c^S$) and E_a ($= \varphi^M - \varphi_a^S < E_c$) are different by an amount $\varphi_a^S - \varphi_c^S$, which equals IR, the product of $I_{corrosion}$ and the total electrolytic resistance R between the two areas.

It may be seen from the equivalent circuit, Fig. 8.3, that the driving emf $\mathcal{E}$ of the corrosion cell is dissipated in overcoming this electrolytic resistance and the overpotentials at anode and cathode:

$$\mathcal{E} = \eta_a + |\eta_c| + IR \quad (8.1)$$

The anodic and cathodic curves, labelled A and C in Fig. 8.2, may be simple (that is, general corrosion) or composite (that is, localised corrosion). Thus, taking our previous example and assuming that area X corrodes preferentially and Y hardly at all, the potential at X $= E_a$, and X will corrode at a rate given by the current density on the polarisation curve at E_a, even though the measured corrosion potential of (X, Y) may be E_c.

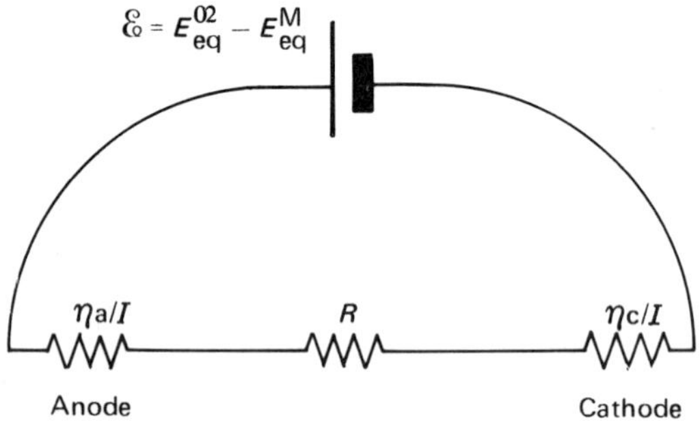

Fig. 8.3 Equivalent electrical circuit of corrosion in aerated water. R is the ohmic resistance due to the electrolyte or any surface films present. The overpotentials contribute nonohmic resistances η/I. Cf. Fig. 13.1.

8.2 INSIDE PITS

Crevices are characterised by diffusion limitation, and so the solution inside them is likely to differ from that elsewhere. Thus, in the interior of a pit or crevice, corrosion is presumed to take place initially by differential aeration, during which metal ions accumulate by dissolution and anions by migration, until both the oxide and anion salt (sulphate or chloride, say) of the metal are precipitated. If equilibrium becomes established inside the pit, it is possible to deduce not only the solution composition but also the equilibrium single potential of the anode and the hydrogen partial pressure. We should recognise from the outset, however, that the slowness of diffusion may not allow equilibrium concentrations to be reached; and moreover that continuing corrosion will mean that the actual anode potential will be a mixed potential ($E_{\text{corrosion}}$ or E_a) which is more noble than this calculated equilibrium value.

We assume that the metal M is in equilibrium with everything inside the crevice: with solid M_xO_y and MCl_n (both suitably hydrated); with $M^{n+}(aq)$, $H^+(aq)$, $OH^-(aq)$ and $Cl^-(aq)$; and with hydrogen gas at a pressure p atm inside the metal. The following equilibria will simultaneously exist:

$$M_xO_y(s) + 2yH^+(aq) + 2ye(M) = xM(s) + yH_2O(l)$$

$$MCl_n(s) + ne(M) = M(s) + nCl^-(aq)$$

$$M^{n+}(aq) + ne(M) = M(s)$$

$$H^+(aq) + e(M) = \tfrac{1}{2}H_2(g)$$

so that there will be a common single potential within the crevice of

$$E_{eq} = E^{\ominus}_{\text{oxide}} + (RT/F) \ln h_{H+} \tag{8.2}$$

$$= E^{\ominus}_{\text{chloride}} - (RT/nF) \ln h_{Cl-} \tag{8.3}$$

$$= E^{\ominus}_M + (RT/nF) \ln h_{Mn+} \tag{8.4}$$

$$= 0.00 + (RT/F) \ln\{h_{H+}/(p/p^{\ominus})\} \tag{8.5}$$

where the various $E^{\ominus}$ are the standard single potentials. We also know that $h_{OH-} = K_w/h_{H+}$, eqn (3.9), and, because all the positive and negative charges in the crevice solution must balance (*electroneutrality* principle), we have in each kg of solvent water

$$m_{H+} + nm_{Mn+} = m_{OH-} + m_{Cl-}$$

or, multiplying throughout by the mean molal activity coefficient (section 2.3),

$$h_{H+} + nh_{Mn+} = h_{OH-} + h_{Cl-}$$

which becomes the quadratic

$$h^2_{H+} + (nh_{Mn+} - h_{Cl-})h_{H+} - K_w = 0 \tag{8.6}$$

The five equations (8.2) to (8.6) permit solution for the five unknowns E_{eq}, p, h_{H+} (hence pH), h_{Mn+} and h_{Cl-} provided that the three standard potentials are known. This usually means guessing the appropriate values for $\mu^{\ominus}_{MxOy}$ and $\mu^{\ominus}_{MCln}$ because, in the confined environment of a pit, it is unlikely that these solids are precipitated in the pure state or that bulk thermodynamic properties apply to thin films (Note 8.1). Table 8.1 shows calculated values of E_{eq}, pH and p for iron, chromium and copper pits. (For copper, there is an added complication of two oxidation states Cu^+ and Cu^{2+} but the calculation follows essentially the same lines. (Note 8.2).

Table 8.1 Equilibrium potential, pH and hydrogen pressure inside a corrosion pit at 25°C.
Assumed values for $\mu^{\ominus}$(kJ/mol) for Fe_3O_4, $FeCl_2.4H_2O$, Cr_2O_3, $CrCl_3.6H_2O$, Cu_2O and CuCl of −1005, −303, −1058, −2020, −146 and −118 respectively.

Metal	Chloride absent			Chloride present			
	E/V, SHE	pH	log(p/atm)	E/V, SHE	pH	log(p/atm)	h_{Cl^-}
Iron	−0.60	8.9	2.4	−0.37	4.8	3.0	560
Chromium	−1.01	7.0	20(!)	−0.39	2.0	9.0	10^{-17}
Copper	+0.06	7.0	−16.0	+0.27	3.5	−2.0	0.01

Evidently, the pH inside a pit is much more acid than the neutral environment outside it. Indeed, there is evidence that, where the diffusion path is long and narrow, for example inside a fatigue crack, the local electrochemical conditions are virtually independent of bulk pH and external potential. This is an excellent example of how corrosion induces differences in *microclimate.* It should be noted, however, that the acid pH values only develop when there are contaminating ions such as chloride present. It is also reasonable to deduce that, inside an iron/chloride pit, the electrolyte is so rich in ferrous and chloride ions as to constitute a 'soup'.

8.3 DIFFERENTIAL AERATION

As we shall see in the next chapter, the presence of air, particularly at alkaline pH values, promotes the formation of a surface film on most common metals. And, because hydroxyl ions are produced by oxygen reduction, eqn (4.30), the process of corrosion in air is normally slowed down by the increased polarisation that then exists for both anodic and cathodic reactions. In the air-restricted (anaerobic) areas of a structure such a film, however tenuous, is unstable and is in any case likely to be further damaged by high anion concentrations such as chloride, Table 8.1. As a result, its anodic polarisation curve (E *vs.* log i_a) is more shallow, Fig. 8.4. Here, the structure is assumed to be made up of a relatively large aerated area and a very small anaerobic area, separated from one another by an electrolytic resistance R. The composite anode curve is represented by curve 'A' and is essentially that for aerated metal in view of the relatively small contribution of current from the anaerobic area. The current density on aerated metal is therefore i', indicated in the right-hand diagram. The corrosion potential is slightly lower in the anaerobic area but, because of the shallower Tafel slope, the corrosion intensity i'' is much higher. This explains why attack is more rapid in areas shielded from oxygen. Typically, such areas occur where they are less readily seen, such as flanges, inside bearings and valves, at broken paint films and under dirt deposits, Fig. 1.1.

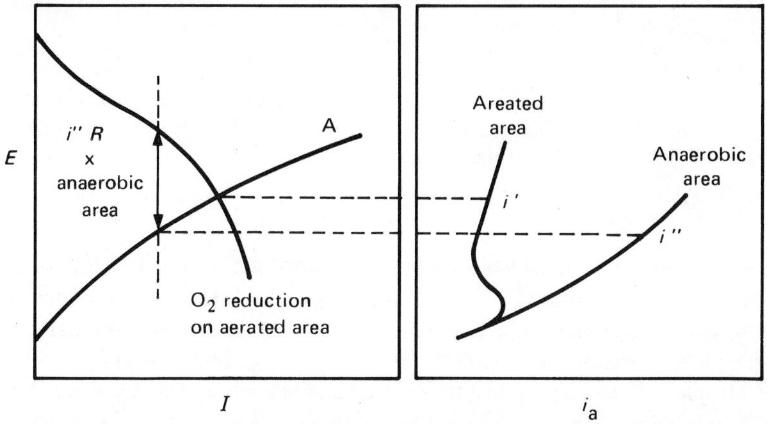

Fig. 8.4 Evans diagram for differential aeration corrosion. 'A' represents the composite curve for both aerated and anaerobic areas. Because the aerated area almost always predominates, the Evans diagram on the left is substantially that representing the corrosion of that area alone: as a result, the point of intersection represents the corrosion potential of the aerated region. This corresponds to an anodic current density i' for the aerated region. The corrosion potentials for the two areas differ very slightly owing to the IR drop between them, for example between the inside and outside of a crevice. The corrosion rate of the anaerobic area is therefore i'' in the RH diagram. Note that both areas corrode but that the oxygen-starved area is attacked faster because of its flatter polarisation curve.

8.4 BIMETALLIC CORROSION

When two metals, or two microstructural phases, are in *electronic* contact with one another, the more reactive metal corrodes preferentially. This is, of course, to be expected. However, because the surface presented to the environment is heterogeneous, the corrosion rate can in fact be enhanced in the same way that anaerobic regions corrode faster in a differential aeration cell. In Fig. 8.5, an aluminium/iron corrosion couple is represented in an appropriate Evans diagram.

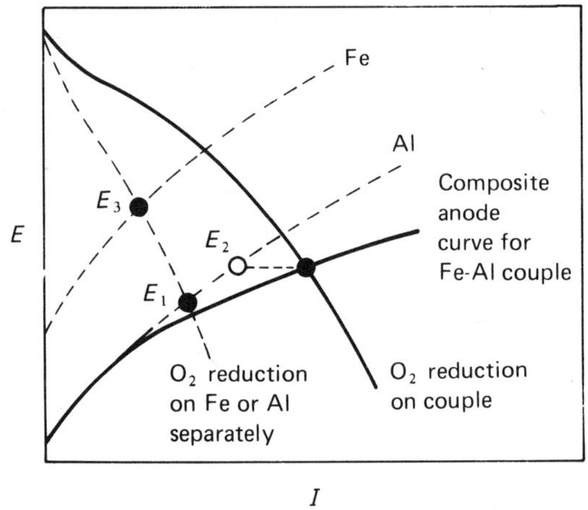

Fig. 8.5 Evans diagram for bimetallic corrosion. The presence of an equal area of iron coupled to aluminium raises the corrosion potential of the aluminium from E_1 to E_2 and lowers that of the iron from E_3.

Both anode and cathode curves are weighted composite curves, and the corrosion potential is E_2. Had there been no iron present, the cathode curve would have been steeper (because of the smaller area) and the corrosion potential at E_1: likewise, the corrosion potential of iron by itself would have been E_3. Evidently, this 'galvanic' effect has raised the corrosion potential, and hence the corrosion rate (A/m^2), of the more reactive metal and lowered that of the more noble one.

The consequences of this effect are that (a) different microstructural phases can be etched at different rates, (b) complex engineering structures display localised attack at the more reactive bits of metal, and (c) corrosion of metals such as iron can be reduced by coupling them to more reactive ones which corrode 'sacrificially'. In Table 8.2 are listed some recent data on the corrosion of mild steel, when coupled to equal areas of various other metals and exposed to a marine atmosphere (Note 8.3). The numbers in the table represent the degree of enhancement or reduction in corrosion rate resulting from bimetallic coupling. As in differential aeration, the *relative areas* are important. When the base metal is present only to a small extent (e.g. steel bolts in a gunmetal casting), there is considerable intensification of attack of that metal. That is, *whenever the cathode area is large compared with that of the anode, anodic attack is faster.*

Other 'galvanic' tables can be compiled for other environments, and both the order of the metals and the actual degree of galvanic enhancement or otherwise alter accordingly. Probably best known of these tables is that for metal actually immersed totally in seawater, Table 8.3. Here, some alloys can be seen to occur twice, in the 'active' and so-called 'passive' conditions: this phenomenon

Table 8.2 – Enhancement of mild steel corrosion in marine atmosphere by galvanic coupling. After Johnson and Abbott, 1975. Approximate acceleration factors for equal areas of mild steel and the named alloy.

Alloy	Acceleration factor
Nickel alloys Aluminium bronze 18Cr–8Ni steel	× 5 to × 10
13Cr stainless steel Copper alloys Weathering steels Tin alloys MILD STEEL Cast irons Lead alloys	No enhancement
Aluminium alloys	× 0.1
Cadmium Zinc	× 0.001
Magnesium alloys	× 0.0001

Table 8.3 – Galvanic series for alloys immersed in seawater. Acceleration effects are some hundred times those observed in moist air (Table 8.2 adjacent) for the same relative areas. Notice also the relative positions of the alloys indicated with an asterisk.

Titanium alloys (passive) Nickel alloys (passive) Stainless steels (passive) Silver alloys	
Copper alloys	
Lead and tin alloys Nickel alloys (active)	*
Stainless steels (active) Cast irons Structural steels Cadmium	 *
Zinc alloys	
Aluminium alloys	*
Magnesium alloys	

Galvanic effects are negligible between alloys in the same groups but become more acute for alloys that are widely separated in the table. The degree of acceleration also depends on relative areas.

is discussed in the next chapter. The various galvanic series, appropriate to various corrosive environments, afford an indication of how mixtures of metals are likely to affect one another. The galvanic effects are most noticeable when

(a) metals are widely separated in the series;
(b) the base metal area is relatively small; and
(c) the electrolytic resistance is low, Fig. 1.2.

In central heating systems, iron and copper are commonly used together with complete safety. This is because initial corrosion rapidly consumes the dissolved air (oxygen) in the system and cathodic reactant can only be reintroduced via 'make up' water added to restore small losses by leakage. It is a different story in the galvanised storage tanks used in many plumbing systems, for here air is plentiful, especially in the meniscus zone, Fig. 1.1. But again bimetallic effects can be avoided if the two metals are kept electronically separated, for example by insulated connections, and the water treated to ensure that it does not dissolve copper. Certain very soft domestic supply waters are *cuprosolvent,* and the $Cu^{2+}(aq)$ ions in solution ($E_{eq} = +0.17$ V, SHE at 10^{-6} activity, section 5.3) can subsequently re-deposit on the zinc coating, part of which dissolves ($E_{eq} \approx -0.76 + 0.03(-6) = -0.94$ V, SHE at a similar trace activity). The small regions of metallic copper so formed are now in *electronic* contact with the coating, where they act as an additional noble cathode for oxygen reduction in a bimetallic cell and so promote more rapid attack. Galvanised tanks in moorland (that is, soft water) areas have been known to fail by pitting corrosion only a few months after installation.

One final example, common in the UK, is pitting corrosion of the urn used for brewing the office tea. Such urns are often manufactured from aluminium sheet, which in turn is electrically connected (for safety!) to the earthed outer sheath of the heating element, usually chromium plated copper tubing. The chromium/aluminium combination carries with it the seeds of its own destruction, particularly as there is invariably a crevice at the gasket where the heating element enters the urn and because such urns are rarely fully emptied, so that salts such as chlorides accumulate. The aluminium often perforates at or close to the chromium/aluminium connection after 1-2 years.

Bibliography to Chapter 8

(1963), *Corrosion and Its Prevention at Bimetallic Contacts,* HMSO, London. Recently replaced by PD 6484 (British Standards Institution).
Ross (1977), *Metal Corrosion,* Oxford University Press.
ASTM Special Technical Publication 516 & 576, Localized Corrosion (1972) and Galvanic Pitting Corrosion.
See also the bibliography to Chapter 11.

Notes to Chapter 8

8.1 The listed values of free energies of formation, Table 2.2, make no allowance for the possible contribution of surface free energy. If 1 mole of substance forms a sphere of volume Lb^3 (b = unit cell parameter of compound), it possesses a surface area of $3.10^{16}b^2$ which, for $b \sim 0.5$ nm and $\gamma \sim 1$ J/m^2, gives an energy contribution of some 10^{-3}J; so that neglect of surface energy is justified. If, however, the mole of substance is flattened out into a round disc of thickness x, its surface area is $2Lb^3/x$ and the surface energy some $10^{-4}/x$. When $x \sim 2$ nm (say), this means that $\mu^{\ominus}$ is raised (less negative) by some 100 kJ/mol or more. Consequently, the effective $\mu^{\ominus}$ may fall to only a small fraction of the tabulated value.

8.2 The first published calculations of this kind were by Pourbaix (Ailor, *loc cit.* chapter 6; also *Lectures in Electrochemical Corrosion* (Plenum Press 1973)). See also Oldfield and Sutton, *Brit. Corrosion J.* 1978 **13** 13 for a somewhat different approach.

8.3 Johnson and Abbott, Brit. Steel Corp. report CEL/CC/5(1975). These authors used a series of concentric plates of various diameters bolted together and exposed to rural, urban/industrial and marine environments. The acceleration factors have been computed from their results.

Chapter 9

Surface Films in Aqueous Corrosion

9.1 CONDITIONS FAVOURING FILMS

A solid oxide or hydroxide will precipitate from aqueous solution when its solubility product is exceeded. For example, from Table 3.1, ferric hydroxide forms

$$Fe^{3+}(aq) + 3OH^{-}(aq) = Fe(OH)_3(s) \tag{9.1}$$

when the ionic product is

$$h_{Fe3+} \times h^3_{OH-} = 10^{-39}$$

and, by expulsion of water molecules, the hydroxide then converts to the oxide or hydrated oxide:

$$2Fe(OH)_3(s) = Fe_2O_3(s) + 3H_2O(l) \tag{9.2}$$

However, when there are no metal ions in solution, there is a problem of defining the conditions under which the metal itself can convert to the oxide. It could perhaps do this as a result of chemical combination with adsorbed oxygen from solution, for example

$$2Fe(s) + \tfrac{3}{2}O_2(ads) = Fe_2O_3(s) \tag{9.3}$$

but, although such a reaction is believed to take place, it is more likely that *electrochemical* oxidation occurs since oxygen is a powerful cathodic reactant. Hence,

$$Fe(s) = Fe^{3+}(aq) + 3e(Fe) \tag{9.4}$$

at a sufficiently noble potential, followed by reaction (9.1), or else

$$2Fe(s) + 3H_2O(l) = Fe_2O_3(s) + 6H^{+}(aq) + 6e(Fe)\ . \tag{9.5}$$

Clearly, oxidising conditions are called for by eqn (9.4) (9.5) and/or the presence of oxygen, eqn (9.3). Moreover, eqn (9.1) indicates that oxide formation is favoured by increasing the activity of hydroxyl ions. For example, at pH 3 we have $p\mathrm{OH} = 14 - 3 = 11$ and $h_{\mathrm{OH^-}} = 10^{-11}$ so that the critical ferric ion activity is $h_{\mathrm{Fe3+}} = 10^{-39}/10^{-33} = 10^{-6}$; whereas, at pH 8, $h_{\mathrm{OH^-}} = 10^{-6}$ and the $h_{\mathrm{Fe3+}}$ required is only 10^{-21}. For less stable oxides such as $Fe(OH)_2$ ($K_s = 10^{-15}$), a pH of 9.5 requires $h_{\mathrm{Fe2+}} = 10^{-6}$.

When the conditions of potential and pH are appropriate, surface films of oxide or hydroxide develop which hinder corrosion and may even stop it completely. We should appreciate that such films may be discontinuous and inhomogeneous and, above all, very thin (2 – 10 nm). The spontaneously-formed 'passive' film on iron has been found to consist of a complex oxide approximating to Fe_3O_4 and Fe_2O_3 at its inner and outer surfaces, the whole being stabilised by an absorbed layer of oxygen molecules. Clearly, the first stage in the formation of such a complex film is the adsorption of oxygen, but this is rapidly followed (a few seconds) by oxidation reactions such as eqn (9.5) until growth is slowed by electrical resistance offered by the film itself. There is some thickening of the film over a long period (several days), but the most important period is the first few minutes, when the thickness attains a few atomic layers.

9.2 SURFACE FILMS AND POLARISATION

Although serving as a more or less effective ionic barrier between metal and electrolyte, 'passive' films are sufficiently thin to allow electron tunnelling and sustain cathodic reactions such as oxygen reduction and proton reduction. What is more, they do not display the bulk semiconducting properties of simple oxides but tend instead to 'metallic' behaviour and, because of lattice defects (section 14.2), allow a restricted amount of cation conduction and so continued – but slow – anodic dissolution.

The residual semiconducting character has two effects. The first is to lower the electron concentration in the electrical double layer, and this apparently lowers the exchange current density i_o. Although the evidence for this is sparse, as much as a hundredfold reduction in the exchange currents of redox reactions have been reported (Note 9.1). The second effect is more significant: an increase in the Tafel slope. The theory is as follows.

It is first assumed that the single potential is developed across the film itself and across the double layer at the film/solution interface, but that the potential difference across the metal/film interface is negligibly small. This means that, for proton reduction on the film surface, the overpotential driving the process may be split into two (negative) potential differences

$$\eta = V_f + V_{dl} \qquad (9.6)$$

At the double layer itself, charge transfer will be characterised by a symmetry factor α_{dl} (see Fig. 6.1) and by a rate constant k_{dl} related to the exchange current density i_o by $i_o = k_{dl}a_H$, where a_H is the proton activity in the outer plane of the double layer (Note 9.2). From eqn (6.6) and putting $z = 1$ for proton reduction,

$$i = k_{dl}a_H \exp\{-(1 - \alpha_{dl})FV_{dl}/RT\}$$

or, rearranging and taking decadic logarithms,

$$V_{dl} = \{-2.303RT/(1 - \alpha_{dl})F\}\{\log i - \log(k_{dl}a_H)\} \tag{9.7}$$

Likewise, for field-dependent electron transport through the film (other than by tunnelling, section 14.1), the rate is characterised by a symmetry factor α_f, a rate constant k_f and an electron activity a_e, so that

$$V_f = \{-2.303RT/(1 - \alpha_f)F\}\{\log i - \log(k_f a_e)\} \tag{9.8}$$

Finally, from eqn (9.6) to (9.8), and because the two currents are in series,

$$\eta = (-2.303RT/F)\,[\{1/(1 - \alpha_{dl})\} + \{1/(1 - \alpha_f)\}]\,\log i + \text{concentration terms} \tag{9.9}$$

whence, substituting eqn (6.11) (6.12) for the film-free slope b_c,

$$d\eta/d(\log i) = \{(2 - \alpha_{dl} - \alpha_f)/(1 - \alpha_f)\}\,b_c \tag{9.10}$$

Since in most cases both α_{dl} and α_f are close to 0.5, *the value of b_c is approximately doubled by the presence of the film:* typical values are 1.8 times (oxygen reduction on aluminium) and 1.7 times (hydrogen evolution on zirconium), whilst the calculation at the end of Chapter 6 led to a factor of 113/59 = 1.9 times for oxygen reduction on iron.

This increase in polarisation occurs for anodic dissolution also, except that the species conducted through the film are metal cations rather than electrons. In these circumstances $V_f \gg V_{dl}$ and eqn (9.8) (9.9) approximates to

$$\eta = (2.303RT/\alpha_f' F)\{\log i - \log(k_f' a_V)\} \tag{9.11}$$

where a_V is the activity of cation vacancies (for that is how the cations move through the film) and α_f', k_f' are the appropriate symmetry factor and rate constant. Both k_f' and a_V are small so that, once a film forms, the anodic current density falls sharply, Fig. 9.1. The change in behaviour is so dramatic that we say the metal has become 'passive'. Dissolution through the surface film shows an anomalously high Tafel slope, but this is not in fact attributable to the especially small size of α'_f. It is because the limited vacancy activity (concentration) at room temperature imposes a *diffusion control* on the anodic current analogously to eqn (6.16). When vacancies are plentiful, as may occur with alloying or changes in the oxidation state of the cations in the film, the slope approximates to the usual Tafel value, with α'_f replacing the α $(= \alpha_{dl})$ of eqn (6.8). But in many instances i_p, the current density in the passive state, approximates to the limiting rate at which vacancies may be induced to move in the potential gradient across the film and the slope is virtually infinite.

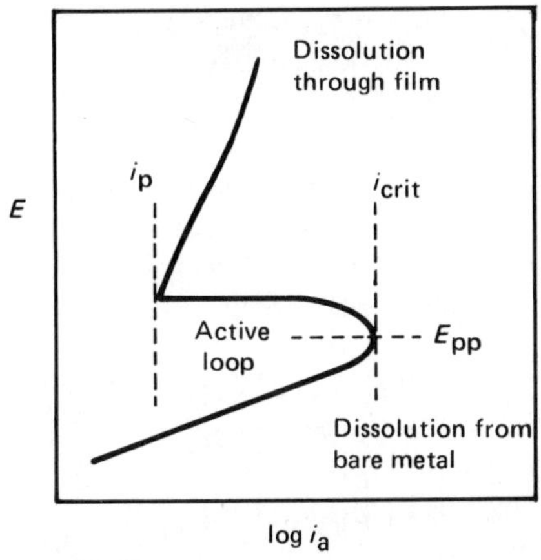

Fig. 9.1 Anodic polarisation curve showing passivity. E_{pp} is the peak passivation potential, i_{crit} is the critical passivating current density, and i_p is the minimum current density in the passive state. For values, see Table 9.1.

9.3 POTENTIAL *vs.* *p*H DIAGRAMS

The thermodynamic information describing the onset of passive film formation can be usefully presented in the form of an isothermal phase diagram. The equilibrium of interest, expressed in the form of a reduction, is

$$M_xO_y(s) + 2yH^+(aq) + 2ye(M) = xM(s) + yH_2O(l) \quad (9.12)$$

$$E = E^{\ominus}_{oxide} + (RT/F) \ln h_{H+} \quad (8.2)$$

so that the experimental variables are potential and *p*H. Diagrams for the system metal/water are usually referred to as *Pourbaix diagrams* (Note 9.3). That for Fe/H_2O is shown in Fig. 9.2: it indicates the experimental conditions of potential and pH for which iron, its various solvated ions and two principal oxides, are stable at 25°C. Thus, the region of stability for Fe^{2+}(aq) is bounded by two horizontal lines representing the equilibria between (a) Fe(s)|Fe^{2+}(aq) and (b) Fe^{2+}(aq)|Fe^{3+}(aq); and two sloping lines representing the equilibria between (c) Fe^{2+}(aq) | Fe_3O_4(s) and (d) Fe^{2+}(aq) | Fe_2O_3(s). At 25°C, these are respectively

(a) $Fe^{2+}(aq) + 2e(Fe) = Fe(s)$

$$\begin{aligned} E &= E^{\ominus} + (RT/2F)\ln(h_{Fe^{2+}}/a_{Fe}) \\ &= -0.44 + 0.0295\log(10^{-6}/1) \\ &= -0.61 \text{ V, SHE.} \end{aligned}$$

(b) $Fe^{3+}(aq) + e(Fe) = Fe^{2+}(aq)$

$$\begin{aligned} E &= E^{\ominus} + (RT/F)\ln(h_{Fe^{3+}}/h_{Fe^{2+}}) \\ &= +0.77 + 0.059\log(10^{-6}/10^{-6}) \\ &= +0.77 \text{ V, SHE.} \end{aligned}$$

(c) $Fe_3O_4(s) + 8H^+(aq) + 2e(Fe) = 3Fe^{2+}(aq) + 4H_2O(l)$

$$\begin{aligned} E &= E^{\ominus} + (RT/2F)\ln(h^8_{H^+}/h^3_{Fe^{2+}}) \\ &= +0.98 - 0.236pH - 0.088\log(10^{-6}) \\ &= +1.51 - 0.236pH \text{ V, SHE.} \end{aligned}$$

(d) $Fe_2O_3(s) + 6H^+(aq) + 2e(Fe) = 2Fe^{2+}(aq) + 3H_2O(l)$

$$\begin{aligned} E &= E^{\ominus} + (RT/2F)\ln(h^6_{H^+}/h^2_{Fe^{2+}}) \\ &= +0.73 - 0.177pH - 0.059\log(10^{-6}) \\ &= +1.08 - 0.177pH \text{ V, SHE.} \end{aligned}$$

It may be seen that the lines are horizontal when no hydrogen ions are involved in the equilibrium, and sloping when they are involved. Vertical lines, such as that separating the Fe^{3+}(aq) and Fe_2O_3(s) regions, result when no electrons (that is, no oxidation) are involved. In every case the activities of all ions except H^+(aq) are taken to be 10^{-6}. This is partly because even nominally 'pure' water contains traces of many salts, partly because in any case small amounts of metal dissolution give rise to micromolal quantities of ions; but most especially because phase boundaries drawn in this way correspond rather well to observed corrosion behaviour. Thus, iron tends to corrode above a potential around −0.6 V, SHE (cf. the calculation in section 5.3).

The Pourbaix diagram is commonly simplified in terms of *domains of corrosion behaviour.* Those regions corresponding to the stable ionic state (Fe^{2+}, Fe^{3+} and $Fe(OH)_3^-$ in Fig. 9.2) are designated 'corrosion' domains; those corresponding to passivating solid compounds (Fe_2O_3 and Fe_3O_4) are designated 'passive'; whilst the metallic state (Fe) is designated 'immune'. Such a simplified diagram summarises the corrosion behaviour to be expected for the pure metal immersed in pure water, assuming that the 'passivating' solids are truly protective.

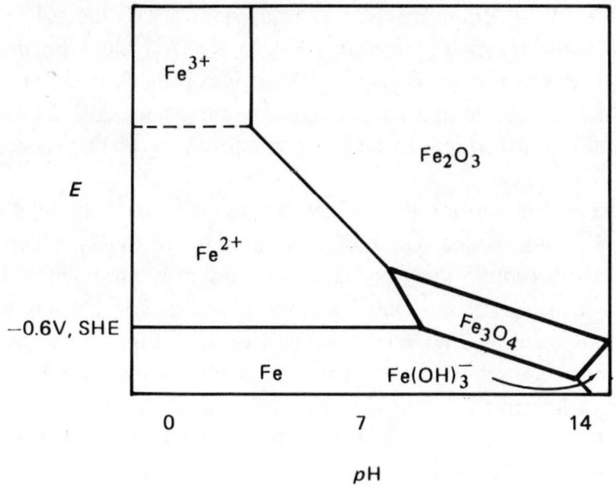

Fig. 9.2 Pourbaix diagram for iron in pure water at 25°C. The boundaries separating the various phase fields represent thermodynamic equilibria for which all ionic activities are 10^{-6}.

Real corrosive environments are less pure and are at temperatures other than 25°C. At higher temperatures, for example, the acid and alkaline regions corresponding to the dissolved state are somewhat larger. A more dramatic change is effected by chloride ion, Fig. 9.3. Here, we see that the passive region corresponding to hydrated magnetite (Fe_3O_4) is no longer present and that the Fe^{2+}(aq)

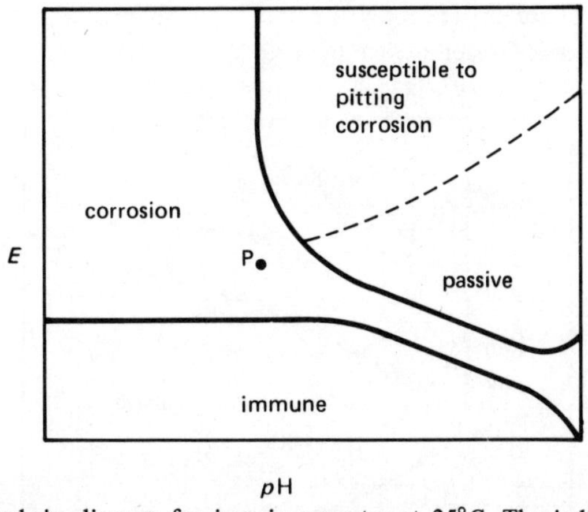

Fig. 9.3 Pourbaix diagram for iron in seawater at 25°C. The individual phase regions have been omitted for clarity and instead replaced by domains of corrosion behaviour. The point P indicates the conditions inside a corrosion pit, section 8.2. The broken line corresponds approximately to the breakdown potential E_b on p. 120.

region, already expanded somewhat, extends right across the *p*H range until it merges with that of ferroate (trihydroxy Fe(II), $Fe(OH)_3^-(aq)$). Furthermore, the hitherto protective region of $Fe_2O_3(s)$ now divides roughly into two regions, the lower of which corresponds to truly 'passive' behaviour and the upper to an unstable situation in which localised breakdown to pitting attack becomes possible.

The presence of chromium in steel is known to be beneficial. This arises from the high stability and low ionic conductivity of Cr_2O_3, which exists as a passive film on chromium itself and also on numerous alloys, in which it exists even at low concentrations. The Pourbaix diagrams for chromium and 12% chrome iron are given in Fig. 9.4. A comparison with Fig. 9.3 will show that the passive area has been extended and the area of pitting susceptibility contracted, so corrosion is less likely when chromium is added as an alloying element to steel. The actual *rate* of corrosion is best demonstrated by reference to Fig. 9.1, where we saw how 'passivation' was a term introduced to describe the sharp deviation from Tafel behaviour as a surface film was established. The maximum rate of anodic dissolution is a critical value of current density i_{crit}, which occurs at the *peak passivation* potential E_{pp}, and the minimum rate in the passive state is i_p. These three quantities are tabulated in Table 9.1 for iron and a variety of Fe-Cr alloys and shown graphically in Fig. 9.5 (Note 9.4). It may be seen that alloying lowers E_{pp} by two-thirds of a volt, the critical current density at this potential by between one and three orders of magnitude and, once passivity is established, the rate of corrosion by a similar amount. The chief advantage of further alloying additions is to improve the tenacity of the protective film so that pitting is less likely in chloride solutions. For example, in the 300 series of austenitic stainless steels (18Cr-8Ni), some 3% molybdenum addition improves pitting resistance in seawater environments.

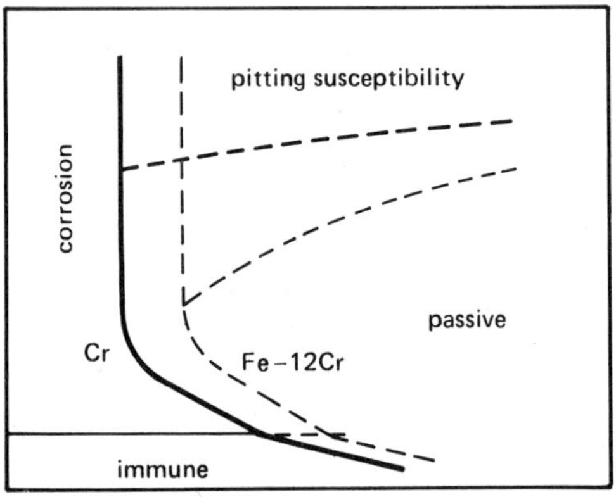

Fig. 9.4 Pourbaix diagrams for chromium and Fe-12% Cr in dilute chloride solutions at 25°C.

Table 9.1 Peak passivation potentials and critical and passive current densities. Deaerated sulphuric acid at 25°C.

Alloy	E_{pp} V, SHE	i_{crit} A/m²	i_p A/m²
Iron	+0.52 to 1.00	$10^{4.0}$	$10^{0.3}$
Fe-14Cr	−0.10	$10^{3.0}$	$10^{-1.3}$
Fe-18Cr	−0.15	$10^{2.5}$	$10^{-2.0}$
Fe-18Cr-5Mo	−0.20	$10^{0.3}$	$10^{-1.7}$
Fe-18Cr-8Ni	−0.20	$10^{1.0}$	$10^{-2.2}$

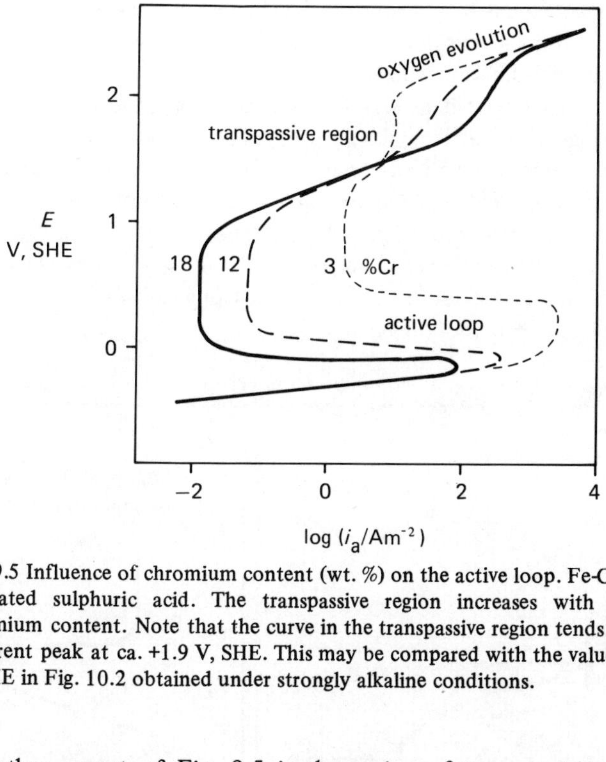

Fig. 9.5 Influence of chromium content (wt. %) on the active loop. Fe-Cr alloys in deaerated sulphuric acid. The transpassive region increases with increasing chromium content. Note that the curve in the transpassive region tends to display a current peak at ca. +1.9 V, SHE. This may be compared with the value of +0.55 V, SHE in Fig. 10.2 obtained under strongly alkaline conditions.

A further aspect of Fig. 9.5 is the region of *transpassivity* indicated at potentials greater than about +0.9 V, SHE. This corresponds to the oxidation of Cr(III) in the passive film to Cr(VI) in solution:

$$Cr(III) + 4H_2O = HCrO_4^-(aq) + 7H^+ + 3e(metal), \tag{9.13}$$

and this obviously occurs the more readily as the chromium activity in the film is raised. The dissolution of the film is not complete, for oxidation of chromium metal to Cr(III) continues at the metal/film interface while the further oxidation (9.13) takes place at its outer surface (Note 9.5). There are further repercussions, for the Cr(III) oxidation injects cation vacancies into the oxide surface in order to preserve electroneutrality, with the result that film conductivity rises. This situation is typical of the behaviour of *multivalent oxides,* and one finds that, as the single potential is raised, i_p for such a passive film displays a maximum as the film gradually converts from the lower-valency to the higher-valency form.

Before leaving Fig. 9.5, we should note how sensitive is the active loop to the amount of chromium available in the underlying metal. It is, therefore, not altogether surprising that heat treatment of the metal can strongly influence its corrosion behaviour. 304-type stainless steels are prone to 'weld decay' if their carbon contents are too high. The heat-affected zone in the parent metal adjoining the weld is subjected to temperatures in the region of 600–800°C, sufficient to cause precipitation of chromium carbide ($Cr_{23}C_6$ in 18Cr–8Ni, Cr_7C_3 in 13Cr steels). Because diffusion and nucleation are more rapid at the grain boundaries, a chromium-depleted zone is produced whose passivity is severely undermined. Fig. 9.6 shows how, in nitric acid solutions, the corrosion potential lies below E_{pp} for the depleted ('sensitised') grain boundaries. The resultant bimetallic corrosion causes the welded metal to fall apart. The remedy is to adjust the alloy composition so that chromium carbide does not form. This is accomplished by lowering the carbon activity: either the steelmaking process ensures that the carbon content lies below about 0.05% or else strong carbide formers such as Ti or Nb are added. See also section 10.5.

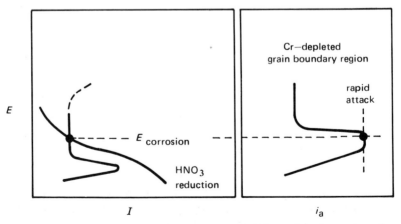

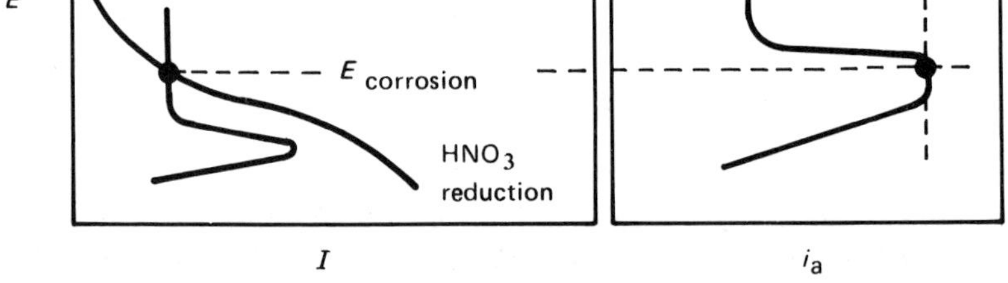

Fig. 9.6 Weld decay of austenitic stainless steels. Carbide precipitation at the grain boundary means that a narrow anodic region remains active at the corrosion potential while the majority of the surface is passive.

9.4 FILM BREAKDOWN AND REPAIR

Most metals acquire a thin oxide film when exposed to dry air at room temperature. A similar film forms as a result of electrochemical action, for example eqn (9.5), and is likewise favoured by the presence of air. Recent work has shown how the discrepancy between E_{pp} and the calculated equilibrium potential, eqn (8.1), is partly due to the presence of adsorbed oxygen on the surface of the film (Note 9.6). And again, one might suppose that the passive film possesses an equilibrium partial pressure of oxygen given by

$$\mu^{\ominus}_{MxOy} = G^{\bullet}_{MxOy} = (yRT/2)\ln(p_{O2}/p^{\ominus}) \qquad (9.14)$$

and restricting the supply of air, so that p_{O2} falls below this equilibrium value, will cause the film to decompose. If, allowing for surface energy effects in a thin film, we take 10% of the bulk values for $\mu^{\ominus}_{MxOy}$ (Notes 8.1 and 9.7), the pressures calculated for Fe_3O_4, Cr_2O_3 and Cu_2O are respectively 10^{-10}, 10^{-13} and 10^{-6} atm. These low pressures can plausibly be achieved inside crevices, and this may explain why differential aeration attack works as in Fig. 8.4. The sequence of film stabilities implies that chromium oxide is the least likely to decompose under such conditions.

In practice, surface films are heterogeneous. Not only are there usually chemical variations in the underlying metal, as for example at segregated grain boundaries and in weld decay, but there are scratch lines, inclusions and sheared edges which are likely to introduce internal stresses in the film. There are, therefore, a number of points ('pores') in the film where it is less thick, less strong or more permeable than elsewhere. The metal may therefore start dissolving at these sensitive points when it is immersed in an electrolyte. After that, three things may happen:

(a) the film grows again at the pores;
(b) localised corrosion continues at the exposed bare metal; or
(c) breakdown extends sideways from the pores until there is no film left.

That is, (a) film repair prevents further corrosion, or else film breakdown causes (b) pitting or (c) general attack. The factors causing one or other of these outcomes are the solubility of the oxide, the anion concentration and, of course, potential and pH.

Film repair takes place if, for the conditions inside the pores, the corrosion potential exceeds E_{pp}. The exposure of a number of small areas of bare metal in an otherwise filmed surface constitutes an **'active-passive' cell** akin to a bimetallic couple, for example Table 8.3. The corrosion current density at these areas is, therefore, enhanced and, if this exceeds i_{crit}, the corrosion potential simultaneously exceeds E_{pp} and induces repassivation in the form of a 'plug' of oxide. The corrosion potential therefore rises with time and levels off at some potential $>E_{pp}$, Figure 9.7.

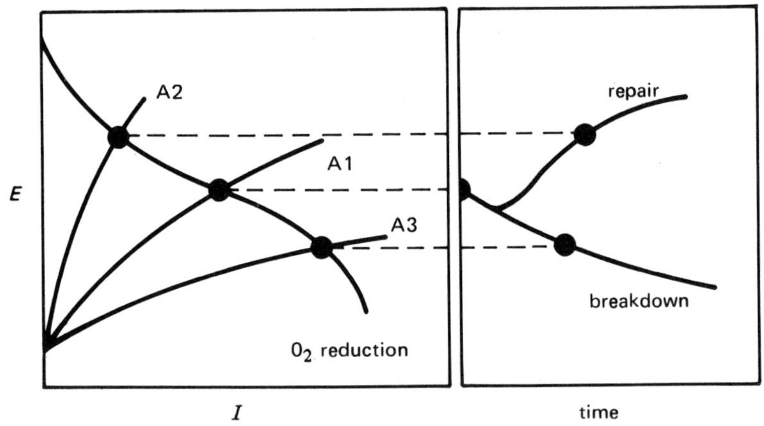

Fig. 9.7 Film breakdown and repair. The anodic polarisation curve A1 is a composite curve for pores and filmed metal. If the pores are repaired the curve moves to A2; if the film breakdown continues the curve moves to A3. The right-hand diagram shows how the corrosion potential changes with time.

The diagram also shows how the corrosion potential falls if film breakdown continues, corresponding to general corrosion. This condition often results when the 'microclimate' in the pore becomes enriched by anions migrating there from outside the film. If hydrolysis of precipitated chloride salts, say, lowers the *p*H to such a value, Table 8.1, that repassivation can no longer take place, anion exchange with the surrounding oxide film may raise its vacancy concentration so that it too becomes permeable to metal cations: the pore extends sideways. Anion penetration of the passive film is also aided by sufficiently high single potentials. That is what happens in the area designated 'pitting susceptibility' in Fig. 9.4. Such localised breakdown depends on the chloride ion concentration but is generally characterised by a critical potential called the **breakdown potential** E_b. (Note 9.8). The breakdown potential in Fig. 9.4 is about +0.0 to +0.5 V, SHE for Fe-12Cr, depending on *p*H, and a constant +0.5 V, SHE for pure chromium. Table 9.2 lists further values in neutral solution (*p*H 7, although buffered values of *p*H 8 were also employed in some cases). These data reinforce the observation that E_b falls with increasing chloride concentration but is raised by additions of chromium to iron. Since the penetration and contamination of the passive film depends on time, the measurement of pitting/breakdown potentials is prone to error.

Table 9.2 Breakdown (pitting) potentials in neutral chloride solutions.

Alloy	E_b in V, SHE			Ref
	0.01 M	0.1 M	1.0 M chloride	
0.2C steel	0.45	0.22	0.02	1
Weathering steel	0.06	0.03	−0.03	1
Fe-13Cr		0.32	0.14	2
Fe-17Cr		0.36	0.20	2
Fe-28Cr		0.75	0.59	2
Pure Al		−0.40		3
Al-1.3Mn		−0.45		3
Al-4Si		−0.48(0.5 M)		3
Al-5Zn		−0.71(0.5 M)		3

References:
1. Szauer & Jakobs, *Corros. Sci.* 1976 **16** 945
2. Kolotyrkin, *Corrosion* 1963 **19** 261
3. Böhni & Uhlig, *J. Electrochem. Soc.* 1969 **116** 906

Bibliography to Chapter 9

Evans (1960), *Corrosion and Oxidation of Metals,* Arnold.

Pourbaix (1963), *Atlas of Equilibrium Diagrams,* Gauthier-Villars, republished by Pergamon, London in 1966.

Uhlig (1963), *Corrosion and Corrosion Control,* Wiley.

West (1970), *Electrodeposition and Corrosion Processes,* Van Nostrand Reinhold 2nd edn.

Young (1961), *Anodic Oxide Films,* Academic Press.

Notes to Chapter 9

9.1 Makrides, *J. Electrochem. Soc.* 1964 **111** 392; Vijh and Conway, *Chem. Revs.* 1967 **67** 623. A general reference to this subject. Vijh, *Electrochemistry of Metals and Semiconductors* (Dekker, 1973), from which the derivation of eqn (9.10) has been adapted.

9.2 In eqn (6.1) the rate constant was defined as the ratio [activities] $/(i_o/zF)$. For convenience, in this treatment of films the zF is included in the rate constant itself. It follows that

$$i_o/k_{dl} = a_{kink}h^n_{OH-} = a_H$$

since forward and backward reactions are equal at equilibrium.

9.3 Pourbaix diagrams are published in a comprehensive atlas: Pourbaix, *Atlas of Equilibrium Diagrams* (Gauthier-Villars, 1963) and the chloride-modified diagram for iron in *Lectures in Electrochemical Corrosion* (Plenum Press, 1973).
9.4 Morika, Sawada and Shiobara, *Studies in Metallurgy* (Tohuku University, 1969); Olivier, Thesis (Leiden University, 1955); Rockel, *Corrosion* 1973 **29** 393.
9.5 This is precisely the reverse process to chromium electrodeposition from CrO_3 solutions. The final stage of metal formation is the reduction of Cr(III) at the inner interface of a passivating Cr_2O_3 film. Conductivity is enhanced by contamination of the film by sulphate and fluoride anions.
9.6 The reactivation potential, at which an initially passive metal exhibits an increase in current as the potential is made more negative, is called the **Flade potential** E_F. For iron, this has been shown by Mayne and Turgoose, *Brit. Corros. J.* 1976 **11** 140 to correspond to the Fe(III)/Fe(II) redox equilibrium potential, which in turn depends on the availability of oxygen. E_F is therefore not an intrinsic property of the oxide film.
9.7 The oxygen partial pressure in the ambient air is 0.2 atm. If the partial pressure at the bottom of a pit or crevice is determined solely by diffusion of oxygen, which is consumed there at a rate $i = i_L - \Delta i$, it will adopt a value $p_{O2} = 0.2(\Delta i/i_L) = 10^{-8}$ atm for a concentration overpotential of -0.2 V, eqn (6.19). This low pressure could very well be sufficient to decompose the oxides of iron and copper if these are present as very thin films. The reader should also consult recent papers by Oldfield and Sutton, *Brit. Corros. J.* 1979, who have developed a technique for evaluating pitting resistance of Fe-Cr-Ni-Mo alloys. They have shown that the composition of the 'critical crevice solution' leading to permanent breakdown of passivity in seawater is 1M Cl^-, *p*H 2.9 for 16% Cr steel, 4M Cl^-, *p*H 1.7 for 316 steel and 6M Cl^-, *p*H 0.0 for the nickel base alloy Inconel 625.
9.8 The breakdown potential is sometimes referred to as the pitting potential. Other authors make a further distinction between that potential which will initiate pits on a pit-free surface and the potential required to activate pits already present.

Chapter 10

Some Complications

This chapter may be omitted at first reading. It contains material whose importance depends upon the reader's interests. Sections 10.1 and 10.2 are simply an extension of earlier material on complexants (sections 4.5 and 6.1). Sections 10.3-10.5 are likely to be of most interest to practising engineers, 10.4 especially to chemical engineers and 10.5 to metallurgists.

10.1 COMPLEXANTS

As we saw in section 4.5, the first effect of complexing is that the single potential of the corresponding metal-ion/metal equilibrium is lowered according to the Nernst equation (4.23):

$$E = E^{\ominus}_{\text{aq}} + (RT/zF)\ln h_{\text{aquo-ion}}$$

$$= E^{\ominus}_{\text{aq}} - (RT/zF)\ln K_{\text{n}} + (RT/zF)\ln(h_{\text{complex}}/h^{n}_{\text{ligand}}) \qquad (4.43)$$

$$= E^{\ominus}_{\text{complex}} + (RT/zF)\ln(h_{\text{complex}}/h^{n}_{\text{ligand}})$$

The decrease in potential $E^{\ominus}_{\text{complex}} - E^{\ominus}_{\text{aq}} = -(RT/zF)\ln K_{\text{n}}$ is shown in the last column of Table 4.3, whence it may be seen that the very stable cyano complexes lower the equilibrium potential by 0.6 to 1.6 V and that hydroxylo and ammine complexes lower it by 0.2 to 0.6 V. The general result is to enlarge the 'corrosion' areas in the Pourbaix diagram, so that metal wastage is easier.

The second effect of complexing is to slow down the kinetics of electrode processes. The exchange current density is reduced, for example by a factor of about 10^5 in the case of the $Ag(CN)_2^-/Ag$ equilibrium discussed in Chapter 4, and, because the complex is either more bulky than the corresponding aquo-ion or else negatively charged, the limiting current density i_L due to diffusion of the ion is also lowered. There are important consequences of this for electrodeposition. From the point of view of corrosion it means simply that the slope of the anodic polarisation curve in the (linear) Evans diagram is steeper.

10.2 SPECIFIC ADSORPTION

Both anions and cations are usually solvated, in the sense that one or more solvent water molecules are more or less permanently associated with each ion. For anions, this association is less complete and less rigid than for the 'sheath' that surrounds cations, but it nevertheless involves re-orientation of adjacent water molecules from the pure solvent structure. However, when anions enter the double layer of a metal, they are often stripped of their associated water molecules and adsorb strongly by sharing electrons with the substrate: such anions are said to be 'specifically' adsorbed (because the strength of the bond is specific to the combination of anion and metal substrate). Their closeness to the metal lowers the potential φ^M of the metal. This alteration in the potential and charge distribution in the double layer has the effect of altering the kinetics of charge transfer, so that anodic dissolution is slowed down (η_a increases for a given anodic current density) and cathodic deposition is accelerated (η_c decreases).

The principal anions of interest are chloride, sulphide and cyanide and, of these, perhaps the first two play a significant part in corrosion. Cyanide is important in electrodeposition, for example specifically adsorbed CN^- stimulates proton discharge during plating of silver and copper from their cyano-complexes. The evidence for the influence of chloride adsorption on anodic dissolution is difficult to disentangle from the simultaneous effects of film breakdown and chloro-complexing, although the Tafel slope falls in very concentrated chloride solutions (that is α in eqn (6.8) increases almost to unity). For sulphide S^{2-} and hydrosulphide HS^- ions, corrosion is considerably enhanced: steels, for example, corrode faster than pure iron owing to their sulphur content. There is evidence that part of this acceleration is due to enhancement of the cathodic reaction, but, as with chloride, the anodic Tafel slope is reduced also.

Finally, as we shall see in the next chapter, the presence of adsorbed ions influences the subsequent adsorption of other species such as inhibitor molecules. Thus, positively charged amines R_3NH^+ (aq) adsorb more easily on iron when chloride ions are also present. A similar cooperative effect obtains when differently charged inhibitor molecules are used together. Such a cooperative effect is called **synergism**.

10.3 BACTERIAL CORROSION ('Microbial corrosion')

Corrosion can be accelerated by the presence of microbial organisms, either because they manufacture aggressive species, such as protons or sulphide ions, or because they catalyse the electrochemical reactions themselves. The majority of active organisms are bacteria, about 1-5 μm long, which either oxidise or reduce sulphur compounds as some part of their life process. One group, for example, use externally supplied oxygen to oxidise sulphur or sulphide to sulphuric acid, e.g.

$$S(s) + \tfrac{3}{2}O_2(g) + H_2O(l) = H_2SO_4(aq) \qquad (10.1)$$

for which $\Delta G^{\ominus} = -508$ kJ/mol ($\mathcal{E} = 0.88$ V, eqn (4.12)), and this and similar reactions lower the pH to between 1 and 4. Perhaps the most dramatic of the aerobic bacteria is *Thiobacillus concretivorus,* which is responsible for many instances of acid corrosion of concrete and building stone; other strains attack cellulose-based wrapping materials to generate acid where it is least expected or else promote corrosion of aluminium fuel tanks in aircraft. The second group, whose ravages are more common, flourish in anaerobic conditions and reduce sulphate to sulphide or H_2S, for example

$$SO_4^{2-}(aq) + 10\,H^+(aq) + 8e(\text{bacterium}) = H_2S(g) + 4H_2O(l) \qquad (10.2)$$

for which $E^{\ominus} = +0.25$ V, SHE, with $E_{eq} \approx -0.3$ V, SHE at pH 7, the electrons being supplied by oxidation of organic material or of elementary hydrogen. The most abundant is *Desulfovibrio,* which flourishes in the pH range 5–9. It occurs readily in natural waters of all kinds, including seawater, and is active over a wide range of temperature. Bacterial corrosion of iron and steel usually occurs in polluted waters, in seabed silt and in clay soils.

Perhaps the chief characteristic of sulphate-reducing bacteria is the fact that they allow corrosion to occur in circumstances where it would not otherwise have been predicted, viz. at neutral pH and in the virtual absence of oxygen. Although sulphates are a constituent of most soils, the reduction reaction (10.2) is normally highly polarised, that is, it possesses a low exchange current density and is therefore kinetically slow. Corrosion of iron ($E \approx -0.6$ V, SHE, section 6.4) is, therefore, very slow unless bacteria are available to catalyse the reduction by providing an easy metabolic path. The bacteria have two further effects. The first is to stimulate hydrogen ion reduction, probably by HS^- or S^{2-} adsorption in the double layer, although bacterial enzymes such as *hydrogenase* may also be responsible. The second is to precipitate sulphide films. As discussed in section 9.2, surface films cause an increase in the Tafel slopes of both anodic and cathodic processes, although often insufficiently to stop attack. The sulphide films are generally nonprotective and lead to enhanced attack if oxygen becomes available at some later time.

There are several *macro*organisms that also contribute to corrosion, largely by interfering with the access of oxygen and so producing differential aeration corrosion. Thus, fungal growth results from the deposition of mould spores on metal surfaces stored in moist conditions. Besides sometimes initiating crevice attack, fungi liberate organic acids such as oxalic and acetic acid which accelerate the formation of unsightly tarnish films. In seawater immersion, the commonest macro-organisms are barnacles and mussels. These proliferate in warm, slow-moving water and are responsible for the 'fouling' of ships' hulls and heat exchanger tubes. Pitting attack usually results and, in addition, heat transfer is impeded in the latter. The initial attachment of the organism occurs at a very early stage in its life cycle, when it is found to be especially sensitive to various toxic substances such as $Cu^{2+}(aq)$ and $Cl_2(g)$ and also to sharp changes in temperature. Hence, when seawater is used in once-through cooling systems, as may occur in electrical power generation, it is common practice to warm the incoming water at intervals and thereby prevent mussel attachment.

10.4 FLOWING ENVIRONMENTS

As corrosion proceeds, corrosion products accumulate at the metal surface and reactants such as dissolved oxygen become depleted. Diffusion counters this situation somewhat, although in the extreme case of a crevice or pit the 'microclimate' may eventually change beyond recognition, section 8.2. Because the diffusion layer thickness δ depends critically on the stirring in the electrolyte the limiting current is also affected by stirring:

$$i_L = zFDc/\delta \tag{10.3}$$

in which the h_{Mz+} of eqn (6.16) has been replaced by the bulk concentration c of diffusing species, as on p. 87.

For example, for a metal corroding in aerated water, the rate of arrival of oxygen at the surface is

$$r_1 = k_1(c_{O2}^{\text{bulk}} - c_{O2}^{\text{surface}}) \qquad \text{mol/m}^2\ \text{s} \tag{10.4}$$

oxygen concentrations here being expressed in mol/m^3, whilst the consumption rate will be

$$r_2 = k_2 c_{O2}^{\text{surface}} \tag{10.5}$$

So that in the steady state $r_1 = r_2 = r$ the rate of corrosion is

$$\begin{aligned} r &= c_{O2}^{\text{bulk}}/\{(1/k_1) + (1/k_2)\} \\ &= c_{O2}^{\text{bulk}} . k_1 k_2/(k_1 + k_2) \end{aligned} \tag{10.6}$$

The proportionality 'constants' k_1 and k_2 have units of m/s and depend respectively on the flow rate u of the electrolyte and on charge transfer kinetics. When k_2 is very small, say 10^{-5} m/s as may occur for a passive metal, r becomes independent of flow rate. On non-passive metals, however, k_1 and k_2 are comparable so that r/c_{O2}^{bulk} depends on k_2 through eqn (10.6). This functional dependence on flow rate is experimentally found to be of the form $r \propto u^n$, in which n is a constant. For example, for passage through a pipe, $n = 0.33$ for laminar flow and 0.6–0.8 for turbulent flow; whilst for passage over a plate the exponent becomes respectively 0.5 and 0.9.

The power-law dependence of corrosion rate upon flow rate may be derived from hydrodynamics (Note 10.1). The important parameters are the dimensionless quantities

$$\text{Reynolds number} \qquad Re = uL/\nu \qquad (10.7)$$

$$\text{Schmidt number} \qquad Sc = \nu/D \qquad (10.8)$$

where ν is the kinematic viscosity of the electrolyte and L is a 'characteristic' length which is identified with pipe diameter or slit width, depending on the geometrical configuration of the system. It is possible to show that, for a smooth surface, the diffusion layer thickness is

$$\delta = 1.61\, Re^{-0.5} Sc^{-0.33} \qquad (10.9)$$

so that, substituting in eqn (10.3),

$$i_L = 0.62\, zFDc\, Re^{0.5} Sc^{033} \qquad (10.10)$$

It may readily be seen that, for passage over a flat plate, the limiting current density is proportional to $u^{0.5}$. This in turn means that, where corrosion is under cathodic control, Fig. 6.5, the corrosion rate ($\approx i_L$) is also proportional to the square root of the flow rate (Note 10.2). There is a transition from laminar (that is, smooth) flow to turbulent flow at some critical value of the Reynolds number: in pipes, for example, Re_{crit} = 2000–3000. For turbulent flow regimes eqn (10.10) becomes

$$i_L \approx 1.7\, zFc\, u\, Sc^{0.83} \qquad (10.11)$$

so that the corrosion rate is approximately proportional to the flow rate.

The foregoing treatment has neglected the actual mechanism of corrosion. For passive metals, for example, the presence of oxygen is essential to maintain the integrity of the passive film. Consequently, at very small flow rates and oxygen concentrations, the rate of oxygen replenishment may be insufficient to maintain passivity so that pitting results. Such pitting is common in 304-type steels (18Cr-8Ni) exposed to stagnant chloride-containing environments. Because rapid flow restores the necessary oxygen concentration and also removes the localised variations in solution composition that develop during pitting attack, the use of the same steel as a pump impeller, say, is perfectly satisfactory. This benefit resulting from high flow rates can take place even at low oxygen concentrations. This is because i_L increases with increasing flow rate and finally reaches the point where it exceeds i_{crit}, the critical passivating current density, section 9.3.

However, at very high flow rates, in the region of 10 m/s and greater, erosion of the metal surface may take place because of *cavitation.* Here the turbulence is of such magnitude that it causes mechanical damage to the passive film and may even tear out small particles of the metal itself. Erosion damage is especially marked when the electrolyte carries a high concentration of suspended solids.

Taking all these effects into account, we arrive at Fig. 10.1. There is a change in exponent n as conditions change from laminar to turbulent flow. There then follows a plateau where the corrosion rate is determined largely by charge transfer kinetics; that is, $i_{corrosion}$ is given by the point of intersection of the anodic and cathodic Tafel lines in Fig. 6.3 because i_L exceeds this value (there is no concentration polarisation). The dashed curve A represents the corrosion of a stainless steel for which $i_L > i_{crit}$, so that increasing oxygen availability promotes increasing passivity. Finally, the rate increases again at the onset of cavitation corrosion.

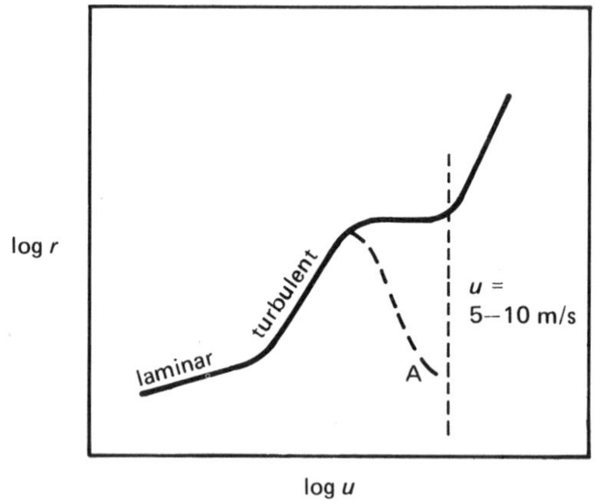

Fig. 10.1 The dependence of corrosion rate r upon solution flow rate u. Note log-log plot. The change in slope reflects a change in the exponent n at the transition from laminar to turbulent flow. The plateau occurs when corrosion is no longer under cathodic control but instead $i_L > i_{corr}$; whereas the curve A results when $i_L > i_{crit}$. The increase in rate above 5–10 m/s is due to cavitation.

In conclusion, there is a complicated dependence of corrosion rate upon the flow of electrolyte. From the design viewpoint, however, this is rarely important. Thus, provided a suitably corrosion-resistant material is selected in the first place, the two- or three-fold change in rate that results from minor turbulence at such surface features as flanged joints in pipes is not damaging. Where rate does become important is when $u >$ ca. 5 m/s, for cavitation can then lead to rapid attack, especially in copper-base alloys. Section 16.2 refers to pitting attack in a stainless steel that resulted from excessive entry velocities into a heat exchanger.

10.5 METALLURGICAL CONSIDERATIONS

It is a well-known observation that, the finer the dispersion of precipitated second-phase particles and the greater the coherency stresses at the particle interfaces, the faster is the rate of corrosion. Thus, lightly tempered martensite etches more rapidly in acid solutions and the corrosion rate passes through a maximum at 400°C temper, whereafter particle coarsening leads to a decline in rate. This observation points to (a) the importance of phase boundaries as preferential sites of cathodic reactions such as hydrogen ion reduction, and (b) the influence of elastic strain energy in these boundaries on anodic dissolution, section 5.2. The boundaries may be regarded as a special form of second phase contributing to bimetallic corrosion, section 8.4. Of course, galvanic effects are also introduced by the chemical differences that exist between matrix and precipitate. This is especially noticeable in precipitation-hardened aluminium alloys. In Al-Cu alloys, the $CuAl_2$ phase is more noble than the surrounding aluminium matrix and so provides a cathodic area in intimate contact with it: because the $CuAl_2$ tends to form preferentially along grain boundaries the result is intergranular attack in the alloy. The effect is most marked at peak hardness and may, indeed, be ameliorated by slightly overaging, which reduces the coherency of the precipitate. Similarly, $MgZn_2$ and Mg_2Al_3 are electrochemically more active than aluminium in Al-Mg-Zn alloys: the intermetallics dissolve preferentially as a series of small anodes immersed in a large cathode. Again, attack is normally concentrated along grain boundaries, although the grain interiors are also attacked when the precipitation lies along crystal planes in the aluminium.

These kinds of galvanic effects are sometimes exaggerated by selective leaching of the more reactive *atoms* in an alloy. The α/β brasses, which contain the relatively zinc-rich β phase (ca. 40% zinc), are prone to **dezincification** in near-boiling soft domestic supply waters containing chloride. Zinc atoms in this β phase are leached out preferentially if the oxygen potential of the water is low whereas, in aerated waters, the process is a two-stage one: the β phase first dissolves uniformly and porous copper then re-deposits. The phenomenon of redeposition is partially poisoned by the addition of arsenic to the alloy. However, the only satisfactory solution is to avoid the high-zinc brasses, since single-phase α brasses are much less prone to the effect.

The carbides in steel, especially alloy carbides, also differ chemically from the iron matrix, so that corrosion is enhanced both by the phase boundary area and by the galvanic local cells that develop. In pearlite, the interleaved layers of carbide and ferrite act in much the same way except that the lamellar nature of the carbide dictates the mode of attack. As a result, although pearlite in steels etches preferentially, the attack produces a series of parallel slots similar to that in Fig. 5.2 This means that surface energy factors become important quite quickly, and there is no significant effect of pearlite upon the gross corrosion behaviour.

In grey cast irons, however, where graphite also acts as a cathode, the flakes provide a more or less continuous open network and corrosion attack on the ferritic matrix can proceed until only the graphite remains (p. 17). White irons and spheroidal graphite cast irons are immune to this so-called *graphitisation.* (Note 10.3)

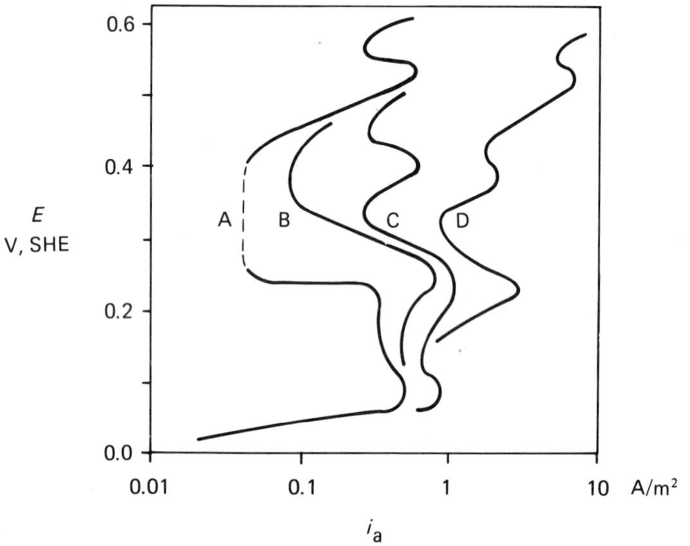

Fig. 10.2 Anodic behaviour of various Cr-Ni austenitic alloy steels in 40% NaOH at room temperature.
Compositions and heat treatments are:

Steel A:	13Cr–25Ni–3Mo	1150°C, WQ (γ)
Steel B:	35Cr–30Ni	1250°C, WQ ($\gamma+\alpha$)
Steel C:	20Cr–12Ni–3Mo	1050°C WQ, 1h 500°C ($\gamma+\sigma+$ trace α)
Steel D:	33Cr	1150°C WQ, 400h 650°C ($\alpha+\sigma+Cr_7C_3$)

After Evans and Brennan (1962).

Where corrosion behaviour is largely determined by the nature and extent of a passive film, alloy composition and heat treatment are often critical. In Fig. 9.5 we saw how addition of chromium to iron led to a progressive lowering of E_{pp} and i_{crit} so that the resultant alloy became passivated by milder and milder oxidants. We also saw how, as a result of adverse heat treatment in the HAZ during welding, grain boundary precipitation of chromium carbide led to denudation of chromium in the surrounding matrix, so rendering it more prone to attack ('weld decay'). It is evident, however, that alloying elements besides chromium are important in determining chemical activity. Most useful in this respect are nickel and molybdenum, Table 9.1. But because the different microstructural phases contain different proportions of alloying elements, for example:

Austenite: contains preferential quantities of Ni,
Ferrite: contains preferential quantities of Cr and Si,
Sigma: contains preferential quantities of Cr and Mo;

we find that the 'transpassive' peaks (p. 115) in the anodic polarisation curves of these phases tend to occur at characteristic potentials. Thus, in Fig. 10.2, there is a ferrite peak at ca. +0.25 V, SHE in the ferrite-containing steels B, C and D; likewise there is a sigma peak at ca. +0.40 V, SHE in steels C and D; and the austenite transpassive peak occurs in all four steels at ca. +0.55 V, SHE. This conclusion is supported by the observation that potentiostatic etching of these steels, that is, etching electrolytically at a controlled potential, leads to preferential light etching of ferrite at +0.25 V, SHE; heavy etching of sigma with some slight attack of ferrite at +0.40 V, SHE; and general etching of austenite and carbide phases at +0.55 V, SHE.

Bibliography to Chapter 10

The reader is advised to consult the useful monograph by Booth (1971), *Microbiological Corrosion,* Mills and Boon. A more comprehensive work is that of Miller (1971), *Microbial Aspects of Metallurgy,* MTP Company, Aylesbury.

The following ASTM Special Technical Publication covers aspects of laboratory evaluation tests as well as microstructural effects in alloy steels and some nickel-based alloys: Steigerwald (1978), *Inter-granular Corrosion of Stainless alloys,* STP 656, ASTM.

Notes to Chapter 10

10.1 Levich, *Physicochemical Hydrodynamics* (Prentice-Hall, 1962).

10.2 Mahato, Steward and Shemilt, *Corros. Sci.* 1968 **10** 737 have considered the influence of thick, porous films of corrosion product upon the corrosion rate inside pipes containing a flowing electrolyte. Their final result gave

$$r = A(t) \, . \, u^{0.54}$$

where the time-dependent function A resulted from the progressive clogging of the pipe by corrosion product.

10.3 The term 'graphitisation' that is sometimes applied to this phenomenon is misleading since the graphite is already present. (Compare the term 'crystallised' as in the phrase 'This steel has crystallised' that used to be applied to steels that had undergone cleavage fracture!) However, the more correct *de-ferritisation* is too clumsy.

Chapter 11

Stopping Low Temperature Corrosion

11.1 DESIGN CONSIDERATIONS

There is no magic lozenge for stopping corrosion. At best, we can effect total and permanent separation of the metal from any kind of oxidising environment. Such remedies tend to be expensive. So, instead, we generally adopt measures that hold the corrosion to economically tolerable levels – although all too frequently unforeseen changes in the corrosive environment or inadequate care in the protective measures adopted can cause failure.

The first approach to the problem is to design engineering components and structures in such a way that corrosion is less likely. Where intermittent wetting takes place the design should allow for *adequate drainage* at points where water is likely to accumulate, in order that the contact time is minimised and so that high salt concentrations cannot accumulate by evaporation. One aspect of this is the higher corrosion rates that occur on the underside of aluminium roofing sheet: although both surfaces are regularly wetted by condensation, salt accumulation is prevented on the uppermost surface as a result of regular washing by rainwater. But in any case, intermittent wetting is always likely to offer the possibility of high localised salt concentrations, for example in the 'splash zone' of structures partly immersed in seawater. Such areas need particular attention, either as regards the material of construction or the protective method adopted.

Whether a structure is partly or fully immersed in a liquid environment, it is always essential to *minimise heterogeneities.* Geometrical factors are most important in this respect. Where, for example, there is a crevice present, either as an integral feature of the design, Fig. 1.1 (a) (b) (d), or because of the accumulation of wet soil or debris, differential aeration leads to crevice attack. Soil accumulation can often be prevented by the suitable location of drainage holes or by elimination of horizontal ledges, whilst, where crevices cannot be avoided, they can often be filled in with suitable plasticised resins. Bimetallic corrosion is also a frequent contributor to component failure. The designer should therefore avoid combinations of metals unless, for the environment in question, the metals are known to be close to one another in the appropriate galvanic series. Otherwise the two metals must be electrically insulated from one another. The matter is complicated somewhat by differences in electrochemical behaviour that can follow welding treatments, as we saw in section 10.5. A further source of heterogeneity is relative motion of metal and environment. Erosion and cavitation are predictable hazards, and it is not surprising that geometrical features can introduce turbulence. However, there are more subtle effects such as the relative accessibility of dissolved oxygen or the influence of thermal convection or flow rate on localised concentrations of salts and/or corrosion inhibitors. Design features that decrease fluid velocities and streamline the flow will be beneficial, as will measures to minimise direct impingement on to critical parts of the system. In practice, it is often helpful to use a more corrosion-resistant alloy.

Variations in internal (residual) stress are an additional source of heterogeneity and, as far as possible, the designer should seek to minimise these by annealing treatments. Moreover, as we shall see in the next chapter, mechanical stress effects can often promote premature failure by corrosion fatigue or stress-corrosion. The design approach is directed, first, to *minimise tensile stress* and, second, to *select a suitable material* or surface coating. Thus, for example, the tensile stress level in the surface may be reduced by stress-relieving treatments, by the avoidance of sharp changes in section or by the introduction of compressive stress by surface peening. An alternative material may be considered on the grounds of its superior mechanical properties, such as a higher yield strength or fatigue limit, or because of reduced susceptibility to hydrogen embrittlement or chloride cracking.

Finally, it should not be forgotten that *accessibility* is an important feature of any good design. This means not only that component thickness can be measured in-situ if necessary but also that surface coatings can be readily applied and inspected. All too frequently a design project is virtually completed before corrosion prevention is thought of, so that the preventive measures taken are inappropriate or inadequately applied.

11.2 SOLUBLE INHIBITORS

One way to ameliorate corrosion in closed (for example, recirculatory) systems is to treat the system itself with soluble inhibitors. These are of two main kinds. The first is a reagent which removes oxygen, and the second is one that promotes passivity. In section 6.4 we saw how the rate of corrosion in aerated water is roughly proportional to the amount of oxygen present: 10 ppm ≡ 0.6 A/m² (mm/yr). So that removal of oxygen to the parts-per-billion† level will lower the rate to some 10^{-3} mm/yr or less, at the same time preventing differential aeration attack. Typical additives are reducing agents such as sulphite and hydrazine:

$$SO_4^{2-}(aq) + H_2O(l) + 2e(M) = SO_3^{2-}(aq) + 2\,OH^-(aq) \qquad (11.1)$$

$$E^\ominus = -0.94 \text{ V, SHE}$$

†USA billion (10^9)

$$NO_2^-(aq) + 7H^+(aq) + 5e(M) = N_2H_5^+(aq) + 2H_2O(l) \qquad (11.2)$$

$$E^\ominus = +0.28 \text{ V, SHE}$$

both of which, after correcting for *p*H and ionic concentrations, have potentials below that of oxygen. (Note that eqn (11.1) (11.2) are written as reduction reactions, so that the additives of interest, SO_3^{2-} and $N_2H_5^+$ – which is how hydrazine N_2H_4 appears in acid and neutral solutions – are on the RHS.)

The Evans diagram representing the effect of such inhibition is shown in Fig. 11.1. This is typical of inhibition which exploits a cathodic 'poison'.

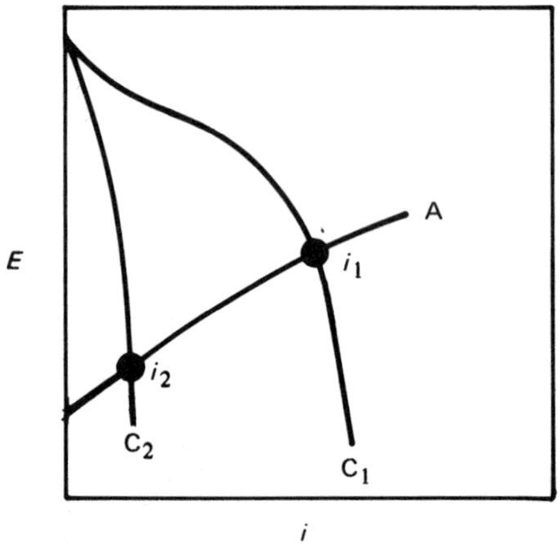

Fig. 11.1 Evans diagram showing effect of oxygen removal. Note that there is no change in the anodic and cathodic areas, so that we may draw the diagram with current density as abscissa.

The soluble inhibitor reduces the limiting current density for oxygen reduction. This means that, whilst the anodic curve A remains unchanged, the cathodic curve changes from C1 to C2. The anodic current density therefore falls from i_1 to i_2.

The second kind of reagent encourages the formation of a surface film, by raising either the *p*H or the potential into a suitable region of the Pourbaix diagram. Alkalis such as NaOH add hydroxyl ions directly whilst the salts of weak acids, such as Na_2CO_3 or Na_2SiO_3, hydrolyse and raise the *p*H indirectly:

$$Na_2SiO_3(aq) + 2H_2O(l) = H_2SiO_3(aq) + 2Na^+(aq) + 2OH^-(aq) \qquad (11.3)$$

besides adding film-promoting anions such as insoluble carbonate and silicate. Raising the potential is effected by oxidising agents, that is, salts whose anions have high redox potentials, Table 4.2. Among these are nitrite and chromate:

$$NO_2^-(aq) + 8H^+(aq) + 6e(M) = NH_4^+(aq) + 2H_2O(l) \qquad E^\ominus = +0.90\text{ V, SHE} \tag{11.4}$$

$$HCrO_4^-(aq) + 7H^+(aq) + 3e(M) = Cr^{3+}(aq) + 4H_2O(l) \qquad E^\ominus = +1.20\text{ V, SHE} \tag{11.5}$$

Although both kinds of passivating inhibitor achieve the same end result – a more or less protective surface film – there is, however, a difference in *reliability*. Oxidising inhibitors, just *because* they raise the corrosion potential, can have disastrous consequences if added in insufficient quantity. This is because, if $E_{corr} < E_{pp}$, passivation does not occur but the inhibitor has nevertheless increased the corrosion rate; whilst, if $E_{corr} > E_b$ the breakdown potential, pitting may result. We can think of this simply in terms of inhibitor ions plugging up most but not all of the pores in a heterogeneous film: those pores that remain unplugged (because of insufficient inhibitor) serve as small anodic areas in a largely cathodic surface.

This behaviour is illustrated in Fig. 11.2. The initial uninhibited polarisation curves in the Evans diagram are labelled 'initial A' and 'initial C' respectively in (a). Oxidising inhibitors, by providing an additional cathodic reactant, effectively reduce cathodic polarisation, so that the point of intersection becomes 2. If no passivation results, the raised corrosion potential means that anodic dissolution increases from i_1 to i_2 and the inhibitor addition has produced the reverse of its intended effect. Only if the new potential lies between E_{pp} and E_b does inhibition occur (i_2') – and we have to remember that E_b varies according to which inhibitor is used. Carbonate is a cathodic inhibitor for iron, precipitating a chalky film in the alkaline conditions generated at the cathode. This film increases cathodic polarisation (section 9.2) and as a result the corrosion rate falls to i_3. Its influence upon anodic polarisation varies, depending for example on sulphate or chloride concentration. When these are low the carbonate behaves as a typical filming inhibitor, such as phosphate or silicate. That is, E_{pp} is lowered and a passive film develops, thereby moving the point of intersection to 4. The corresponding corrosion rate is i_4 in (c).

There is yet a third type of inhibitor, which is used in acid pickling to remove millscale from hot rolled steel. This is essentially an *adsorption inhibitor,* that is, a surface-active organic substance which serves to exclude water and protons from the bare steel revealed by the pickling process. It is an ingenious way of exploiting the corrosion medium so that it effectively applies a monomolecular film of oil to the reactive surface while allowing chemical attack of the millscale to continue. Typical inhibitors are long-chain alkyl amines for hydrochloric acid and aryl thioureas or thioethers for sulphuric acid. Suitable combinations of inhibitors often reinforce one another ('synergism', section 10.2). (Note 11.1).

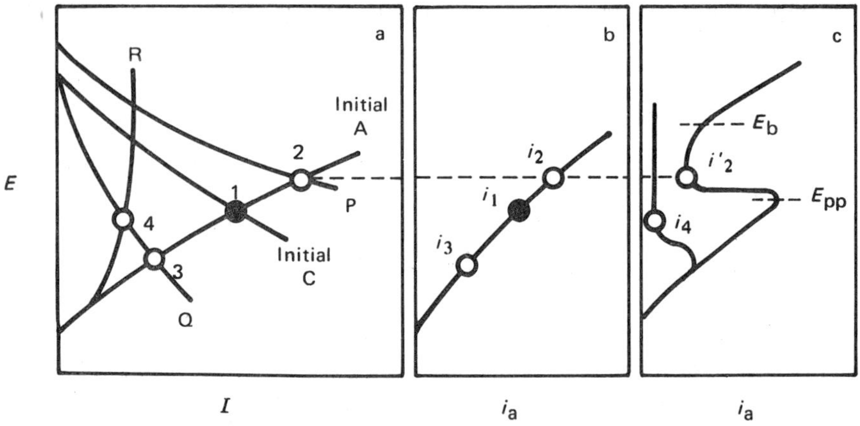

Fig. 11.2 Evans diagram showing effect of various inhibitors. Because anodic and cathodic areas can be affected to different extents, the 'heterogeneous' Evans diagram is used, with current as abscissa.

An oxidising inhibitor P (for example chromate) increases the effective cathodic current from 1 to 2, raises the corrosion potential and hence i_a from i_1 to i_2 in (b). The corrosion rate only falls if the raised potential lies between E_{pp} and E_b in (c).

A cathodic inhibitor Q (for example carbonate) steepens the cathodic curve, and the intersection point falls to 3, simultaneously lowering i_a to i_3.

If additionally passivation is induced, as for a filming inhibitor R (for example silicate or phosphate), the anodic curve is also steepened and the intersection point falls to 4. In (c) the lowering of E_{pp} can be seen to have resulted in a reduced current density of i_4.

11.3 ANODIC PROTECTION

The action of oxidising inhibitors can be parallelled by means of an impressed anodic polarisation, with the added advantage of control over the potential to avoid corrosion enhancement or pitting. In practice, the technique of anodic protection is confined to systems where the active loop and i_{crit} are small, in order to reduce electrical power drain, especially at the commissioning stage. A good example is the use of Cr-Ni austenitic steels in sulphuric acid cooling plant, with added anodic protection to eliminate crevice attack on the acid side, Chapter 16. Suitable inert cathodes, such as graphite or lead, are inserted in the acid and, once the voltage is applied, a high anodic current density exists on neighbouring parts of the steel structure, sufficient to exceed i_{crit} and thoroughly passivate it. The current is thereby deflected to more remote parts of the structure, which passivate in turn. In this way, current penetrates to the outermost recesses, including crevices. The process is accordingly said to have excellent 'throwing power'. Once the system is established and the entire structure passivated, the current drain falls dramatically (Table 9.1) and, for a minimal running cost, ensures integrity of the plant thereafter.

11.4 CATHODIC PROTECTION

Cathodic protection is different in principle from anodic protection. Not only is the polarity reversed, so that the single potential of the metal is lowered, but also the protection afforded is thermodynamic rather than kinetic. That is, instead of introducing a diffusion barrier in the form of a protective film, we establish a condition in which the metallic and not the ionic state is the stable one: for example, we lower the potential of a steel structure below the E_{eq} line for Fe^{2+}(aq)/Fe(s) in Fig. 9.2 into the 'immune' region. There is a side effect of doing this. The current that flows between the external anode and the (cathodic) system being protected causes oxygen to be reduced on the cathode surface. The protected metal is therefore bathed in an alkaline 'soup' which, by promoting the build-up of basic salts, confers additional long term protection in the event of power failure.

We can get cathodic protection in two ways. The first is to exploit the bimetallic phenomenon encountered in section 8.4, by metallically connecting the system to a more reactive metal, to give *sacrificial protection.* 'Galvanising' zinc coatings on steel work in this way, as do the lumps of zinc, aluminium or magnesium alloys that are attached at intervals to steel pipe lines buried in soil or seawater. The sacrificial corrosion of the base metal lowers the corrosion potential of the couple so that any exposed parts of the steel are below, or at least not too much above, −0.61 V, SHE (the equilibrium potential for iron in 10^{-6} mol/kg Fe^{2+}(aq)). The system is not as wasteful as it sounds. In the case of galvanised coatings, the zinc soon acquires a protective film of basic salts which allows the ca. 100 μm coating to last for several years. Its sacrificial action is only manifested for a few days whenever the zinc layer is damaged, during which period any exposed steel acquires its own protective plug of basic salts because of the alkalinity developed there (the 'soup' referred to above). When sacrificial anodes are used, they are supplemented by an inert barrier coating, so that current drawn from them passes only to the small areas of steel exposed at pores ('holidays') in the coating. Typical coatings for submarine oil lines are glass-fibre-reinforced pitch-enamel several millimetres thick, whilst adhesive plastic-tape wrappings are used on land. Both kinds of coating are able to resist the alkaline soup. Moreover, the presence of dissolved calcium ions in the surrounding environment often ensures that the 'soup' precipitates a hard, impermeable calcareous coating at defective areas, so that the cathodic system augments the coating in two ways. But, whereas the galvanised coating for atmospheric exposure wastes away only slowly, sacrificial anodes for total immersion conditions have to remain electrochemically active all the time. That is why such anodes are usually specially compounded alloys that passivate only with difficulty. The amount of anodic alloy required is carefully calculated to last the economic lifetime of the protected structure, for example a buried pipeline. If a protected line becomes mechanically damaged (or if local bacteria discover a liking for the coating material, section 10.3), there is an increase in the current drain, and the anodes will not last as long.

The second way of getting cathodic protection is to use *impressed current* from a suitable d.c. source. The structure being protected may or may not be given a back-up coating of alkali-resistant paint. After all, the fabrication or installation of harbour works or offshore oil platforms may render such coatings impractical and, in any case, electricity is still relatively cheap. So suitable anodes are placed at intervals along the structure and the current adjusted until the corrosion potential has fallen to an economically 'safe' value (Note 11.2). On land, the anode usually consists of a so-called 'groundbed' of steel scrap and graphite placed some 200 m from the system being protected. This allows the protective current to throw through the soil to remote parts of the structure before returning through the structure itself and the drain-point connection, Fig. 11.3 (Note 11.3). At sea, the anode is a rod or 'button' of inert metal. This may be Pb, alloyed with Ag to give mechanical strength and to improve the electronic conductivity of the PbO_2 film; or else platinised titanium, in which a thin Pt layer affords easy oxygen evolution at low overpotential and the underlying Ti remains passive if exposed at pores in the coating.

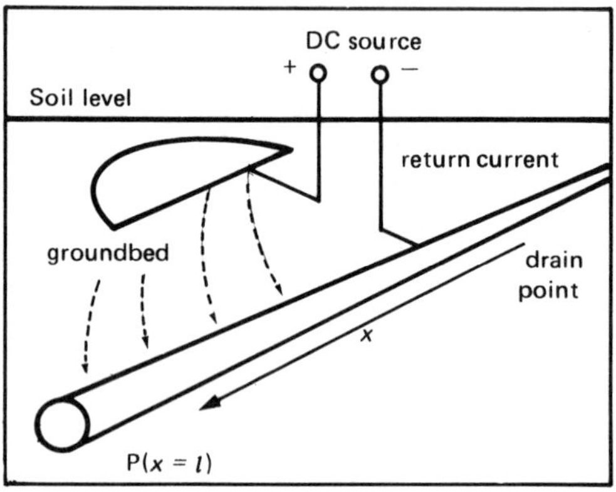

Fig. 11.3 Cathodic protection of a buried pipeline on land. The potential of the line at P must not exceed the 'safe' value. The voltage source and the siting of the groundbed(s) are adjusted accordingly.

The spacing of the anodes, in both sacrificial and impressed current systems, depends on the potential drops in the electrical circuit and hence upon the electrical resistivity of the metal and of the electrolytic medium in which it is placed, Table 11.1. It will be seen from the table that the critical spacing also depends on the anode system employed. This is because the natural 'drain point' potential of the sacrificial anodes, that is, essentially their free corrosion potentials, is not so negative as that obtainable by impressed current. The only limiting factor in impressed current cathodic protection is the cathodic evolution of hydrogen gas (Note 11.4), which may disrupt the coating or embrittle weldments in the steel.

Table 11.1 Critical throw of cathodic protection on iron
Unless otherwise stated, the iron is assumed to be 'moderately well coated with $\beta = 10^{-3}$.

Protection system	Drain point potential V, SHE	Condition	Distance of throw m
Zn anodes	–0.85	Seawater: Bare	3
		Seawater: Coated	300
Mg anodes	–1.3 to –1.5	Soil: 50Ωm	30
		Soil: 3Ωm	300
Impressed current	–2.5 to –25*	Soil	1 – 15 km
		Seawater	5 – 25 km

*Coating damage likely below –2.5 V, SHE

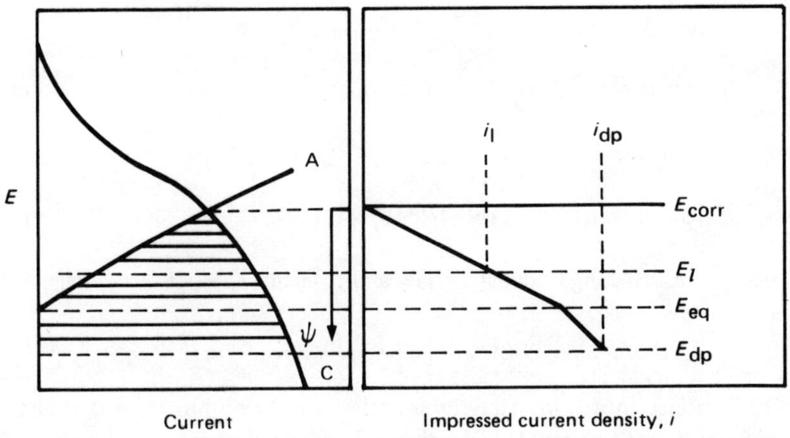

Fig. 11.4 Cathodic protection calculation. The horizontal lines in the shaded region correspond to the impressed currents at different potentials. The diagram on the right shows how the impressed current *density* varies with the potential difference ψ below the free corrosion potential of the structure.

Although the values in Table 11.1 are empirical ones derived from experience, it is possible to calculate them as follows, Fig. 11.4. The Evans diagram on the left shows that, if we ignore electrolytic resistance, the potential at the drain point (where the connection is made to the groundbed) is E_{dp} and the electrolyte current to the pipeline is i_{dp} per unit area of metal exposed at pores in the coating; and the potential of the line rises to E_l at the midpoint, where the cathodic current density from the electrolyte has fallen to i_l. To simplify the problem further, it is convenient to measure all the single potentials with respect to the free corrosion potential E_{corr} of the pipeline, that is, $\psi = E_{corr} - E$, as shown in the right-hand diagram. As we shall see, this mathematical device removes an inconvenient minus sign in eqn (11.8). Next, we approximate the ψ *vs.* i curve to a straight line

$$\psi = ki \tag{11.6}$$

Because only a fraction β ($\lesssim 0.1\%$ in general) of the metal is actually exposed, the current flowing from the electrolyte into unit length of a pipeline of diameter D is $\beta\pi Di$. The return current flowing in the line at that point will include all the incremental currents out to the midpoint at $x = l$. If this current is I, then

$$\mathrm{d}I/\mathrm{d}x = -\beta\pi Di = -(\beta\pi D/k)\psi \tag{11.7}$$

Writing R (Ω/m) for the resistance of the line, the potential change along the line, *which is assumed to be due only to R*, is

$$\mathrm{d}\psi/\mathrm{d}x = -RI$$

or

$$\mathrm{d}^2\psi/\mathrm{d}x^2 = -R.\mathrm{d}I/\mathrm{d}x = +(R\beta\pi D/k)\psi \tag{11.8}$$

for which a solution is

$$\psi = \text{a constant} \times \exp\{-(R\beta\pi D/k)^{\frac{1}{2}}x\} \tag{11.9}$$

Whence, by substituting boundary values and reverting to single potentials,

$$l = -(k/R\beta\pi D)^{\frac{1}{2}} \ln\{1 - (E_l - E_{dp})/(E_{corr} - E_{dp})\} \tag{11.10}$$

For zinc anodes protecting steel in seawater, the logarithm term is about 0.7 whilst for impressed current it lies between 2 and 10, depending on how negative a drain point potential can be tolerated (which really means how high a hydrogen pressure the coating can withstand). Eqn (11.10) gives answers of the right magnitude but requires some modification when there is significant electrolyte resistance, as in soils, or the geometry of the system is different.

Impressed current systems have a longer 'throw' and are more flexible, being able to accommodate damage to the coating, that is, an increase in β. They are sometimes cheaper to run but have the disadvantage that anodes are expensive to install and easily damaged by heavy seas. Sacrificial anode systems are, therefore, generally more reliable if initially installed with a degree of 'overkill'.

11.5 COATINGS

Corrosion-resistant coatings can be broadly divided into the following categories:

(a) oils and greases
(b) conversion coatings, including anodised coatings
(c) glasses and vitreous enamels
(d) organic coatings, including paints and lacquers
(e) metallic coatings,

from which it may be seen that man's ingenuity has devised many and various forms of barrier, differing in their cost, ease of application, effectiveness and permanence. Although the different kinds may depend on several protective mechanisms, they all unite in having as their main aim the exclusion of water and air from the metal surface. And, because in many instances this exclusion is not total, *they may best be regarded as introducing a large ionic resistance into the corrosion cell.* As such, they may be represented by Figs. 8.2 and 8.3, with R taking very large values and thereby reducing the corrosion current to negligible proportions. For example, the resistivity of many varnish and paint films is some 10^4 to 10^5 times that of aqueous electrolytes, and the corrosion rate is reduced in much the same proportion.

Oils and greases are temporary protectives. Being water-repellent, they limit the availability of solvent water molecules and present a diffusion barrier to oxygen. Some greases contain chemically active groups such as the carboxylic radical $-COOH$ and so form metal soaps, limiting still further the area of metal able to corrode.

Typical **conversion coatings** are phosphate for steels, chromate/oxide for aluminium, and fluoride for magnesium. The metal is subjected to an oxidising chemical treatment which produces a relatively thick (ca. 2 μm) layer of corrosion product, of a form suitable for resisting further attack. There are many proprietary processes, but one example – phosphating – should suffice to illustrate the principle. Phosphate coatings are essentially temporary in nature, being used mainly as a basis for paint on iron, cadmium plate, and aluminium. As a result of chemical reaction with free phosphoric acid, iron phosphate and one or other of the phosphates of zinc and manganese are precipitated in the form of an insoluble film. Thus, zinc phosphate dissociates:

$$Zn(H_2PO_4)_2(aq) = Zn^{2+}(aq) + 2HPO_4^{2-}(aq) + 2H^+(aq) \qquad (11.11)$$

followed by proton reduction

$$H^+(aq) + e(Fe) = \tfrac{1}{2}H_2(g) \qquad (11.12, cf. 4.15)$$

and simultaneous oxidation of iron to Fe^{2+}(aq). The film forms as the double layer becomes denuded of protons and the *p*H rises. Oxidising agents, such as NO_3^- and/or Cu^{2+}, may be added in 0.1 mol/kg quantities to accelerate the process and may give rise to some Fe(III) in the film, without it seems damaging its properties (Note 11.5).

An alternative method of thickening the naturally passive film is to employ anodic polarisation. Because aluminium, in common with silicon and tantalum, produces a semiconducting oxide film which can be persuaded to grow if the potential gradient reaches approximately 1 GV/m, **anodising** is an effective method of producing complex films of thicknesses up to 30 μm. This dimension is somewhat misleading because the true barrier layer, which conducts only electrons, is generally ca. 20 nm thick. The remaining outermost layer, which makes up most of the film thickness, is porous and needs to be sealed by further hydrolysis treatment before the coated metal is put into service. Anodised aluminium coatings can withstand many years exposure to mild atmospheres but fail by pitting after a few months in sulphate/chloride-contaminated air.

Weathering steels contain small amounts of alloying elements, principally copper and phosphorus, which modify the normal rust to one which grows slowly over two or three years to a compact, protective film. The mechanism is not yet understood (Note 11.6). But it may be cited as an example of a 'conversion' coating produced by natural weathering processes.

Vitreous enamel coatings are essentially thick (ca. 0.7 mm) glass barrier coatings. They totally isolate the metal and, as such, are useful in preventing corrosion of steel and cast iron in mild environments. Because silicate glass dissolves in strong alkalis, enamels are confined to the containment of acids, or else to neutral electrolytes such as bathwater.

Paints are, perhaps, the most varied and complex of all anticorrosion coatings. In essence they consist of an organic polymer film (the 'binder') containing a filler ('pigment') dispersed throughout its thickness. In order to ensure freedom from pores it is customary to apply several layers, either by brush, roller or spray, taking suitable care to ensure that successive layers bond to one another to give an integrated coating. Most of the organic binders are initially dissolved in a solvent which prevents the polymerisation process while the paint is being stored, facilitates spreading, and then evaporates as the paint 'dries'. The degree of polymerisation is governed by the frequency of cross-linking: the more extensive the cross-linking, the stronger and more stable the final film (and the more expensive in consequence). Some solvent-free paints, such as epoxides, are catalysed just prior to application and 'dry' (that is, polymerise) at a rate depending on temperature and catalyst concentration.

'High build' paint coatings, some 300 μm per layer, can be designed by combining epoxide resin with long-chain organic fillers such as pitch. However, most pigments are inorganic and the coatings only ca.100 μm per layer when dry. The pigments used are of three kinds: inert, inhibitive, and sacrificial. As the name implies, inert pigments serve no other function than to thicken the paint film and so lengthen the ionic diffusion path. Micaceous iron oxide (MIO) is typical of this class, the flat platelets of pigment lining up parallel to the metal surface as the solvent evaporates. Inhibitive pigments, for example Pb_3O_4, $ZnSiO_3$ or $ZnCrO_4$, act as a controlled source of inhibitive anions (section 11.2) and are, therefore, embodied in the 'primer' coat in contact with the metal. The zinc cation is thought to control the degree of hydrolysis by water that penetrates the film and may also help to de-activate sulphide ions originating from the steel (section 10.2), by precipitating zinc sulphide. Metallic zinc, in the form of a dust, is incorporated in 'zinc rich' primer paints, an example of the use of a sacrificial pigment. The other principal sacrificial metal is aluminium. Both require the pigment to be present in sufficient proportion to ensure continuous metallic contact throughout the coating.

It is a common observation that a paint coating is only as effective as the degree of surface preparation allows it to be. This is partly a matter of adhesion, which is destroyed by residual grease or millscale. A more insidious agent is rust on steel. Rust itself is not particularly deleterious if mechanically scrubbed to remove loose particles. It is the sulphate and chloride anions that it harbours, more especially in surface pits (section 8.2). If they are not removed, these anions remain to contaminate the pigment and prevent passivation. Hence the need to remove them before painting begins. Blast cleaning, which employs hardened steel or slag grit entrained in a stream of high pressure air or water, is an effective method of doing this, while at the same time roughening the surface to improve mechanical 'keying' of paint and metal. (Note 11.7).

Metallic coatings are distinguished as much by the manner in which they are applied, whether by high-temperature diffusion from gas, liquid or solid phase or by 'cold' coating by metal spraying or electrodeposition, as by their electrochemical properties. Considering only the electrochemical behaviour, a reactive metal will afford sacrificial protection of the underlying metal, exposed at pores in the coating, section 11.2 and Fig. 11.5. In contrast, a relatively noble metal coating leads to a higher corrosion potential (section 8.4) and hence a faster corrosion rate. Even so, more noble coatings are often used because they give adequate protection over several years and may have the added advantage of attractive appearance and high wear resistance. Chromium-nickel coatings come in this category. They consist of some 20 μm nickel, electrodeposited under conditions that eliminate through-thickness pores, and then overlaid with 3-5 μm chromium. To reduce the rate at which the composite coating is penetrated by corrosion, the chromium is usually deposited in such a way that it contains many minute discontinuities (cracks or pores) amounting to some 10^{-2} m^2 nickel exposed per m² of coating, that is, 1%. This relatively high anode/cathode ratio, compared with < 0.1% in 'conventional' chromium coatings, keeps the nickel current density low and so prolongs its life.

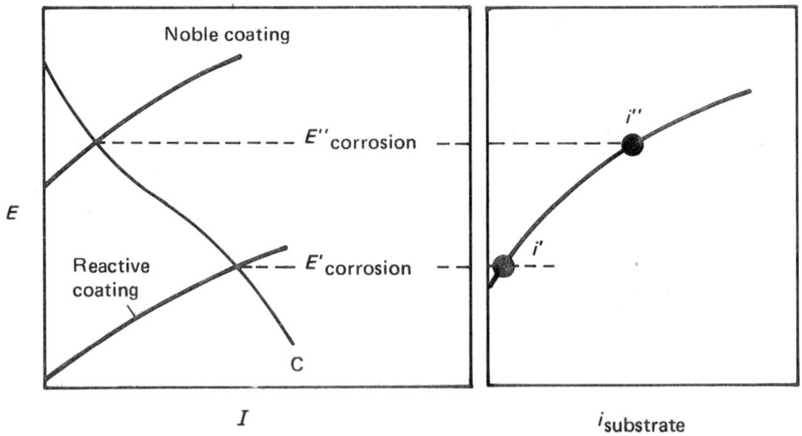

Fig. 11.5 Corrosion rate at pores in metallic coatings. The corrosion potential of a reactive (base) coating $E'_{corrosion}$ gives a lower corrosion rate i' of the underlying metal than i'' resulting from the high corrosion potential $E''_{corrosion}$ of a noble coating.

Bibliography to Chapter 11

Diamant (1967), *The Prevention of Corrosion,* Business Books.
Evans (1960), *Corrosion and Oxidation of Metals,* Arnold with two supplementary volumes.
Fontana and Greene (1978), *Corrosion Engineering,* 2nd edn., McGraw Hill.
Gellings (1976), *Introduction to Corrosion Prevention and Control,* Delft Univ. Press.
Ministry of Defence (1968), *Treatments for the Protection of Metal Parts of Service Stores and Equipments,* DG–8 Pt. 2, HMSO, London.
Ross (1977), *Metal Corrosion,* Oxford Univ. Press.
Scully (1975), *Fundamentals of Corrosion,* Pergamon.
Shreir (ed.) (1963), *Corrosion,* 2 vols., Newnes.
Tomashov (1966), *Theory of Corrosion and Protection of Metals,* MacMillan.
Uhlig (1948), *Corrosion Handbook,* Wiley and (1971), *Corrosion and Corrosion Control,* Wiley.

Books specifically on metal finishing include:

Biestek and Weber, (1976), *Conversion Coatings,* Portcullis Publications.
Drummond and Bews (eds.) (1967), *Introduction to Paint Technology,* OCCA.
Gabe (1972), *Principles of Metal Surface Treatment and Protection,* Pergamon.

Lowenheim (1978), *Electroplating*, McGraw Hill.
Metals Handbook (1979), vol. 2: *Heat Treating, Cleaning and Finishing*, 8th edn. Chapman & Hall.

The reader is also referred to two recent publications by the Department of Industry (HMSO 1978):
Corrosion Control in Engineering Design and *Sources of Corrosion Information.*

Notes to Chapter 11

11.1 Synergism, and the detailed adsorption mechanism of inhibitors, has been extensively studied. Our present understanding is still usefully summarised by Hackerman, *Corrosion* 1962 **18** 332 and a more general discussion of adsorption in the double layer is given by Reeves, *Modern Aspects of Electrochemistry, No. 9*, ed. Conway and Bockris (Plenum, 1974) p. 239. As regards iron, Thomas and Davies, *Brit. Corros. J.* 1977 **12** 108 have shown that the passive film is different over different potential ranges, consisting essentially of hydrated Fe_2O_3 at noble potentials and of 'quasi-magnetite' (Fe_3O_4 containing varying amounts of Fe(II)) at lower potentials, cf. the Pourbaix diagram, Fig. 9.2. Each film is characterised by a breakdown potential and a Flade potential (for a given oxygen concentration), stability at both potentials being influenced by the anions in solution. Thus, in uninhibited neutral solutions, the corrosion of steel depends on the stability of the magnetite film whilst, as inhibitor is added, the corrosion behaviour hinges on the increased stability of the Fe_2O_3 film which develops.

11.2 The economically accepted *rate* of corrosion may be as little as 0.05 mm/yr, that is, after 25 years' economic life the tolerable reduction in component thickness is no more than 1 or 2 mm. Hence the anodic overpotential must not exceed $\eta = b_a \log (0.05/i_o)$. For iron in the absence of microbial action, $b_a \sim 0.06$ V and $i_o \sim 3.10^{-5}$ A/m^2 at 20°C so that the acceptable $\eta \ngtr 0.19$ V or $E \ngtr -0.42$ V, SHE (−0.74 V, SCSE). The 'safe' potential is usually taken to be 60 to 100 mV more negative than this whilst, if bacteria are present, it is the equilibrium potential −0.61 V, SHE.

11.3 This need to 'throw' current through the electrolyte accounts for the fact that sticking lumps of zinc on a car is unlikely to constitute a workable cathodic protection system. The electrolyte is present as little more than a thin layer, usually of fairly high resistance, so that the throw from each sacrificial anode is little more than a few cm.

11.4 Many protective coatings are unable to withstand hydrogen pressures resulting from impressed potentials more negative than −7.5 V, SHE, although glass fibre reinforcement improves matters. Steels for submerged seawater applications are generally immune to hydrogen embrittlement in the wrought state, having yield strengths ca. 500 MN/m^2 or less. However, strengths in the HAZ of welds can exceed 1000 MN/m^2, rendering them susceptible to embrittlement, Chapter 12.

11.5 The mechanism of phosphating has been examined, for example, by Lakeman, Gabe and Richardson, *Trans. Inst. Metal Finishing* 1977 **55** 47.
11.6 The mechanism of rust formation on weathering steels is not understood but may be associated with growth poisoning by the Cu and P alloying additions. Two recent papers are by Bruno, Agabio and Bombara, *Brit. Corros. J.* 1972 **7** 122 and by Misawa, Asami, Hashimoto and Shimodaira, *Corros. Sci.* 1974 **14** 279.
11.7 The advantage of wet cleaning is that the (pure) water used helps to wash away contaminating salts. The light 'bloom' of rust that develops has not been found to be deleterious provided the primer coat repels any residual water. The size of the grit particles cannot be controlled so readily as in the dry method of blasting: this size determines the 'anchor pattern', that is, the roughness of the final surface.

Chapter 12

Stress and Corrosion

12.1 CONJOINT EFFECTS

Stress-corrosion cracking, usually abbreviated to SCC, is a common phenomenon in alloys subjected to extremes of stress and corrosive environment. It also occurs in less severe circumstances under the combined action of *residual* stress and specific environments encountered in service. It is manifested as mechanical failure by cracking under circumstances where, in the absence of corrosion, no failure would have been expected. Normally ductile alloys, such as brasses and austenitic steels, can display apparently brittle behaviour, whilst high-strength aluminium alloys and martensitic steels fail at stress intensities well below half the normal critical value. The phenomena are widely different in their basic mechanisms. What they have in common is *cracking*: cracks initiate spontaneously and propagate to fracture under the influence of some kind of corrosion process.

The phenomenon of fatigue, which is likewise characterised by a crack initiation and propagation process as a result of cyclical stressing, is also influenced by corrosive environments. In **corrosion fatigue**, failure occurs at stresses well below the fatigue limit, and cracks, once initiated, appear to propagate faster. The initiation of fatigue cracks is sometimes a direct consequence of surface pitting induced by corrosion. However, it may also result from **fretting corrosion**, which occurs especially in wire ropes. Here the steel wires rub together and, if not sufficiently lubricated, their surfaces weld locally over areas of a few $(\mu m)^2$. Such welds are broken by small-amplitude relative movement, producing small sheared particles of bare metal. The rupture process is almost certainly made more damaging by any corrosive environment such as seawater and, in any case, the metallic debris oxidises to form an abrasive powder.

Because all these 'conjoint' processes lead to fracture, we shall begin by examining cracking phenomena in general.

12.2 FRACTURE MECHANICS

Arising from the manufacturing or fabrication process, interior and surface flaws are found in all metal structures. Not all such flaws are unstable under service conditions, and fracture mechanics is the analysis of flaws to discover those that are safe (that is, do not grow) and those that are liable to propagate as cracks and so cause failure.

Internal and external flaws act as stress raisers. For example, a crack of length $2a$ and tip radius ρ, raises the effective stress normal to the crack plane from a nominal value σ_{app} to

$$\sigma = \sigma_{app}\{1 + 2(a/\rho)^{\frac{1}{2}}\} \approx 2\sigma_{app}(a/\rho)^{\frac{1}{2}} \qquad \text{for } a/\rho \gg 1 \qquad (12.1)$$

More important for the purpose of predicting instability, we can estimate the elastic stress field in the neighbourhood of the crack tip and thereby determine the elastic strain energy that would be released if the crack were to grow. If there is no significant plastic deformation and the crack is sharp ($\rho < 4b$ or thereabouts), a tensile stress regime that permits simple crack opening ('mode I' opening, cf. modes II and III which involve shearing of the two crack surfaces past one another) leads to an energy release of

$$\begin{aligned} \Delta U &= -\sigma_{app}^2 \pi a(1-\nu^2)/E \qquad &\text{for plane strain} \\ &= -\sigma_{app}^2 \pi a/E \qquad &\text{for plane stress} \end{aligned} \qquad (12.2)$$

per unit area of new cracked material; E and ν are respectively Young's modulus and Poisson's ratio. In order for the crack to propagate spontaneously, this incremental energy release must exceed the surface energy 2γ (that is, γ is the surface energy per unit area and there are two new crack surfaces produced) so that, for plane strain,

$$\sigma_{app}^2 \pi a(1-\nu^2)/E \geqslant 2\gamma \qquad (12.3)$$

This condition for instability is modified when plastic deformation takes place at the crack tip, as occurs for metal (Note 12.1). The energy to propagate the crack increases by several orders of magnitude from 2γ to $(2\gamma + \gamma_p)$, where γ_p represents the plastic work done as the crack extends unit area. The LHS of eqn (12.3) is commonly represented by the symbol $\mathcal{G}_{Ic}$ and is called the critical **energy release rate** (or sometimes the 'crack extension force' since $J/m^2 \equiv N/m$). We then have

$$\mathcal{G}_{Ic} = \sigma_{app}^2 \pi a(1-\nu^2)/E = 2\gamma + \gamma_p \approx \gamma_p \qquad (12.4)$$

In ductile alloys, it is also convenient to express $\mathcal{G}_{Ic}$ in terms of the critical **crack opening displacement** δ_c, which is the amount that the crack tip has to stretch before the crack can extend:

$$\mathcal{G}_{Ic} = \sigma_y \delta_c \qquad (12.5)$$

where σ_y is the uniaxial yield stress. A small correction to the crack length may be made by adding to a the size of the plastic zone

$$r_y = (a/6)\,(\sigma_{app}/\sigma_y)^2 \tag{12.6}$$

in plane strain for example, but this correction is very small. More significant corrections may also be needed to take account of the shape of the flaw and its relationship to the shape and size of the component. This has led to the concept of **stress intensity factor** K, usually (misleadingly) abbreviated to **stress intensity**. For a sharp planar elliptical flaw the stress intensity takes the form

$$K = 1.12\sigma_{app}(\pi a/Q)^{\frac{1}{2}}M_k \tag{12.7}$$

where the 1.12 is introduced for any crack or flaw initiating at the surface of a component, Q is the flaw shape parameter (0.8 to 2.4 depending on σ_{app}/σ_y and the eccentricity of the ellipse) and M_k is the Kobayashi correction, which allows for the proximity of a free surface close to and ahead of the crack tip (normally between unity and 2.0). All the terms multiplying σ_{app} are lumped together as a *compliance function* which may be computed for most simple crack geometries, including multiple and branching cracks. From eqn (12.3) to (12.7) and neglecting the Poisson ratio term, the condition for an unstable crack is

$$K_c^2/E = \gamma_p \tag{12.8}$$

where the subscript 'c' to the stress intensity indicates the critical condition at energy balance. Mode I opening offers the most severe test of a material, especially in plane strain, for these conditions provide the least opportunity for plastic deformation to dissipate energy. The critical value of K_I in plane strain that satisfies the equality in eqn (12.8) is, therefore, regarded as a measure of the **fracture toughness** of the material, represented by K_{Ic}. Typical values of K_{Ic} and the corresponding $\mathcal{G}_{Ic}(=K_{Ic}^2/E)$ are listed in Table 12.1.

Table 12.1 Some typical fracture toughnesses and energy release rates for structural materials.

Material	K_{Ic} MN/m$^{\frac{3}{2}}$	$\mathcal{G}_{Ic}$ kJ/m^2
Very tough metals	150	50–150
Brittle metals	25	1–5
Glasses and brittle polymers	1–10	0.01–0.5

When there is extensive plastic deformation in a component, the linear-elastic approach of calculating a fracture toughness K_{Ic} is no longer valid. It is necessary to determine the compliance function experimentally, and from this it is possible to compute a quantity J_{Ic} equivalent in its predictive value to $\mathcal{G}_{Ic}$. Alternative elastic-plastic treatments may also be used. They all recognise that the plastic zone consumes the major part of the work of fracture and modifies the elastic stress field in the crack tip region. As yet, however, there exists no satisfactory treatment for very small cracks whose dimensions are comparable with microstructural features in the metal.

12.3 SUBCRITICAL CRACK EXTENSION

In the foregoing treatment, the basic idea is that, once there is enough elastic energy present to do the work of fracture, any pre-existing flaw rapidly extends through the component at a speed governed by the rate at which an elastic stress wave is able to move through the solid. That is, a 'critically' sized crack immediately produces fast failure. We shall now learn how a corrosive environment may cause smaller cracks than this – *subcritical* cracks – to grow spontaneously, although at a much slower rate. When eventually such cracks achieve the 'critical' size, their rate speeds up to bring about fast final fracture.

We begin with the observation, eqn (12.4), that plasticity effects dominate in metal fracture, that is, $\gamma_p \gg 2\gamma$, so that

$$\mathcal{G}_c = K_c^2/E = \gamma_p \tag{12.8}$$

for unstable cracks. Hence we might justifiably deduce that cracks will propagate independently of the value of the surface energy γ. This conclusion, though, is misleading. Intuitively, we might expect that, if we could in some way reduce γ to zero, the crystal planes would merely separate spontaneously without the expenditure of plastic work. Indeed, detailed calculations of how the work of fracture is altered by the presence of a reactive environment (see later) are consistent with the supposition that γ_p is directly proportional to γ. If this were the case then

$$\gamma_p = k\gamma \qquad (k = \text{constant}) \text{ (Note 12.2)} \tag{12.9}$$

and

$$K_c^2/E = \gamma_p = k\gamma \tag{12.10}$$

In such circumstances a crack can spontaneously extend when K exceeds a critical value given by

$$K_c = (k\gamma E)^{\frac{1}{2}} \tag{12.11}$$

From eqn (12.7) with $Q = M_k = 1$, we may calculate the stress intensity for a sharp through-thickness edge crack of length a normal to some critical net-section tensile stress σ_c in a large component:

$$\sigma_c \approx K_c/(2a^{\frac{1}{2}}) \tag{12.12}$$

$$\approx (k\gamma E/4a)^{\frac{1}{2}} \tag{12.13}$$

A subcritical crack will extend at some tensile stress $\sigma < \sigma_c$ only if there is some additional source of stress or energy available. That is, for an additional tensile stress $\Delta\sigma$, the nominal fracture stress becomes

$$\sigma = \sigma_c - \Delta\sigma \tag{12.14a}$$

or, where an additional 'decohesion' energy $\Delta\gamma$ is available to lower the surface energy,

$$\sigma \approx \{(\gamma - \Delta\gamma)kE/4a\}^{\frac{1}{2}} \tag{12.14b}$$

As we shall see, $\Delta\sigma$ is a pressure term that can manifest itself in hydrogen embrittlement, and $\Delta\gamma$ occurs in a variety of embrittling processes due to chemical interaction with the environment. Typical examples are hydrogen embrittlement, liquid metal embrittlement, and stress-corrosion cracking.

In the absence of a corrosive environment, the fracture toughness is K_{Ic}. Likewise, when chemical embrittlement of any kind reduces the effective value of K_{Ic} to some subcritical value, the critical stress intensity below which crack propagation will not take place is designated K_{Iscc}. The ratio K_{Iscc}/K_{Ic} is often in the region of 0.2 for hydrogen embrittlement and may fall to as low as 0.05 for SCC by yield-assisted dissolution, section 12.5.

12.4 HYDROGEN EMBRITTLEMENT

High-tensile steels and, to a lesser extent, high-strength alloys of aluminium and titanium, are subject to SCC as a result of absorbed hydrogen. The phenomenon is so widespread as to constitute a special case of SCC. Hydrogen can originate from the molten state, for example from steel refining or especially welding, but in most cases it originates from atomic hydrogen adsorbed on the surface of the solid metal and is produced by gas dissociation or by proton reduction:

$$H_2(g) = 2H(ads) \tag{12.15a}$$

$$H_2S(g) = 2H(ads) + \tfrac{1}{2}S_2(g) \tag{12.15b}$$

$$H^+(aq) + e(Fe) = 2H(ads) \tag{12.16}$$

where eqn (12.16) represents the first step leading to hydrogen gas evolution, for example eqn (4.15). The atomic hydrogen diffuses into the steel, where it exists interstitially. At interior cavities, such as the interfaces produced when sulphide inclusions contract on cooling from the melt or decohere during rolling, the hydrogen atoms are free to recombine to form gas. Otherwise the atoms segregate to ferrite or prior-austenite grain boundaries and to dislocations, possibly assisted by chemical association with other segregated impurities such as phosphorus. The significant features are (a) that hydrogen gas formed at the interior surfaces is at high pressure and so exerts an expansive (that is, tensile) force tending to separate the iron atoms, and (b) that hydrogen atoms in the grain boundaries lower the cohesive forces between adjacent grains (Note 12.3).

The first effect may be readily demonstrated from a consideration of the argument advanced in section 8.2, where it was shown that the equilibrium partial pressure of hydrogen in a chloride-contaminated pit in a steel surface can be of the order of 10^3 atm. Of course, such an equilibrium gas pressure cannot be attained in the electrolyte, for it would blow the electrolyte away and destroy the double layer, but steel is much more able to resist stress than water is. Its high yield strength, some 300 to 2000 MN/m^2, can support a pressure of $(0.3 \text{ to } 2) \times 10^9/1.03 \times 10^5 = 3$ to 20 thousand atmospheres, so that the equilibrium can be attained in principle on the metal side of the interface. If we write the equilibrium constant between adsorbed hydrogen and gaseous hydrogen as $K = a_H/(p_{H_2}/p^{\ominus})^{\frac{1}{2}}$, the Nernst equation (4.26) becomes

$$\begin{aligned} E &= (RT/F) \ln (K h_{H^+}/a_H) \\ &= -0.059\,(pH + \log a_H - \log K) \qquad \text{V, SHE at } 25°\text{C} \end{aligned} \tag{12.17}$$

The equilibrium activity of H(ads) can attain high values. For example, at pH 4.8 and $E = -0.37$ V, SHE (Table 8.1) we get $a_H/K = 30$ and, at more acid pH values or more negative potentials, it may reach several hundred. In equilibrium with this adsorbed hydrogen is hydrogen gas inside voids in the metal:

$$\text{H(ads)} = \text{H(abs)} = \tfrac{1}{2}\text{H}_2(\text{g; internal}) \tag{12.18}$$

whose pressure will be $p = p^{\ominus}.a_H^2/K^2 = 900$ atm in this example but could obviously rise to some 10^4 atm without the onset of yielding in many steels. This hydrogen pressure can augment any applied or residual tensile stress, as indicated by eqn (12.14a) with $\Delta\sigma = p$. However, the equilibrium pressure may not have time to develop ahead of a crack that is propagating, and its effect may in any case be small compared with that of decohesion.

The lowering of the cohesive strength of the grain boundaries may be thought of as a reduction of the surface energy γ, because γ corresponds to the energy required to separate atomic planes in the solid. The surprising result is that K_c falls as γ falls, even though a substantial part of the fracture process involves plastic deformation at the crack tip. This is because, in spite of γ_p greatly exceeding γ, the amount of deformation – and hence K_c – depends sensitively on how easily the atoms at the tip can be parted, eqn (12.9). It may be shown that the incremental reduction in energy of the two fracture surfaces formed as the crack advances is

$$\Delta\gamma \approx \propto RT \ln(p/p_o) \quad (\propto = \text{constant in mol/m}^2) \tag{12.19}$$

where p ($> p_o$) and p_o are the hydrogen partial pressures in the embrittled and unembrittled states. A similar relationship holds when pressure is replaced by the concentration of dissolved hydrogen in the metal: this concentration is proportional to the ambient $p^{\frac{1}{2}}$ (Sievert's law) at the time that equilibrium was established, so that p/p_o is replaced by $(c/c_o)^2$. It follows from eqn (12.10) (12.14) (12.19) that the reduction in the work of fracture due to hydrogen adsorption is

$$\Delta\left(\frac{K_c^2}{E}\right) = \frac{K_{Iscc}^2 - K_{Ic}^2}{E} = -k\Delta\gamma$$

$$= -\propto kRT \ln(p/p_o) \tag{12.20}$$

$$\text{or } -2\propto kRT \ln(c/c_o)$$

from which it may be seen that the degree of embrittlement depends upon the logarithm of the hydrogen pressure or concentration (Note 12.3). The effect is most notable (a) when the metal is already fairly brittle, as occurs for steels having yield strengths greater than 1000 MN/m^2, and (b) when the ambient hydrogen pressure does not exceed a few atmospheres. For high pressures of the order of 10^4 atm, it is possible that the 'planar pressure' mechanism dominates (Note 12.4).

In practice, corrosion can usually generate the surface hydrogen necessary for embrittlement. In pits and cracks alike, the ingress of anions and subsequent hydrolysis of salts leads to acidity and so to hydrogen evolution, even in apparently neutral solutions. Moreover, the ionic potential drop between the crack tip and the external environment can produce local single potentials more active than the external corrosion potential might suggest, p. 99. Consequently, hydrogen evolution can take place when external conditions are seemingly inappropriate. It should also be noted that hydrogen embrittlement is not a *necessary* accompaniment of hydrogen evolution. Embrittlement only occurs when

(a) there is a high yield stress, so that limited plasticity allows $\Delta(K_c^2/E)$ to become comparable with K_{Ic}^2/E; and

(b) there is a mechanism favouring the ingress of atomic hydrogen (Note 12.5).

Of course, the higher the external hydrogen activity the greater the chance of cracking, which is why impressed-current cathodic 'protection' can be dangerous.

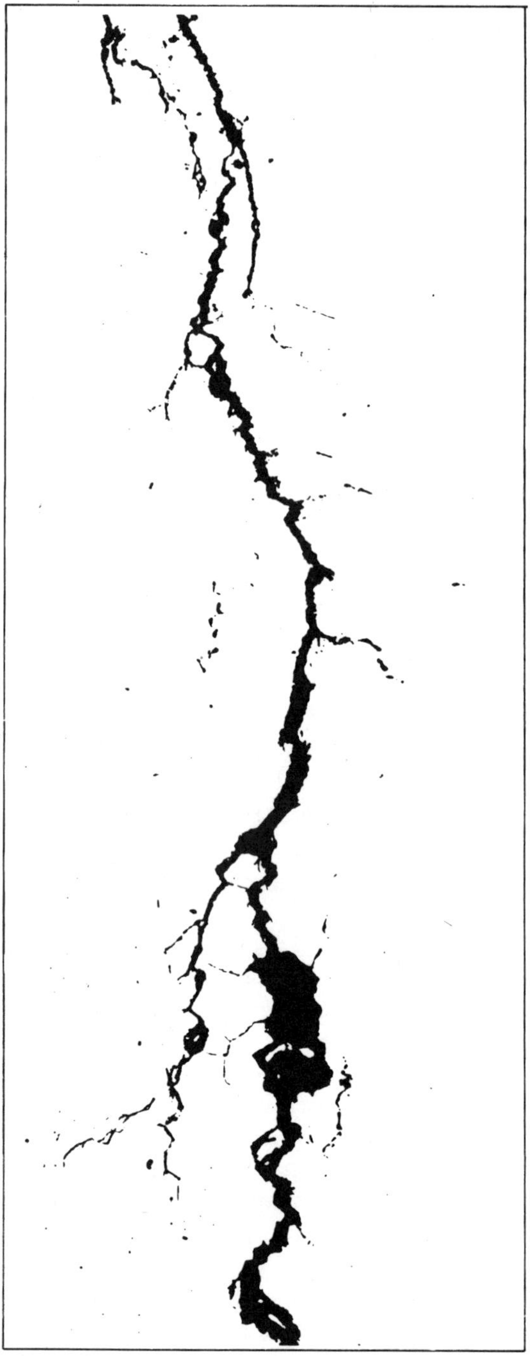

Fig. 12.1 An example of stress-corrosion cracking. Branching hydrogen-embrittlement cracks on the surface of polished 20Co–14Cr–5Mo maraging steel after exposure to 3% NaCl solution. The cracks are intergranular.

12.5 YIELD ASSISTED DISSOLUTION

In section 5.2 we saw how localised attack can be directed down suitably activated grain boundaries because

$$\Delta\tilde{G}^{ox} = -zF\eta_a - u_{gb} + 0.4Lb^2\gamma \tag{5.8}$$

Provided there exists a suitable mechanism for limiting corrosion to a groove of width δ, the electrochemical free energy change (J/mol) accompanying dissolution at the tip of such a groove is

$$\Delta\tilde{G}^{ox} = -zF\eta_a + 2Lb^3\gamma/\delta \tag{12.21}$$

augmented by a release of $-u_{gb}$ if attack is directed down a grain boundary (smaller than $-u_{gb}$ if $\delta > 5b$). Evidently, such a groove is thermodynamically favoured only if there is an additional source of energy release numerically greater than $2Lb^3\gamma/\delta$. When a tensile stress acts normally to the plane of the groove, elastic energy K^2/E (J/m^2) can provide this source and so, converting to J/m^2 by multiplying J/mol by δ/Lb^3,

$$\Delta\tilde{G}^{ox} = -(\delta/Lb^3)zF\eta_a + 2\gamma - K^2/E \tag{12.22}$$

and, recognising that the mechanically-assisted propagation of a groove in a ductile material also involves some plastic work, we get an energy balance ($\Delta\tilde{G}^{ox} = 0$) of

$$K^2_{Iscc}/E = 2\gamma + \gamma_p - (\delta/Lb^3)zF\eta_a \tag{12.23}$$

Having regard to eqn (12.10) and Note 12.2, and making the substitution $\Delta\gamma = (\delta/Lb^3)zF\eta_a$ in eqn (12.20)

$$\Delta(K^2_c/E) = -2\delta zF\eta_a k/Lb^3 \tag{12.24}$$

That is, anodic dissolution at the tip of a propagating crack provides a 'decohesion' energy of $(\delta/Lb^3)zF\eta_a$ and, in spite of the important role of plasticity in the fracture process, the degree of embrittlement is proportional to the anodic overpotential at the tip.

The phenomenon requires localisation of attack on a narrow front of width δ, generally 1-10 nm. Such localisation is best effected by conditions favouring **borderline passivity.** We should, therefore, expect to find SCC by this mechanism to be highly specific, so as to provide an electrochemically active crack (groove) tip while everywhere else, including the crack walls, is passive. But the specificity lies not only in the electrolytic environment, for a further condition for continuing anodic activity at the crack tip is that mechanical yielding at the tip should be sufficiently intense to prevent repassivation. If we imagine that yielding first ruptures a passive film to reveal a (bare) crack tip one atomic diameter wide and that further yielding at a rate $\dot{x}$ normal to the crack plane causes the tip to open to a width δ in a time $\delta/\dot{x}$, then the tip will remain essentially unfilmed if the repassivation time $\tau > \delta/\dot{x}$. For, if $\tau = \delta/\dot{x}$, the repassivated tip of width δ is deemed to rupture once more, thereby again revealing a sharp crack one atom wide and the cycle continues. Whereas, if $\tau < \delta/\dot{x}$, the passive film is sufficiently substantial to resist rupture and corrosion stops. There is, therefore, a delicate balance between crack geometry, yielding rate and repassivation rate (Note 12.6). Since the yielding rate depends on dislocation density and mobility and the repassivation rate on chemical heterogeneity of the metal (as well as on the electrolytic environment), these factors will determine whether an alloy is susceptible or not to SCC and whether the path taken is intergranular or transgranular.

A system that displays both inter- and transgranular cracking is alpha-brass (copper containing up to 30% zinc) in ammoniacal solutions, being characterised by intergranular cracking in dilute aqueous solutions at *p*H *ca.* 7.5 and by transgranular cracking in concentrated ammonia. The mechanisms are probably different. Intergranular failure of internally-stressed cartridge brass was first observed at the turn of the century when, during the monsoon season (hence the description **'season cracking'**), the close conjunction of ammunition dumps and horse lines provided the necessary moist ammoniacal environment. The brass tarnishes to form a 300 nm layer of Cu_2O and CuO. As the appropriate Pourbaix diagram demonstrates, Fig. 12.2, the tip can dissolve to the ammine complex of Cu(I), point A, while coexisting with cuprous oxide; the principal cathodic reaction outside the crack is reduction of Cu(II) to Cu(I), point C, allied to

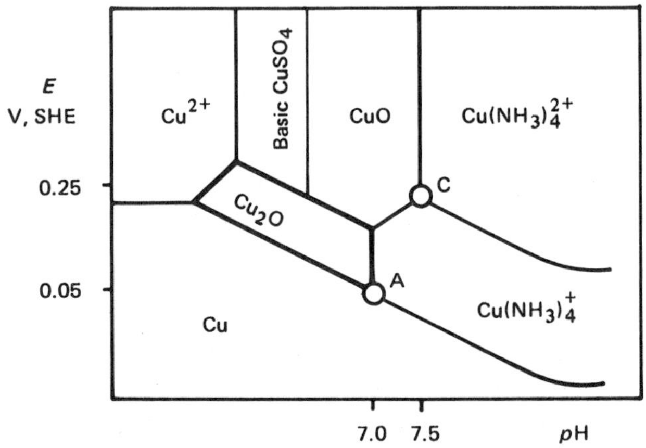

Fig. 12.2 Pourbaix diagram for copper in ammoniacal solution at 25°C.

oxygen reduction if air is present. The difference in potential is the *IR* drop down the crack electrolyte. The crack tip probably remains continuously active as a result of significant plastic deformation and the sides of the crack carry a very thin passivating film. In contrast, there is recent evidence that, in the non-tarnishing concentrated ammonia environment, cracks propagate by cleavage, and the localisation of attack is apparently associated not with a passive film but with decohesion of the lattice following preferential dissolution of zinc solute atoms.

Austenitic stainless steels in the 300 series, that is, based on the 18%Cr–8%Ni composition, are susceptible to transgranular SCC in hot concentrated chloride solutions. The chloride ion activity is critical in determining the mode of attack, Fig. 12.3, indicating the importance of borderline passivity conditions. The boundaries in the diagram are virtually independent of *p*H, as might be expected if the 'micro-climate' in pits and cracks tends to some equilibrium composition. In spite of the ductility of the steel in normal circumstance, crack surfaces commonly resemble cleavage fractures. This has led some observers to suggest that hydrogen embrittlement is involved in the fracture process – and indeed hydrogen gas evolution does sometimes (always?) occur within the crack. However, the decohesion resulting from anodic overpotential, eqn (12.23), is sufficient to explain this, and cracking stops when cathodic protection is applied.

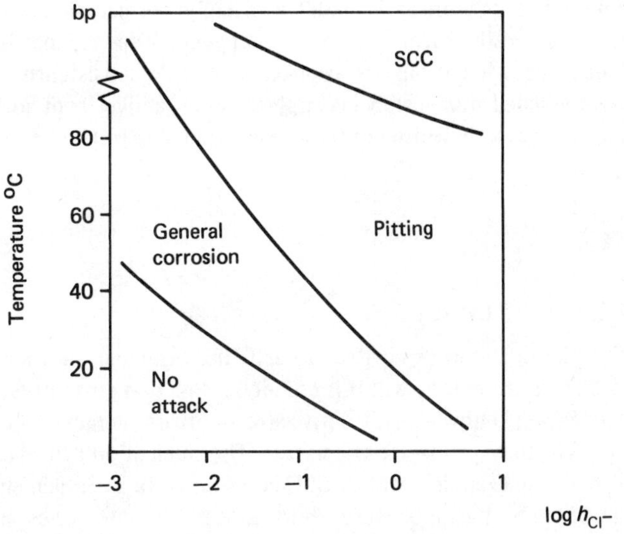

Fig. 12.3 Behaviour of residually stressed tubes of 304 alloy (18Cr–8Ni steel) after 15 months' exposure to chloride solutions at *p*H 7. (Truman, 1976).

It is possible that further lattice disruption follows upon the preferential dissolution of the metal in the form of a network of microscopical tubular 'tunnels', some 20 to 500 nm in diameter. But these are only observed at the pitting/SCC boundary in Fig. 12.3 and may be no more than a curious side effect of borderline passivity and tensile stress. The most powerful arguments for a film-breakdown mechanism of localised attack are

(a) the borderline passivity behaviour in Fig. 12.3;
(b) the high degree of specificity of the SCC environments; and
(c) the experimental observation of anodic current transients when the passivated surface is mechanically scratched.

A third example of a yield-assisted dissolution mechanism is the **'caustic cracking'** of ferritic steels stressed in highly alkaline environments. Fig. 9.2 showed that iron and its oxides dissolve as ferroate ions at $pH > 14$, a condition readily achieved at heat transfer surfaces in steam-raising plant. The effect of surface yielding has been shown to give a large increase in anodic dissolution rate at potentials just above the active loop of Fig. 9.1. Unlike chloride cracking of austenitic stainless steels, it appears that inhibition of caustic cracking is possible by means of soluble silicates.

All these quoted examples of SCC are found to satisfy eqn (12.24). Thus, for α-brass in ammonia, $\Delta(K_c^2/E)$ is some -300 kJ/m^2 whilst, for $\eta \sim 0.1$ V, the RHS of the equation yields this energy provided that $k\delta \sim 2.10^{-5}$; since $k \sim 2000$ in this instance, this implies that $\delta \sim 10$ nm for the actively propagating crack tip dissolving as Cu(I). Similarly, for 18Cr–8Ni steel in chloride, $\Delta(K_c^2/E)$ is some -200 kJ/m^2 and $\delta \sim 6$ nm if $\eta \sim 0.2$ V. Finally, for caustic cracking of mild steel, $\Delta(K_c^2/E) \sim -200$ kJ/m^2 and δ lies between 3 and 15 nm if $\eta \sim 0.5$ V. Although all three calculations are approximate, they consistently indicate that SCC by yield assisted dissolution takes place on an active front some ten times broader than the crack tip width normally associated with brittle fracture processes in air.

12.6 THE RATE OF CRACKING

As with the phenomenon of corrosion itself, the principal question of practical interest in SCC is: how long will this component or that structure last? And this means discovering (a) how quickly active stress-corrosion cracks take to form and (b) how quickly they propagate thereafter. The nucleation process is essentially concerned with the establishment of SCC conditions. In hydrogen embrittlement this induction period can be very short indeed because, once surface flaws exceed a certain critical size, all that is needed is a corrosion process able to generate hydrogen inside the flaw, a process which may be present from the outset. But, even without such a flaw, a corrosion pit can often develop after only a few minutes, and the electrochemical conditions sufficient for large hydrogen pressures not long after, so that the important factor is the rate at which cracks propagate. In yield assisted dissolution, electrochemical conditions of borderline passivity may take anything from a few minutes to a few months, depending for example on stress level and chloride ion activity. But, again, a major part of the component life is determined by how quickly SCC cracks propagate from some critically-sized flaw.

Fracture mechanics can usually give an indication of the sizes of such critical flaws. Thus, in noncorrosive environments, the presence of a surface flaw whose elastic strain field is characterised by a stress intensity equal to the fracture toughness K_{Ic} will lead to instability and rapid fracture. We saw earlier that, for a simple crack geometry, the stress and crack length are related by

$$\sigma_c \approx K_{Ic}/(2a^{\frac{1}{2}}) \tag{12.12}$$

$$\approx (k\gamma E/4a)^{\frac{1}{2}} \tag{12.13}$$

so, by rearrangement, the critical flaw length a_c^{air} for a given applied tensile stress σ is

$$\begin{aligned} a_c^{air} &\approx 0.25\,(K_{Ic}/\sigma)^2 \\ &\approx k\gamma E/4\sigma^2 \end{aligned} \tag{12.25}$$

Under SCC conditions, a flaw will propagate subcritically, that is, below K_{Ic}, and the critical size becomes

$$a_c^{scc} \approx 0.25\,(K_{Iscc}/\sigma)^2 = (K_{Iscc}/K_{Ic})^2\,a_c^{air} \tag{12.26}$$

$$\begin{aligned} &\approx (\gamma - \Delta\gamma)kE/4\sigma^2 \\ &\approx \{1 - (\Delta\gamma/\gamma)\}\,a_c^{air} \end{aligned} \tag{12.27}$$

Typical values of K_{Ic} and K_{Iscc} and the corresponding critical flaw sizes are listed in Table 12.2: note the units used. Considerable caution should be exercised over the tabulated values of a_c^{scc} because they are typically of similar dimensions to the grain size and to the plastic zone size. This means that linear elastic fracture mechanics (LEFM) calculations are no longer valid, and as yet no satisfactory theoretical basis exists for predicting such small critical flaws. Nevertheless, it is apparent that environmental effects can lead to instability in flaws whose dimensions are likely to be comparable with those of microstructural features. In short, stress-corrosion is almost inevitable if the electrochemistry is right.

Table 12.2 Some critical flaw sizes and critical stress intensities in stress-corrosion

Alloy	K_{Ic} $MN/m^{\frac{3}{2}}$	a_c^{air} mm	SCC environment	K_{Iscc} $MN/m^{\frac{3}{2}}$	a_c^{scc} μm
Mild steel	120	15	10 M NaOH	1	1
13Cr steel (σ_y=1.5GN/m^2)	60	0.2	3% NaCl	12	8
18Cr–8Ni steel	200	75	42% $MgCl_2$	10	180
18Mn–5Cr steel	145	3	Hot halides	8	10
Cu–30Zn	200	13	NH_4OH, pH7	1	0.3
Al–3Mg–7Zn	25	0.5	Aqueous halides	5	40
Ti–6Al–1V	60	1.1	0.6 M KCl	20	120
Ti–3Al–8V	35	0.2	MeOH–HCl	6	6

Note Critical flaw sizes in SCC (in *micro*metres) calculated assuming LEFM valid, eqn (12.26).

Let us suppose that, after an appropriate induction period, we have a flaw for which $K > K_{Iscc}$ so that it begins to propagate as a fairly sharp crack. The rate of propagation then depends on the slowest process. At low stress intensities this is likely to be the rate of charge transfer, either for metal dissolution or of proton reduction, both of which will depend on the amount of bare metal present and its degree of mechanical disturbance. These factors in turn depend on the strain rate of the surface constituting the crack tip and so upon the stress intensity. At higher stress intensities, the strain rate will now be sufficiently great that other processes become rate determining. In hydrogen embrittlement this next-slowest process is probably the rate of hydrogen diffusion in the grain boundary. Thus, the cracking of martensitic steels reaches a 'plateau', designated region II in Fig. 12.4 (Note 12.7), which varies as the square root of hydrogen partial pressure and upon the source of atomic hydrogen, whether from dissociation of H_2S or from proton reduction in water. Similarly, in SCC by yield assisted dissolution, the next-slowest process is ionic diffusion in the crack electrolyte. Some representative rates in the plateau region are listed in Table 12.3.

It is a relatively simple matter to deduce minimum component life once an SCC flaw starts to grow. When the rates have been determined and expressed analytically as a rate equation, integration of this equation between the limits a_c^{scc} and a_c^{air} gives the time to propagate to final fast rupture. This, of course, applies only to a system where the stress intensity increases as the crack grows. It is fortunate that some engineering structures are self-loading 'fixed beam' systems where K falls progressively until the crack stops.

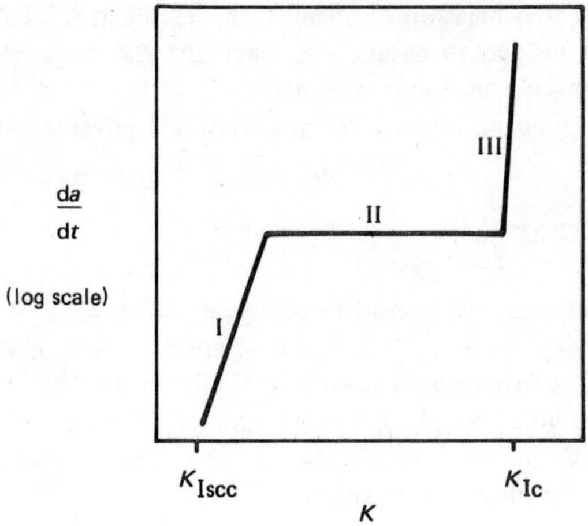

Fig. 12.4 Influence of stress intensity factor on the rate of SCC propagation. Note how the rate becomes very fast as K_{Ic} is approached (region III).

Table 12.3 Region II propagation rates of SCC

System	Rate m/s
13Cr steel: H_2 (g, 1 atm)	10^{-3}
H_2S (g, 1 atm)	10^{-1}
aqueous halides	10^{-4}
18Cr–8Ni steel: 42% $MgCl_2$	10^{-7}
18Mn–5Cr steel: hot halides	10^{-8}
Ti alloys: aqueous halides	10^{-3} to 10^{-4}
Al alloys: air (RH 0.1%)	10^{-10}
aqueous halides	10^{-5} to 10^{-6}
Brass: aqueous ammonia	10^{-6}

12.7 CORROSION FATIGUE

SCC is the result of conjoint action between corrosion and tensile stress. When the stress is cyclical, the resulting fatigue failure is likewise accelerated by electrochemical action. In the absence of a reactive environment, cyclical strain leads to surface crack initiation by dislocation processes that are relatively well understood. The crack then propagates subcritically because the cycling process at the crack tip leads to a measure of decohesion, $\Delta\gamma$ in eqn (12.14b), lowering the maximum stress needed to extend the crack. At the stage where surface dislocation mechanisms are no longer important, the fatigue crack propagates at right angles to the principal stress direction, at a rate governed by the *Paris equation*

$$da/dN = C(\Delta K)^n \tag{12.28}$$

where da/dN is the incremental extension per cycle, $\Delta K = K_{max} - K_{min}$ is the range of stress intensity for $K_{min} \geqslant 0$, and C, n are constants: n generally lies between 2 and 4. This behaviour is portrayed by the broken line in Fig. 12.5. In the case of aluminium alloys, the threshold value of ΔK is approximately that value for which da/dN is one atomic distance per cycle, whereas for steels it often corresponds to the inter-carbide spacing.

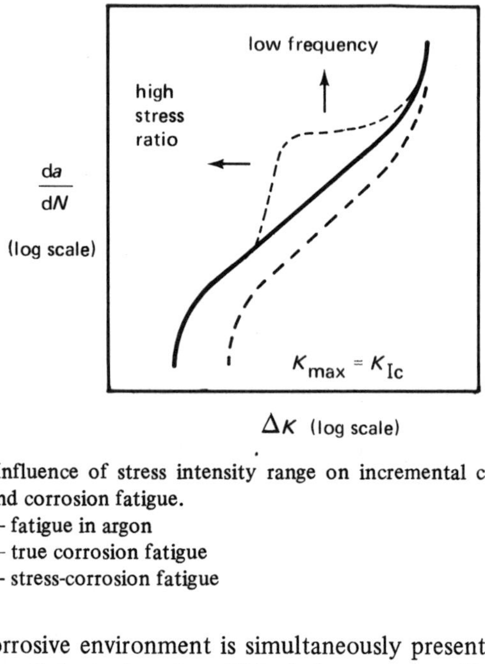

Fig. 12.5 Influence of stress intensity range on incremental crack propagation in fatigue and corrosion fatigue.
---- fatigue in argon
—— true corrosion fatigue
------ stress-corrosion fatigue

When a corrosive environment is simultaneously present with fatigue stressing, we should anticipate that $\Delta\gamma$ will include not only a 'fatigue damage' contribution but also an SCC contribution, thereby further increasing the tendency to crack spontaneously. The threshold ΔK is lowered to a value for which, in fcc alloys, da/dN is now a fraction of an atomic distance, presumably because crack advance occurs as small intrusions of the crack front rather than across the whole front simultaneously. The rate of crack propagation is found to be higher too. There is a small increase, approximately a doubling, which is independent of cycling frequency or stress intensity ratio K_{min}/K_{max}: this has come to be called *'true' corrosion fatigue* and is indicated by the solid line in Fig. 12.5 (Note 12.8). In addition, there is a much larger increase, perhaps 20 times or more, that is also observed at low frequencies and high stress intensity ratios. This is due to SCC superimposed on the true corrosion fatigue, and it is therefore referred to as *stress-corrosion fatigue* by some workers. The dotted line in Fig. 12.5 can be seen to be the curve of Fig. 12.4 superimposed on the 'Paris' line of eqn (12.28). It moves bodily upwards with decreasing frequency (since $da/dN = da/dt$ divided by the frequency dN/dt) and to the left with increasing ratio K_{min}/K_{max} (since $\Delta K = K_{max}\{1 - (K_{min}/K_{max})\}$). Evidently, the phenomenon of corrosion fatigue, as commonly understood, is a complex mixture of mechanisms. The presence of the corrosive environment ensures that, sooner or later, surface flaws will develop, which is why the phenomenon is so frequently encountered. The enhancement of propagation rate, however, is not really significant unless the stress cycling rate is sufficiently slow (at or below 1 Hz) for SCC to take effect.

Bibliography to Chapter 12

Knott 1973, *Fundamentals of Fracture Mechanics,* Butterworths.
Logan 1966, *The Stress Corrosion of Metals,* Wiley.
Rhodin (ed.) 1954, *Physical Metallurgy of SCC Fracture,* Interscience.
Scully (ed.) 1971, *Theory of SCC in Alloys,* NATO, Brussels.
Staehle, Forty and Van Rooyen (eds.) 1969, *Fundamental Aspects of SCC,* NACE, Houston.
Westwood and Stoloff (eds.) 1966, *Environment-Sensitive Mechanical Behaviour,* Gordon & Breach.
McCright, Slater and Staehle (eds.) 1976, *SCC and Hydrogen Embrittlement in Iron Base Alloys,* NACE, Houston.
Read 1961, *Hydrogen Embrittlement in Metal Finishing,* Reinhold.
Robertson (ed.) 1956, *SCC and Hydrogen Embrittlement,* Wiley.
Science et Industrie (ed.) 1977, *Proc. 2nd. Internat. Congr. on Hydrogen in Metals,* Paris.
Plumbridge 1972, *J. Mater. Sci.,* (on corrosion fatigue survey).
Waterhouse 1972, *Fretting Corrosion,* Pergamon.
Foroulis (ed.) 1979, *Environment-Sensitive Fracture of Engineering Materials,* AIME, New York.

Notes to Chapter 12

12.1 Even amorphous materials such as glasses have additional energy-wasting processes. 'Hazing', for example, involves microcracking and so additional new surfaces.

12.2 The proportionality between K_c^2, γ and γ_p is strictly valid only for small-scale yielding conditions. When there is significant plasticity, which occurs when $\sigma/\sigma_y > 0.3$, there develop shear stresses parallel to the crack plane, and the energy balance is no longer properly expressed by eqn (12.8). However, the errors introduced by assuming a constant value of k in eqn (12.9) et seq. are substantially cancelled out when we consider the 'difference' equations (12.20) and (12.24). Experimental observations, although limited, bear out these two equations to within 10%, West, *Metal Science J.* 1980. The nonlinear behaviour of ductile alloys is considered, for example, by Rice, *J. Mech. Phys. Solids* 1974 **22** 17.

12.3 See previous note. The experimental validity of eqn (12.20) is one justification for the assumption of eqn (12.9) that $\gamma_p \propto \gamma$. The other is the similar validation of eqn (12.24).

12.4 These two aspects have given rise to the 'planar pressure' and 'decohesion' models of hydrogen embrittlement. The first of these envisages that an expansive pressure in the incipient fracture plane may originate from dissolved hydrogen atoms in the lattice, besides giving rise to gaseous pressure in any internal voids, see for example Morlet, Johnson and Troiano, *J. Iron Steel Inst.* 1958 **189** 37. The 'decohesion' model, see for example Oriani, *Proc. Symp. Fundamental Aspects of SCC* (NACE 1969) p.32, assumes that the lattice expansion caused by hydrogen serves to lower the residual lattice binding energy so that the cohesive strength falls with increasing hydrogen content. In essence this latter model is indistinguishable from the adsorption model, described in the text and proposed by Petch, *Phil. Mag.* 1956 **1** 331, since binding energy and surface free energy are closely related.

12.5 The initial ingress of atomic hydrogen is greatly favoured by surface poisons such as sulphur and arsenic. Thereafter the evidence indicates that hydrogen diffusion is assisted by a dislocation-sweeping mechanism resulting from crack tip plasticity.

12.6 Scully, *Corrosion Science* 1975 **15** 207 has, for example, developed an interesting treatment based on the total electrical charge needed to form a coherent film. Although specifying a two-stage model, in which film rupture and anodic dissolution alternate, the treatment can be applied to a continuous model in which the crack tip is permanently (almost) bare. It would appear that Scully's two-stage model of slip-step dissolution applies especially to the transgranular failure observed in austenitic stainless steels that are in the *transpassive* condition; whilst the continuous model best describes the intergranular failure that occurs when these steels are in the passive region.

12.7 Regions I and II may be compared with the Tafel and concentration-limited regions of the polarisation curve, Fig. 6.2 and 6.5.

12.8 Dawson and Pelloux, *Met. Trans.* 1974 **5** 723. The idea that corrosion fatigue crack propagation may be inferred from a superposition of fatigue and SCC contributions was first put forward by Wei and Landes, *Mat. Res. Stand.* 1969 **9** 25 and more recently developed by Austen and Walker, *Proc. Internat. Conf. on Influence of Environment on Fatigue* (Instn. Mech. Engrs, London 1977).

Chapter 13

High Temperature Corrosion

13.1 THE DRIVING FORCE

At high temperatures, where water is no longer stable in the liquid phase, reaction of metals with their environment may be regarded as occurring by direct chemical combination. Thus, in dry air, copper forms cuprous oxide:

$$2Cu(s) + \tfrac{1}{2}O_2(g) = Cu_2O(s) \qquad (13.1)$$

and so on. Nevertheless, because most oxidation products grow as reasonably coherent solid films, there develops a spatial separation of simultaneous oxidation and reduction reactions:

At the metal/film interface:

$$Cu(s) = Cu^{+}(\text{film}) + e(Cu) \quad .$$

(13.2)

At the film/air interface:

$$\tfrac{1}{2}O_2(g) + 2e(\text{film}) = O^{2-}(\text{film})$$

and these clearly parallel the anodic and cathodic reactions of electrochemical corrosion, even though cations are here 'solvated' by an ionic solid rather than water. In fact, the oxidation process is also an electrochemical one, with its driving emf $\mathcal{E}$ given by an equation analagous to eqn (4.12)

$$\mathcal{E} = -\Delta G/nF \quad . \qquad (13.3)$$

From eqn (13.1), ΔG is evidently the free energy of formation of the oxide, in this case Cu_2O, at the temperature of interest. When all products and reactants are in their (Raoultian) standard states of pure metal, pure oxide and 1 atm oxygen partial pressure, then $\Delta G = \Delta G^{\ominus} = G^{\bullet}$, the standard free energy of formation. This quantity may be calculated from published tables of $\Delta H^{\ominus}$ and $S^{\ominus}$ at 298 K, for example, Table 2.1, making due allowance for any phase changes or changes of state involved, pp. 29, 30; otherwise it may be read off directly from the appropriate Ellingham diagram, Fig. 2.2. Thus, taking the room temperature data for $Cu_2O(s)$:

$$\Delta H^{\ominus}(Cu_2O) = -167 \text{ kJ/mol}$$

$\Delta S^{\ominus}$ (Cu_2O) for the reaction (13.1) as written is

$$S^{\ominus}(Cu_2O) - 2S^{\ominus}(Cu) - \tfrac{1}{2}S^{\ominus}(O_2) = 101 - 66 - 102.5$$

$$= -67.5 \text{ J/mol K}$$

so

$$\Delta G^{\ominus}(800K) \approx -167 + (800 \times 0.0675) = -113 \text{ kJ/mol.}$$

From this, using eqn (9.14) and recognising that $\mu^{\ominus}_{MxOy}$ is $G^{\bullet}_{MxOy}$ for the oxide M_xO_y, we get

$$\Delta G^{\ominus} = (yRT/2)\ln(p_{O2}/p^{\ominus}) \qquad (9.14)$$

$$= (RT/2)\ln(p_{O2}/p^{\ominus}) \text{ in the case of } Cu_2O$$

and hence discover that the equilibrium partial pressure of oxygen over solid Cu_2O and Cu at 800K is

$$p_{O2} = p^{\ominus} \exp(-113\,000 \times 2)/(8.31 \times 800)$$

$$= 2.10^{-15} \text{ atm.}$$

That is, copper will not oxidise below this pressure of 2.10^{-15} atm, which is consequently designated the **dissociation partial pressure** of pure Cu_2O at 800K (see p. 37). Some typical values for p_{O2} (oxides) and p_{S2} (sulphides) are listed in Table 13.1.

Of course, we rarely encounter standard states in real life, and the ΔG in eqn (13.3) needs to take account of the copper activity (if the metal is an alloy), the Cu_2O activity (if the oxide is contaminated or dissolved), and the oxygen partial pressure. If, in our example, the metal is a brass having $a_{Cu} = 0.6$, the oxide is essentially pure Cu_2O (because in this instance zinc tends to distil away at 800K), and the oxygen is at 10^{-4} atm, we obtain from eqn (2.40)

$$\Delta G = \Delta G^{\ominus} + RT\ln\{a_{Cu2O}/a^2_{Cu}(p_{O2}/p^{\ominus})^{\frac{1}{2}}\}$$

$$= -113 + (8.31 \times 10^{-3} \times 800)\ln\{1/(0.36 \times 10^{-2})\}$$

$$= -76 \text{ kJ.}$$

Table 13.1 Dissociation partial pressures (atm) of some pure oxides and sulphides.

Oxide	$-\log(p_{O_2}/p^{\ominus})$ at 600	800	1000K
Cu_2O	21.9	14.7	10.3
NiO	32.7	22.1	15.7
FeO	38.5	26.9	19.9
Al_2O_3	86.4	62.1	47.5
Sulphide	$-\log(p_{S_2}/p^{\ominus})$ at 600	800	1000K
NiS	6.1	2.4	−0.2
Cu_2S	7.6	2.7	2.1
FeS	9.0	4.8	2.3

Substituting in eqn (13.3),

$$\mathcal{E} = -\Delta G/2F = 76/(2 \times 96.5) = 0.39 \text{ V}.$$

This result may be compared with the 0.63 V driving the process at room temperature (section 5.3).

We saw in Chapter 6 that the rate of corrosion at room temperature is largely determined by the overpotentials at anode and cathode regions, occasionally modified by a contribution from electrolytic resistance. In Figs. 8.2 and 8.3 this can be summarised by the emf equation

$$\mathcal{E} = \eta_a + |\eta_c| + IR \qquad (8.1)$$

Because surface films in general are effective insulators at room temperature (Chapter 9), we saw also that metals tend to corrode at an effectively constant rate, controlled by charge transfer or bulk diffusion (of oxygen, say) if passive films are absent or, if such a film is present, by very slow cation transport through a film of more or less constant thickness. In either event, the Evans diagram affords a means of estimating this constant rate, which we can express analytically for simple cases of charge transfer, eqn (7.2).

But, as the temperature is raised, so too is the rate of reaction, eqn (3.16): the overpotentials fall dramatically and film transport becomes rapid. Charge transfer and ionic diffusion in water are characterised by apparent activation enthalpies of ca. 40–55 kJ/mol (Table 3.2) whilst ionic transport in oxide films usually displays a higher activation enthalpy around 100–200 kJ/mol. Now the Arrhenius equation

$$k = A \exp(-\Delta H^{\ddagger}/RT) \tag{3.16}$$

may be rearranged to give the ratio of the rate constants at two different temperature (provided that the temperature interval is sufficiently small, p. 51)

$$\ln(k_1/k_2) = -\frac{\Delta H^{\ddagger}}{R}\left(\frac{1}{T_1} - \frac{1}{T_2}\right) = \frac{\Delta H^{\ddagger}}{R}\left(\frac{T_1 - T_2}{T_1 T_2}\right) \tag{13.4}$$

This means that the relative rates of reaction at 800K and room temperature are:

Charge transfer ($\Delta H^{\ddagger} \sim 45$ kJ/mol): $k_{800}/k_{298} = 10^{5\pm1}$

Ionic film transport ($\Delta H^{\ddagger} \sim 150$ kJ/mol):

$$k_{800}/k_{298} = 10^{16\pm5}$$

If we assume for the moment that the pre-exponential constants A remain unaltered (the assumption that underlies eqn (13.4)), this is tantamount to assuming that the mechanisms of interfacial charge transfer and film conduction are still the same at high temperature. On such an assumption, the data of Tables 6.1 and 9.1 indicate that exchange current densities at 800K are likely to be something in excess of 10^4A/m^2 (that is, $> 10^4$ mm/yr, eqn (6.14)) and 'passive film' limiting current densities (i_p) very large indeed, in the neighbourhood of 10^{17} A/m^2 for a film a few nanometres thick. Of course this basic assumption is unfounded. At the metal/film interface, the charge transfer process involves a metal cation in a solid ionic lattice rather than an aquo-ion in a liquid double layer. Likewise, the conduction process in a thin passive film is subject to a very high electrical potential gradient through a medium of rapidly changing composition and probably highly sensitive to surface defects in the underlying metal; whereas conduction in thicker scales (Table 13.2) takes place via a lower potential gradient in a film approaching stoichiometric composition (Note 13.1). Nevertheless, the marked difference in magnitude (10^4 *vs.* 10^{17} A/m^2) indicates that interfacial kinetics are likely to be rate determining in the very early stages of film growth. As the film thickens to a scale, it is found that the interfacial effects can be ignored and the rate is dominated by film conduction processes. *These become slower as reaction proceeds.*

Reverting now to the emf equation

$$\mathcal{E} = \eta_a + |\eta_c| + IR \tag{8.1}$$

we therefore find that, once a substantial scale has developed, the charge transfer overpotentials are insignificant. For all practical purposes, concentration polarisation can occur only at the anode, and then only where diffusion of the reacting

Table 13.2 Some typical thicknesses after oxidation in dry air.

Metal	Temperature °C	Time	Thickness
Iron	20	100 h	1–2 nm
		8000 h	5 nm
	400	3 min	70 nm
	900	24 h	0.6 mm
Aluminium	20	1500 h	3 nm
	600	60 h	200 nm
Copper	20	100 h	2–3 nm
	500	30 min	500 nm
	800	6 h	20 μm
Nickel	20	100 h	ca. 2 nm
	800	1 h	450 nm

metal atoms from the bulk metal up to the metal/film interface may become rate controlling in sufficiently dilute alloys. The concentration overpotential, by analogy with eqn (6.18), is given by

$$\eta = (RT/nF)\ \ln\{(1 - \frac{i}{i_L})\ (\gamma_i/\gamma_b)\} \tag{13.5}$$

where i_L is the limiting current density and γ_i/γ_b is the ratio of the Raoultian activity coefficients for metal atoms at the interface and in the bulk alloy respectively. The limiting current equation is similar in form to eqn (6.16):

$$i_L = nFx_M D_M/\delta_M \tag{13.6}$$

where x_M, D_M and δ_M are the bulk concentration, diffusivity and diffusion layer thickness of the metal atoms within the alloy. If we neglect the activity coefficient correction and substitute eqn (13.6) in (13.5),

$$\eta = (RT/nF)\ \ln\left(\frac{nFx_M D_M - i\delta_M}{nFx_M D_M}\right) \tag{13.7}$$

which tends to zero when $x_M \rightarrow 1$ or D_M is very large. If diffusion through the oxide film is also subject to Fick's law then as will be shown in the next section, when the film has a thickness y its electrical resistance is

$$R = R_i + R_e = y/\kappa t_i t_e \qquad (13.8)$$

where R_i and R_e are the contributions of ionic and electronic resistances, κ is the film conductivity and t_i, t_e are the fractions of the current transported by ions and electrons respectively (that is, the ionic and electronic **transport numbers**). Hence, in Fig. 13.1, the oxidation cell may be envisaged as an emf of $-\Delta G/nF$, eqn (13.3), being dissipated through the small nonlinear resistance η/i, eqn (13.5), and the ohmic resistance R, eqn (13.8). Combination of these equations yields

$$i = -(1/y)\,(\kappa t_i t_e/nF)\,\{RT \ln(\Delta i/i) + \Delta G\} \qquad (13.9)$$

where $\Delta i/i$ represents the quotient in eqn (13.7) (normally close to unity). This equation clearly shows how the rate i depends on the film thickness y.

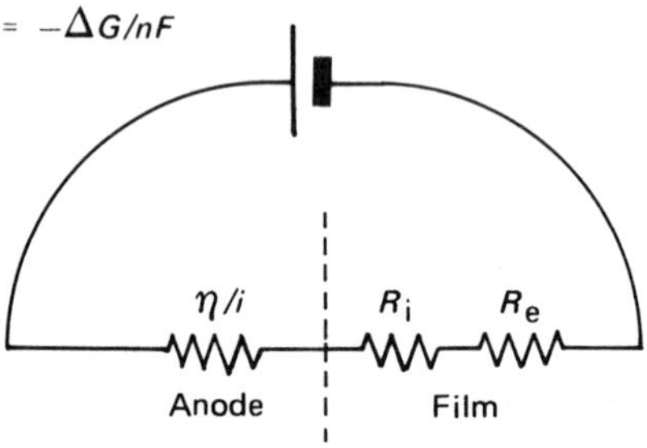

Fig. 13.1 Equivalent circuit for high temperature oxidation. R_i and R_e are the ionic and electronic resistances of the surface film. Cf. Fig. 8.3 for room temperature corrosion.

13.2 PARABOLIC OXIDATION

Whereas passive films may be absent during room temperature aqueous corrosion, in high-temperature corrosion a surface film is almost invariably present. This means that, for oxidation to continue, the film must conduct not only cations but also electrons for the external cathodic process of oxygen reduction. Many oxide films also conduct the oxygen anion, so that the overall process is that represented in Fig. 13.2. The plane in which film growth occurs is P. Here it is shown lying within the film itself but it may equally lie at the oxide/O_2 interface (if $t_O \ll t_M$, that is, the film conducts predominantly by cation transport of M^{n+} rather than O^{2-}) or at the metal/film interface (if $t_M \ll t_O$). The sum of the ionic and electronic transport numbers must of course be unity:

$$t_M + t_O + t_e = 1 \quad . \qquad (13.10)$$

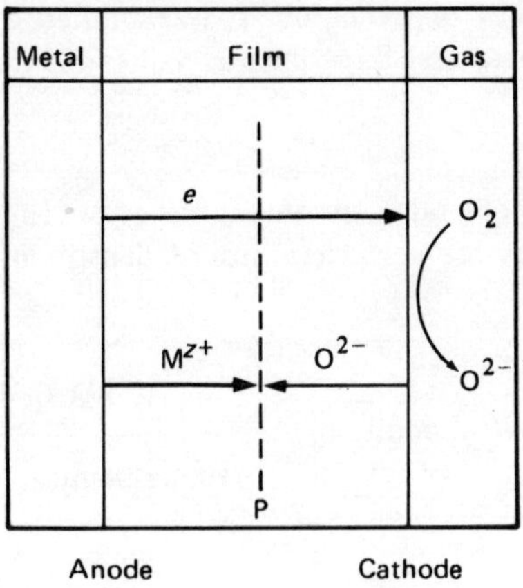

Fig. 13.2 Schematic oxidation process.
P = plane of growth.

The transport mechanism through a coherent film, that is, one free from rifts and cavities, is a combination of diffusion down a concentration (activity) gradient and electrical migration down a potential gradient. However, the mobility u_i of a species i carrying n_iF coulomb/mol is related to the diffusivity D_i by the Nernst-Einstein relation

$$u_i = (n_iF/RT)D_i \tag{13.11}$$

so that the flux Q_i (mol/m^2 s) of the species at concentration c_i (mol/m^3), through a film of thickness y, is

$$\begin{aligned} Q_i &= -D_i(\Delta c_i/y) + u_i c_i(\mathcal{E} - \eta)/y \\ &= -(D_i/y)\,\{\Delta c_i - (n_iFc_i/RT)\,(\mathcal{E} - \eta)\} \end{aligned} \tag{13.12}$$

and Q is evidently proportional simply to D/y for each species. Since the rate of film thickening is directly proportional to the flux of charge, it follows that

$$\mathrm{d}y/\mathrm{d}t = K/y \tag{13.13}$$

in agreement with eqn (13.9). Integrating and putting the integration constant as zero, we obtain

$$\boxed{y^2 = k_\mathrm{p}t} \qquad (k_\mathrm{p} = 2K) \quad . \tag{13.14}$$

This is the **parabolic law of oxidation.** It is exhibited by most metals over a limited range of temperature. Experimental values for the rate constant k_p are listed in Table 13.3.

Table 13.3 Some parabolic rate constants in the equation $y^2 = k_p t$.
The final column gives the corrosion current density, in *mega*amps per square metre, for a 3 nm film.

Metal	Product	Condition	$-\log k_p$ (m^2/s) Experimental	Calculated	i MA/m^2
Silver	Ag_2S	490K	8.66	8.48	5300
	AgBr	470K	13.13	13.28	0.13
Copper	CuI	470K	12.24	12.19	1.1
	Cu_2O	1270K, $10^{-1.1}$ atm	11.15	11.12	21
	Cu_2O	1270K, $10^{-3.5}$ atm	11.60	11.62	7.3

It is possible to predict k_p on the basis of eqn (13.12), but a simpler derivation is as follows (Note 13.2). We should first recognise that, although ionic and electronic conduction proceed by separate paths through the film, the two processes are intimately linked, neither being possible without the other, section 14.2. Electrically speaking, this implies that the two paths are in series, Fig. 13.1:

$$R = R_i + R_e$$

If we write κ for the conductance of the film then the ionic conductance is $\kappa(t_M + t_O)$ and the electronic conductance is κt_e whence, for unit area of film of thickness y,

$$R_i = y/\kappa\,(t_M + t_O) \quad \text{and} \quad R_e = y/\kappa t_e \qquad (13.15)$$

From eqn (13.8) (13.10) (13.15),

$$R = y/\kappa t_e(t_M + t_O) \qquad (13.16)$$

which was used in a slightly different form in eqn (13.8) on p. 168. If nF coulombs are needed to form 1 mole of oxide of relative molecular mass M and density ρ, then

$$dy/dt = (i/nF)\,(M/\rho)$$

which, from Ohm's law

$$i = (\mathcal{E} - \eta)/R = -\Delta G/nFR \text{ for } \eta \ll \mathcal{E} \tag{13.17}$$

becomes

$$\mathrm{d}y/\mathrm{d}t = -\frac{\Delta G.M\kappa t_e(t_M + t_O)}{(nF)^2 \rho}(1/y) \tag{13.18}$$

As we shall see later, κ as well as ΔG depends on the oxygen partial pressure. Equations (13.13) and (13.18) are directly comparable and indicate that, from a knowledge of $G^\bullet$ and the electrical properties of the film, we may predict the rate constant k_p in eqn (13.14). The experimental and predicted values are compared in Table 13.3. The good agreement confirms the model and demonstrates that, the more stable the corrosion product, the faster it forms initially. The final column gives the values of the corrosion current density derived from k_p when the film thickness is comparable with that of a passive film in aqueous corrosion. It may be seen that this current lies in the region of $10^5 - 10^9$ A/m². An Arrhenius-type calculation on the basis of room temperature passive film currents, eqn (13.4), predicts that, for the temperatures and pressures concerned, the current should lie between 10^4 and 10^{11} A/m². This agreement is sufficiently good to indicate that the rate-limiting film conduction processes are kinetically similar to those encountered in aqueous corrosion.

13.3 OTHER GROWTH LAWS

The parabolic law was derived on the assumption that the integrity of the film is perfect, that Ohm's law is obeyed, and that there is no concentration polarisation (Note 13.3). The perfection of the film depends in the first instance on its volume relative to that of the metal which went into it. This ratio, known as the **Pilling-Bedworth ratio**, is less than unity only for the alkali and alkali earth metals, whereas the metals of engineering interest display ratios around 1.5-2.0, Table 13.4. This implies that most oxide films commonly encountered are in a state of compression. In the early epitaxial stage of growth (Note 13.4), when y is little more than 10 nm, this residual stress is relatively unimportant but, as the film thickens, and particularly if flaws develop for other reasons, the stress can lead to local, mechanical failure.

The principal sources of flaws are:

(a) when cation diffusion predominates, because lattice vacancies accumulate at the metal/film interface, section 14.2; and, as with low temperature passive films,
(b) microstructural 'mismatch' features such as grain boundaries; or
(c) geometrical features such as sharp corners.

Table 13.4 The Pilling-Bedworth ratio for some oxides.
The final column gives the multiplication factor required to convert a rate of 1 mg/cm^2 day to mm/yr. Note: 1 Mg/m^3 ≡ 1 g/cm^3.

Oxide	Density Mg/m^3	Pilling-Bedworth ratio	mm/yr / mg/cm^2 day
MgO	3.6	0.8	1.0
Al_2O_3	4.0	1.3	0.9
TiO_2	5.1	1.5	0.7
ZrO_2	5.6		
Fe_2O_3	5.3	2.1	0.7
Cr_2O_3	5.1		
Cu_2O	6.2	1.6	0.55
NiO	6.9		
SiO_2	2.7	1.9	1.4
UO_2	11.1	1.9	0.3
WO_3	7.3	3.3	0.5

Corners are a particular source of decohesion, whether within the film or at the metal/film interface, Fig. 13.3, because the relative rigidity of the film (scale) makes it difficult for it to adapt to the inwardly receding metal. The determining factors are the Pilling-Bedworth ratio and, more importantly, the degree of plasticity of the film relative to its adhesion to the metal. It is difficult to quantify these mechanical factors in any meaningful way; however, see section 13.6.

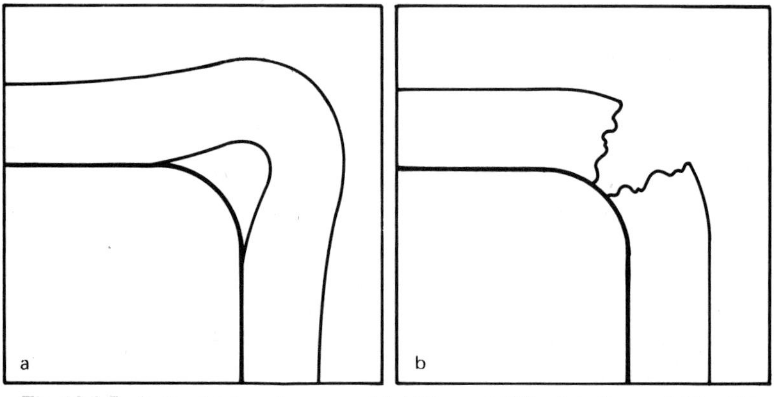

Fig. 13.3 Scale decohesion at corners. (a) At the metal/film interface and (b) within the film itself.

In the light of the foregoing factors, it is hardly surprising that the parabolic law is obeyed over only a limited range of temperature. Typical growth laws are shown schematically in Fig. 13.4. The *parabolic* growth behaviour of eqn (13.14) is represented by curve 'a'. *Rectilinear* oxidation 'b' occurs when the film is nonprotective, for example if the Pilling-Bedworth ratio is less than unity or if the corrosion product is liquid or volatile. It also occurs when the film is very thin, which implies that overpotential considerations at the interface determine the rate rather than the very fast transport that could otherwise occur through the film itself. *Quasi-linear* behaviour 'c' can result when the predominating mechanism is ionic diffusion (that is, parabolic) but the film is sufficiently brittle to crack from time to time. Finally, *logarithmic* behaviour 'd' occurs when the film develops flaws parallel to the interface, for these progressively limit the effective area available to diffusion. In the limit, the rate of oxidation is controlled by the rate of gaseous diffusion across the flaws. However, the logarithmic law

$$y = \ln(Kt) \tag{13.19}$$

is characteristic also of oxidation at low temperatures, for example copper below 400K, aluminium below 500K, iron below 650K, and nickel below 900K. The reason is thought to lie with the reduced electronic conductivity at these temperatures (Note 13.3).

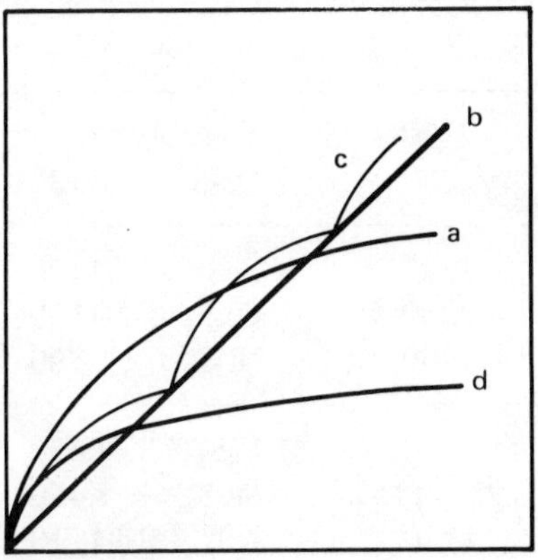

Fig. 13.4 The growth 'laws' of oxidation. (a) Parabolic, (b) rectilinear, (c) quasi-rectilinear and (d) logarithmic.

13.4 FLUID PRODUCTS

Rectilinear (that is, constant rate) oxidation often occurs when the Pilling-Bedworth ratio is less than unity. Rather like Zeno's paradox of Achilles and the tortoise (Note 13.5), this implies that the oxide film can never 'catch up' with the exposed surface area, so that bare metal is always present. However, the facts are otherwise: there first forms a thin epitaxial film similar to the barrier layer in anodised aluminium, section 11.4, which progressively spalls at its outer surface as the expansive tensile stress disrupts the film beyond a certain critical thickness. The film therefore remains of roughly constant thickness and so does the oxidation rate.

Naturally enough, rectilinear oxidation also occurs when there is no film present at all, so that the rate is determined by the rate of arrival of gaseous reactants at the surface. This happens when the corrosion product is volatile or when the film is sufficiently liquid to run off the surface. As may be seen from Table 13.5, the oxides of vanadium, molybdenum, and tungsten melt relatively easily – indeed MoO_3 volatilises and so affords no protection above about 1000°C; the sulphides are generally less stable, nickel significantly joining in the group of vulnerable metals; whilst, if chloride is present, all the metals listed are liable to rapid attack. We should further note that alloying will nearly always lead to the formation of mixed oxides, sulphides and so on which, if mutually soluble, will lower the melting point. All these factors will be taken into account in the next section, when considering oxidation in complex or contaminated atmospheres.

Table 13.5 Melting points of some oxides, sulphides and chlorides (°C).
d = decomposes, s = sublimes, b = boils

Metal	Oxide		Sulphide		Chloride	
Al	Al_2O_3	2020	Unstable		$AlCl_3$	s.178
Cu	Cu_2O	1230	Cu_2S	1130	$CuCl_2$	620
Fe	FeO	1371	FeS	1190	$FeCl_2$	670
Cr	Cr_2O_3	2280	Cr_2S_3	1150	$CrCl_2$	824
Ni	NiO	1960	Ni_2S_3	790	$NiCl_2$	s.973
V	V_2O_5	670	V_2S_3	d.600	VCl_4	b.149
Mo	MoO_3	795, s.1155	MoS_2	s.450	$MoCl_5$	194
W	WO_2	1270	WS_2	d.1250	WCl_5	b.276

13.5 OXIDATION IN COMPLEX ATMOSPHERES

Atmospheres rarely consist of pure oxygen. It is the presence of contaminants such as H_2O, CO_2 and SO_2 that are largely responsible for the very rapid wastage of metals at high temperature, Table 13.6. The action of water is probably to introduce monovalent OH^- anions into an O^{2-} lattice, but it also leads to a reduced oxygen partial pressure, and only in a few instances is the oxidation rate enhanced directly (iron at 700°C); its principal effect is to introduce *liquid* water under conditions of thermal cycling, enabling electrochemical corrosion to alternate with oxidation (section 16.3). Carbon dioxide is a constituent of combustion products and, like H_2O, provides a source of oxygen. The table shows that the pure metals oxidise at much the same rate as in oxygen itself, with the exception of tungsten, where the volatile WO_2 is formed only in O_2 and H_2O atmospheres. As we shall see below, the importance of CO_2 lies in its ability to promote simultaneous carburisation of *alloys,* so that its destructive power is not shown up in this table. Sulphur dioxide is also a common product of combustion and, because of the dissociation

$$SO_2(g) = \tfrac{1}{2}S_2(g) + O_2(g) \quad , \tag{13.20}$$

can lead to simultaneous oxidation and sulphidation. In view of the low melting points of many sulphides, Table 13.5, (and more especially of mixed sulphide eutectics), the rate of attack of iron and nickel base alloys is greatly increased.

Table 13.6 Oxidation rates in various atmospheres.
Averaged over about a week and converted into the equivalent wastage rate in mm/yr assuming *linear* oxidation kinetics.

Temperature °C	Atmosphere	O_2	H_2O	CO_2	SO_2
700	Iron	36	44	41	25
	Chromium	0.33	0.04	0.19	0.11
	Nickel	0.53	0.02	0.21	**51**
	Cobalt	1.9	0.4	1.4	**31**
	Copper	6.6	1.8	3.6	0.07
	Tungsten	21	1.1	7.0	24
900	Iron	87	40	79	**>350**
	Chromium	1.5	0.8	0.9	2.2
	Nickel	1.5	0.8	2.0	**46**
	Cobalt	48	13	23	**86**
	Copper	24	8.4	6.8	0.11
	Tungsten	**188**	**90**	7	15

Catastrophic oxidation is the very rapid corrosion of Fe-Cr-Ni alloys resulting from the formation of fluid oxidation products above 650°C. The cause is a variety of solids carried into the combustion gas stream by fuel ash. One constituent is vanadium pentoxide, V_2O_5, and this is found to give a low-melting complex in combination with Na_2SO_4: the resultant fluid glass provides an oxidising slag which dissolves the oxides of the attacked alloy and allows oxidation to occur at a rectilinear rate.

The combination of carburisation with oxidation is equally disastrous in alloys relying on chromium for their protection. The phenomenon leads to *green rot* in Nimonic alloys and *dusting* in iron-chromium and iron-chromium-nickel alloys. The precipitation of chromium carbide, usually of $Cr_{23}C_6$ (cf. weld decay in section 9.3), sufficiently denudes the matrix for extensive oxidation to green NiO or black Fe_3O_4/Fe_2O_3 to occur unchecked. Figure 13.5 shows the microstructure of a 25Cr–20Ni creep resisting steel after such carburisation has occurred, together with the subsequent grain boundary oxidation. In this instance the carbide precipitation is so extensive that oxidation is pretty general. Reference to the Darken diagram, Figs 15.5 and 15.6, shows that the oxidation-plus-carburisation range of atmospheric mixtures is more extensive (a) at lower temperatures and (b) at higher chromium contents. The influence of temperature on the 'dusting' zone for iron-rich alloys is of some importance in hydrocarbon atmospheres, in view of the fact that wastage tends to occur under seemingly less severe conditions. Many chemical engineers have been surprised to discover that the problem may be cured by *raising* the temperature of their reaction mixture by 100°C. Where this is not possible, resort to higher nickel alloys such as 25Cr–35Ni is usually effective against this phenomenon.

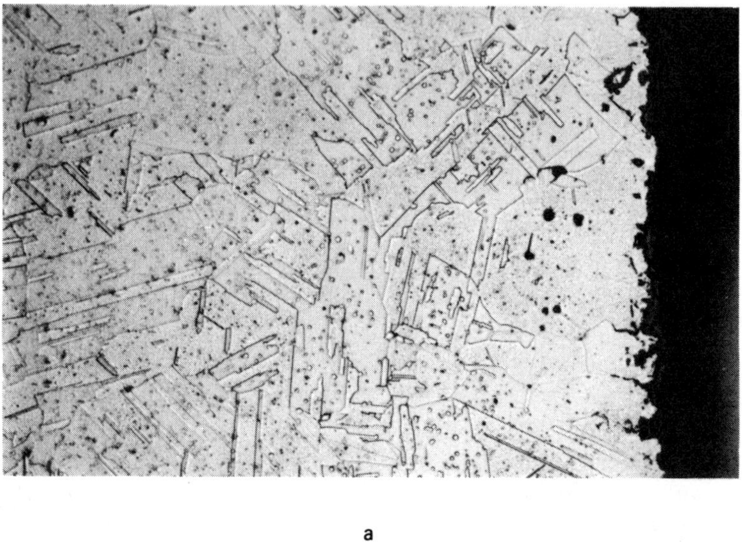

a

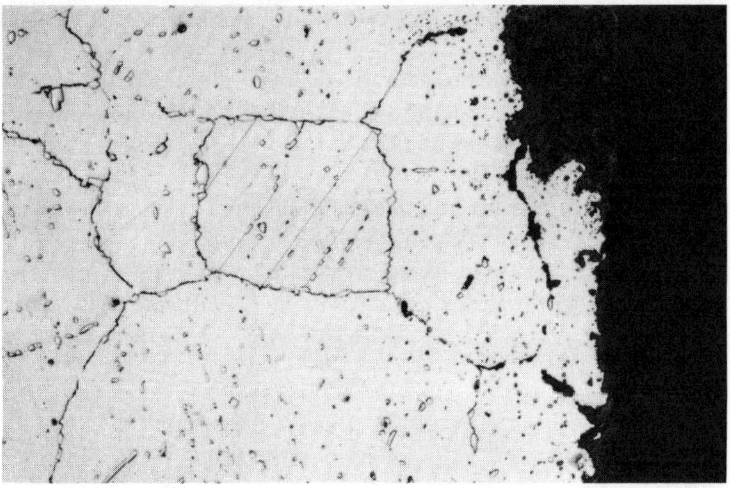

b

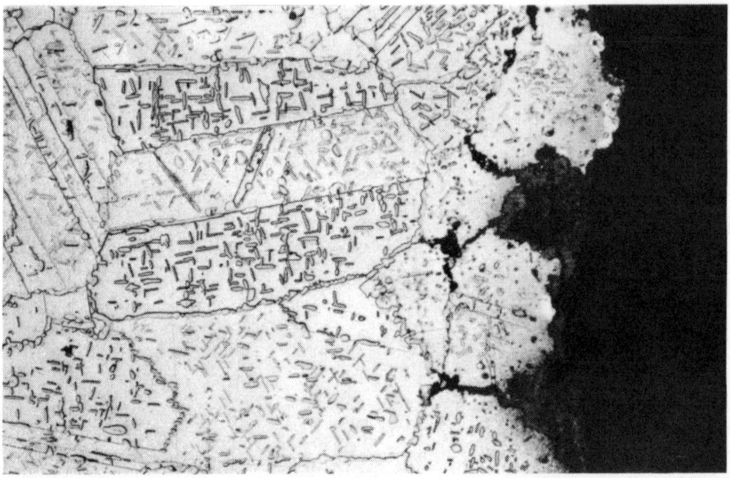

c

Fig. 13.5 Dusting behaviour observed in 25Cr–20Ni steel furnace roof hangers at 1500°C. The change in carbide distribution between relatively cool and hot areas is shown in (a) (b), whilst (c) shows extensive carbide precipitation within the grains. × 400

Black plague is the graphic description of the attack of nickel-base superalloys in the presence of sulphur-bearing combustion gases. The principal product is black NiS. The precise mechanism is not fully understood but it is known that reaction is catalysed by chloride (for example from entrained seawater spray or even originating from human sweat introduced by careless handling). A possible reaction is

$$\tfrac{1}{2}Cr_2O_3 + 2NaCl + \tfrac{3}{2}O_2(g) = CrO_2Cl_2(g) + Na_2O \qquad (13.21)$$

or perhaps various metal chloride eutectics, and this removal of protective chromium allows sulphur attack of the nickel. Table 13.7 shows how Nimonic alloys show marked acceleration at 750°C.

Table 13.7 Corrosion rates of iron, nickel, chromium and some alloys in air as a result of coating with sulphate-chloride pastes.
Rate in mm/yr, calculated from average weight loss in 6h test.
Proc. Internat. Conf. *Mechanism of Corrosion by Fuel Impurities* (Butterworths 1963).

	Wt. % NaCl in Na_2SO_4–NaCl mixture	650°C	750°C
Fe	10	24	400
Cr	10	0.5	8
Ni	10	1	17
Fe-25Cr-20Ni	10	0.7	12
Fe-18Cr-8Ni	0	0.8	0.4
	1	11	37
	10	8	13
Ni-20Cr (Nimonic)	0	0.3	1
	1	0.8	11
	10	3	1200 (!)

13.6 INTERNAL STRESS EFFECTS

As pointed out earlier, it is difficult to quantify the effects of volume change, film plasticity and film/substrate adhesion to give a realistic value for the effective stress level in the growing film. This is not only because data on elastic moduli and surface energies are scarce but also because the oxidation process requires lattice vacancy diffusion, and this in turn contributes towards diffusion creep and the relief of stress. The matter is further complicated by the physical disposition (geometry) of the component and by the complex nature of the scales formed (Note 13.6). To illustrate the difficulty it will be sufficient to perform a simplified calculation of the critical film thickness at which rupture might be expected, and to compare this calculated value with that observed or inferred in practice.

We assume that the film is isotropic and forms coherently with the metal substrate; that is, no interfacial gaps develop spontaneously from the oxidation process (section 14.2). If the Pilling-Bedworth ratio is r, then a length L of the metal surface is converted to a length $Lr^{\frac{1}{3}}$ of oxide (sulphide, etc.). However, because of the constraint offered by the other surfaces, this expansion cannot take place and the oxide retains the same original length L. The linear strain in the film is therefore

$$\epsilon = \frac{Lr^{\frac{1}{3}} - L}{Lr^{\frac{1}{3}}} = 1 - r^{-\frac{1}{3}} \tag{13.22}$$

which becomes $r^{-\frac{1}{3}} - 1$ for $r < 1$. By a similar argument the areal strain in a square surface is

$$\epsilon_a = 1 - r^{-\frac{2}{3}} \tag{13.23}$$

The elastic strain energy associated with this is $(E/2)\epsilon_a^2$ per unit volume and, for a film of thickness y, is $(E/2)\epsilon_a^2(L^2y)$. The compressive stresses in the film will cause it to develop a series of 45° cracks or rifts over the whole area and, for simplicity and because $y \ll L$, we may sum the total fracture surface area as approximately $2 \times (\sqrt{2}L)^2$ (the factor of 2 because of the two surfaces produced; if the cracking is very severe the $\sqrt{2}$ could perhaps increase by a further factor of 2 or so). If we equate the energies and assume brittle fracture, then

$$(E/2)\epsilon_a^2(L^2y) = 4L^2\gamma \tag{13.24}$$

where γ is the surface free energy of the film material, whence

$$y = 8\gamma/E(1 - r^{-\frac{2}{3}})^2 \tag{13.25}$$

This critical thickness has been calculated in Table 13.8, assuming that γ is some 1-2 J/m^2 and that the elasticity modulus E at high temperature lies between 1 and 30 GN/m^2, that is, γ/E lies between 0.02 and 2 nm. The table suggests that cracking should normally take place in films that are at most a few tens of nanometres thick. This conclusion agrees reasonably well with the limited data available: for example, the linear oxidation rate of magnesium is compatible with the presence of a 'pseudomorphic' layer of constant thickness ca. 20 nm thick. In copper at 500°C, however, quasi-linear oxidation results from periodic scale rupture every 4 μm. The fact that this value is some 100 times greater than the largest value calculated is a good indication that film plasticity (that is, creep) continuously relieves the stress at this temperature and/or that rupture involves complex microcracking.

Table 13.8 Approximate upper limit of film thickness to give cracking. Assuming $\gamma/E = 0.02$ to 2 nm where not known.

Pilling-Bedworth ratio r	Typical oxide	y nm
0.8	MgO	10–20
1.3	Al_2O_3	2–10
1.6	NiO, ZrO_2 Cu_2O	4–50
2.1	Fe_2O_3, Cr_2O_3, SiO_2	2–30
3.3	WO_3	1–30

A second source of stress in films and scales is that introduced by *thermal shock.* Because of differences in the expansion or contraction of scale and substrate, or between the different axial directions in crystallographically anisotropic materials, sharp changes in temperature can cause the scale to 'spall', that is, break up into loose fragments. The degree of thermal shock depends upon (a) the rate of change of ambient temperature, (b) the differences in expansion coefficient, and (c) the thermal conductivity of the materials. For a temperature difference ΔT between two adjacent layers having a difference of expansion coefficient $\Delta\alpha$, the strain will be $\Delta\alpha.\Delta T$ and the thermally-induced stress will be

$$\sigma = E\Delta\alpha\Delta T \quad . \tag{13.26}$$

Expansion coefficients of both metals and oxides vary with temperature. They are generally in the region of $1 - 2 \times 10^{-5}\ K^{-1}$ and $\Delta\alpha$ is rarely more than $2.10^{-6}\ K^{-1}$. There are exceptions such as Al/Al_2O_3 ($\Delta\alpha = \alpha_{metal} - \alpha_{oxide} \approx 1.4 \times 10^{-5}\ K^{-1}$) and Cu/Cu_2O ($\Delta\alpha \approx 1 \times 10^{-5}\ K^{-1}$) and there is a dramatic change in coefficient for SiO_2 at 300°C ($\Delta\alpha \approx 4 \times 10^{-5}\ K^{-1}$). But these data are for bulk oxides and, in any case, film plasticity again lessens the incidence of rupture.

Bibliography to Chapter 13

Evans (1960), *The Corrosion and Oxidation of Metals,* Arnold.

Hauffe (1965), *Oxidation of Metals,* Plenum Press.

Kubachewski and Hopkins (1962), *Oxidation of Metals and Alloys,* 2nd edn., Butterworth.

Kofstad (1966), *High Temperature Oxidation of Metals,* Wiley.

Tomashov (1966), *Theory of Corrosion and Protection of Metals,* MacMillan.

Notes to Chapter 13

13.1 Stoichiometry (stow-iki-*om*-etry) is the degree to which the chemical composition conforms to the simple chemical formula. Most oxides and sulphides have an excess of either anions or cations, the charge deficiency being compensated by variable cationic valency. For example, wüstite (FeO) is more properly represented by $Fe_{0.96}O$, since there are usually some 4% iron site vacancies plus some Fe^{3+} ions to compensate (but see the next chapter).

13.2 Hoar and Price, *Trans. Faraday Soc.*, 1938 **34** 867.

13.3 Tomashov (1966), *Theory of Corrosion and Protection of Metals,* Macmillan, who also refers to the possibility of concentration polarisation contributing to logarithmic growth.

13.4 Epitaxy is the conformity of the crystal lattice of a growth film to that of the metal substrate. The orientation tends to be rigidly fixed so that at least one lattice dimension is approximately coincident across the interface. If this conformity is exact, so that the film reproduces the structure of the underlying metal, it is said to be 'pseudomorphic'.

13.5 Zeno's paradox: If Achilles runs ten times faster than the tortoise but gives it a hundred metres start then, when he has run this 100 m, the tortoise is still ahead by 10 m; and when he has run this 10 m the lead is 1 m and so on, so Achilles never catches up. The paradox is of course resolved when we appreciate that the time intervals finally tend to zero.

13.6 But see Stringer, *Corros. Sci.* 1970 **10** 513; also the symposium proceedings *Stress Effects and the Oxidation of Metals* 1975, ed. Cathcart, A.I.M.E.

Chapter 14

How Films Conduct

14.1 VERY THIN FILMS

When a metal is first exposed to an oxidising atmosphere there develop small nuclei of the oxide (sulphide, etc) which subsequently spread laterally to cover the surface. The film lattice is normally **epitaxial** with that of the metal, that is, the two lattices have a fixed geometrical relationship. When the film is still only a few atom layers thick ($\leqslant$ 2 nm), the unfilled electron orbitals from the underlying metal extend through the film, so that there is a finite (but small) probability that 'metallic' electrons are to be found at the outermost interface, for example oxide/O_2. This **electron tunnelling** process behaves as a non-ohmic transport of charge across the film.

A characteristic feature of the early stages of oxidation, especially at low temperatures, is that the initial rate of oxidation is rapid but thereafter the rate follows a logarithmic law:

$$y = \ln(Kt) \quad \text{or} \quad A + B \ln t \tag{13.19}$$

or the inverse logarithmic law:

$$1/y = A + B \ln t \ . \tag{14.1}$$

Many theories have been proposed to account for this behaviour, often on the erroneous assumption that the surface film is compact and of uniform thickness. The most commonly accepted idea (Note 14.1) is that oxygen atoms adsorbed on the outer surface become ionised as a result of electron tunnelling and so develop an electric field across the film: this helps to transport ions through the small distance involved. Ionisation (that is, charge transfer overpotential) at the metal/film interface is assumed to be rate determining, but alternative models have been proposed in which interstitial transport (eqn (13.19)) or vacancy transport (eqn (14.1)) predominate. It is possible that 'space charge' effects take place, that is, electrical charges accumulate locally in the film in rather the same way that aquo-cations concentrate in the electrical double layer of electrodes in water. Such space charges are likely to alter with time because electrons become trapped at lattice defects. The logarithmic equations have also been derived on this assumption, and yet further models have invoked (a) differential conduction along grain boundaries and dislocations in the film or (b) localised heating as a result of exothermic reaction. The matter has not yet been resolved.

14.2 LATTICE DEFECTS

Within the ionic assembly that constitutes a solid oxide or sulphide, electrons are distributed between two broad bands of energy. Those that exist within the inner quantum shells (cores) of the ions or which contribute to the bonding of the lattice are termed **valence band electrons**: these are not free to conduct electricity through the lattice. There are, however, further electrons in higher energy states that are able to move relatively freely through the lattice. These **conduction band electrons** are very numerous in metals but relatively rare in ionic solids. Because of the periodic nature of the lattice electric field, there is an energy gap ΔU separating these two bands, Fig. 14.1 (Note 14.2). In order for such a semiconductor to conduct it is necessary to excite the electrons thermally so that some valence band electrons can enter the conduction band: this requires an energy input of

$$\Delta U = U_c - U_v \qquad (14.2)$$

The thermal energy required is typically of the order of a few hundred kJ/mol, Table 14.1. Conduction caused in this way is termed **intrinsic semiconduction**.

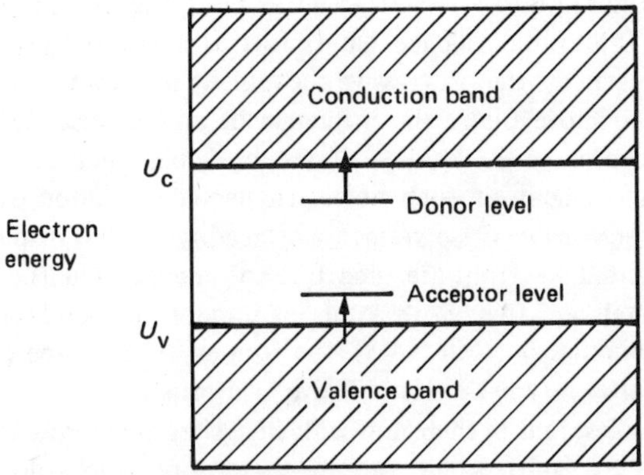

Fig. 14.1 Energy band diagram for a semiconductor. U_V corresponds to the Fermi level (sometimes represented by E_F).

Table 14.1 Band energy gaps in some ionic solids. Vijh, *J. Chem. Phys. Solids* 1969 **30** 1999 and Kofstad, *Nonstoichiometry in Binary Metal Oxides* (Wiley 1972).
ΔU is sometimes represented by the symbol E_g.
96 500 kJ/mol of electrons corresponds to 1 eV per electron.

Solid	ΔU kJ/mol
PbS	50
NbO_2	85
UO_2	ca. 180
CdO	200
V_2O_5	ca. 240
CdS	260
TiO_2	ca. 300
PbCl	370
Ta_2O_5	450
Al_2O_5	ca. 750
MgO	840
NaCl	850
ZrO_2	ca. 1000
CaF_2	1150

However, when lattice defects are plentiful, these modify the local electric fields so that intermediate 'impurity' energy levels exist. Much lower thermal excitation, ca. 5–50 kJ/mol, is then required. For example, a valence band electron can be raised into a vacant **acceptor level**, Fig. 14.1, leaving behind it a 'positive hole' (h) in the valence band. Just as a lattice vacancy can diffuse around in a crystal by the progressive movement of atoms or ions, so positive holes are free to move under the influence of an external electric field. The presence of acceptor levels thereby allows the semiconductor to conduct electrons via the movement of such holes. Higher energy impurity levels, **donor levels**, enable electrons in these states to be readily excited into the conduction band. These excited electrons are then free to move, just as the highest energy electrons in metals are free. Both kinds of impure semiconductors are termed **extrinsic semiconductors** (Note 14.3), the former being **p-type** ('p' for positive holes) and the latter **n-type** ('n' for negative electrons).

In what follows, ions in their normal lattice sites are represented by M and A. Charge symbols are omitted here because such 'normal' ions do not contribute to conduction processes (except by providing the continuum in which point defects can move). However, lattice defects directly influence the conductivity and so are here represented as carrying an appropriate effective charge. Thus, vacancies and interstitials are represented by $V_M(-)$, $V_A(+)$ and $M_i(+)$, $A_i(-)$. The sign of the effective charge is obvious for an ion displaced to an interstitial site: it is simply the 'normal' charge possessed by the ion. For vacancies, however, the sign is reversed from this normal value. When there is an anion vacancy, for example, some or all of the negative charge associated with it 'leaks' elsewhere in the lattice, leaving behind an effective excess positive charge with respect to the perfect crystal (Note 14.4). Hence V_A becomes $V_A(+)$. Similarly, a metal vacancy behaves effectively as a localised negative charge.

In stoichiometric compounds such as MgO and Al_2O_3, there are two types of defect that can occur. *Schottky defects* are paired anion and cation vacancies ($V_M + V_A$), whilst *Frenkel defects* are simply ions displaced into interstitial positions, leaving behind an appropriate vacancy.

$$M = M_i(+) + V_M(-) \quad \text{for a displaced cation}$$

and

$$A = A_i(-) + V_A(+) \quad \text{for a displaced anion} \qquad (14.3)$$

Frenkel defects predominate where M and A are appreciably different in size, Schottky-pair defects when M and A are of comparable size.

Nonstoichiometric compounds are of two main kinds:

(a) *Anion-deficient or metal-excess* (for example TiO_{2-x}, Fe_2O_{3-x}; $Zn_{1+y}O$): Here the predominant defects are V_A and/or M_i. The presence of either defect produces a free electron, so that the compound tends to be an n-type semiconductor. For example, in oxides,

$$O = V_O(+) + e + \tfrac{1}{2}O_2(g) \qquad (14.4)$$

from which it may be seen that such free electrons are generated in order to preserve electroneutrality. The vacancy can acquire additional effective charge from a neighbouring cation in the lattice:

$$M + V_O(+) = V_O(2+) + M(-) \qquad (14.5)$$

in which $M(-)$ represents a decrease in valency of the cation relative to its normal value, for example Fe(III) in Fe_2O_3 becomes Fe(II).

(b) *Metal-deficient or anion-excess* (for example $Fe_{1-y}O$, $Cu_{2-y}O$; UO_{2+x}): Here the predominant defects are V_M and/or A_i and these are associated with the formation of positive holes, in order to preserve electroneutrality:

$$\tfrac{1}{2}O_2(g) = V_M(-) + h + O \qquad (14.6)$$

In this particular equation it may be seen that metal-deficient oxides are normally p-type semiconductors. The cation vacancy can give rise to an *increase* in valency of a neighbouring cation, such as Fe(II) in FeO becoming Fe(III):

$$M + V_M(-) = V_M(2-) + M(+) \tag{14.7}$$

In both kinds of stoichiometric compound, dissolution of foreign cations ('doping') can strongly affect the point defect concentration. Thus, for a crystal MA in which M and A are divalent, addition of a trivalent cation P (that is, P(+) relative to the normal lattice value) increases the concentration of free electrons:

$$P_2A_3 = 2P(+) + 2e + 2A + A(g) \tag{14.8}$$

where for example $A \equiv \frac{1}{2}O_2$. Alternatively, in an anion-deficient crystal,

$$2V_A(+) + P_2A_3 = 2P(+) + 3A \tag{14.9}$$

which simultaneously increases the electron concentration, eqn (14.8), and lowers the population of anion vacancies, eqn (14.9). The converse is true for a metal-deficient crystal:

$$P_2A_3 + 2h = 2P(+) + 2A + A(g) \tag{14.10}$$

and

$$P_2A_3 \qquad = 2P(+) + V_M(2-) + 3A \tag{14.11}$$

which simultaneously results in a decrease in the positive hole concentration and an increase in the population of metal vacancies.

Just as each ionic species in aqueous solution possesses a characteristic standard chemical potential (Table 2.5), so too the various 'structure elements' (anions, cations, vacancies and other point defects) in a solid electrolyte possess standard chemical potentials. As with aqueous solutions, it is impossible to determine experimentally each of these in isolation. The difference is that there is no conventionally agreed reference standard such as $\mu^{\ominus}_{H+(aq)} = 0$ in the solid state. Instead, there are various undefined 'virtual' values of $\mu^{\ominus}_{ion}$ etc, which together combine to form the observed free energy of formation. For example,

$$M(s) + \tfrac{1}{2}O_2(g) = MO(s) = M^{2+}(\text{crystal}) + O^{2-}(\text{crystal}) \tag{14.12}$$

here represented simply by symbols M and O.

$$\Delta G^{\ominus} = \mu^{\ominus}_M + \mu^{\ominus}_O - (\mu^{\ominus}_{M(s)} + \tfrac{1}{2}\mu^{\ominus}_{O2}) \tag{14.13}$$

$$= -RT \ln K = RT \ln \left(\frac{a_{M(s)} \cdot (p_{O_2}/p^{\ominus})^{\frac{1}{2}}}{a_M \cdot a_O} \right) \tag{14.14}$$

The virtual potentials $\mu_M^{\ominus}$, $\mu_O^{\ominus}$ do not in fact need to be separated as it is *changes* in free energy, resulting from changes in activity, that are important in describing behaviour.

We may therefore expect that vacancies exist at some characteristic equilibrium concentration at each temperature. For example, the Frenkel defect, eqn (14.3), is characterised by

$$\Delta G_F^{\ominus} = \mu_{Mi}^{\ominus} + \mu_{VM}^{\ominus} - \mu_M^{\ominus}$$

$$= -RT \ln(a_{Mi} \cdot a_{VM}/a_M) \tag{14.15}$$

In the pure crystal we may arbitrarily write $a_M = 1$ (just as is done for electrons in metals: $\mu_e^{\ominus} = 0$, p. 56), so that, for low defect considerations

$$a_{Mi} \cdot a_{VM} = \exp(-\Delta G_F^{\ominus}/RT) \tag{14.16}$$

Likewise, reactions (14.4) (14.6) for oxides are characterised by

$$a_{VO} \cdot a_e \cdot (p_{O_2}/p^{\ominus})^{\frac{1}{2}} = \exp(-\Delta G_{14.4}^{\ominus}/RT) \quad (a_O \approx 1) \tag{14.17}$$

$$a_{VM} \cdot a_h \cdot (p_{O_2}/p^{\ominus})^{-\frac{1}{2}} = \exp(-\Delta G_{14.6}^{\ominus}/RT) \quad (a_O \approx 1) \; . \tag{14.18}$$

We may further note that, since electroneutrality requires that the numbers of excess negative and positive charges balance,

$$n_e = n_{VO} \text{ (or, neglecting activity coefficients, } a_e \approx a_{VO})$$

$$n_h = n_{VM} \text{ (or } a_h \approx a_{VM}) \qquad \text{(Both 14.19)}$$

whence

$$\boxed{a_e \propto (p_{O_2}/p^{\ominus})^{-\frac{1}{4}}} \tag{14.20}$$

$$\boxed{a_h \propto (p_{O_2}/p^{\ominus})^{\frac{1}{4}}} \tag{14.21}$$

so that the electron and hole concentrations depend on some fractional power of the oxygen partial pressure. Where there are multiple-charged vacancies present it may readily be shown that the $\frac{1}{4}$th-power relationship becomes $\frac{1}{6}$th-power or less. The correspondence between the charge carriers (e, h) and the ion vacancies (V_O, V_M) given in eqn (14.19) shows that there is a similar dependence of lattice vacancy concentration upon oxygen partial pressure. For sulphides, of course, p_{O2} is replaced by p_{S2}.

Finally, because ionic conduction through the surface film is predominantly via lattice vacancies such as V_O, V_M, it follows that ionic vacancies need to be generated at the growth interface P in Fig. 13.2. Where $t_O \ll t_M$ and P lies at the oxide/O_2 interface, this means that V_M vacancies are generated at the outer surface and later arrive at the inner metal/oxide interface. If not immediately annihilated by the passage of cations into the oxide, these vacancies accumulate and aggregate to form a gap between metal and oxide. The film loses adhesion and, if insufficiently plastic, is more readily broken by internal stresses (section 13.6) and may thereby provoke a catastrophic increase in oxidation rate. It is this process of vacancy aggregation that is thought to be responsible for the quasi-linear oxidation of copper, Fig. 13.4c, and the 'breakaway' oxidation of Fe-Cr alloys.

14.3 RATES OF OXIDATION

The rate of oxidation by the so-called Wagner mechanism of mixed ionic-electronic film conduction, section 13.2, is governed by a parabolic rate constant

$$y^2 = k_p t \tag{13.14}$$

where, from eqn (13.13) (13.18)

$$k_p = 2y(\mathrm{d}y/\mathrm{d}t) = -\frac{2\Delta G M \kappa \; t_e \,(t_M + t_O)}{(nF)^2 \, \rho} \tag{14.22}$$

Values of k_p for five oxides are listed in Table 14.2 for various temperatures and oxygen partial pressures.

Obviously, from eqn (2.40) applied to a reaction $M + \frac{1}{2}O_2 = MO$,

$$\Delta G = \Delta G^{\ominus} + RT \ln \frac{a_{MO}}{a_M (p_{O2}/p^{\ominus})^{\frac{1}{2}}}$$

$$= \Delta G^{\ominus} - (RT/2) \ln (p_{O2}/p^{\ominus}) \tag{14.23}$$

so that we should expect that k_p will depend on oxygen partial pressure through its effect on the driving force ΔG. We now see from the previous section that the conductivity κ and the various transport numbers t_i will also be affected by the oxygen pressure, via eqn (14.20) (14.21), and by the degree of stoichiometry. Small 'doping' impurities are likely to have a strong influence, eqn (14.8)-(14.11), and such is found to be the case.

Table 14.2 Some parabolic rate constants (k_p) for oxide formation.
Units are 10^{-9} $(g/cm^2)^2/s$. The numbers in parentheses are the corrosion rate in mm/yr, obtained by multiplying $(k_p)^{\frac{1}{2}}$ by ca. 10^4, assuming that short-term parabolic rate data may be extended from a few hours to 8800 h. In practice, long-term rates are often more nearly linear. The data for chromium are very limited and it is doubtful whether they fit the parabolic equation.

	°C			
		10^{-25} atm		10^{-20} atm oxygen
Chromium	1000	530(7.3)		1500(12)
	900	280(5.3)		1000(10)
	800	150(3.9)		330(5.7)
	700	30(1.7)		40(2.0)
		10^{-3} atm		10^{-1} atm oxygen
Copper	1000	600(7.7)		1800(13)
		0.2 atm (air)		
Iron	1100	1000(10)		
	900	140(4)		
	700	4(0.6)		
		10^{-14} atm		10^{-10} atm oxygen
Manganese	1200	6(0.8)		30(1.7)
	1100	3.5(0.6)		10(1.0)
	1000	1.7(0.4)		7.5(0.9)
	900	0.6(0.2)		1(0.3)
		10^{-4} atm	10^{-2} atm	1 atm oxygen
Nickel	1400	0.6(0.2)	3(0.6)	8(0.9)
	1200	0.3(0.2)	0.7(0.3)	1(0.3)
	1000	0.04(0.1)	0.07(0.1)	0.1(0.1)

Figure 14.2 shows broadly how the transport numbers depend on p_{O2}. The ionic transport contribution varies with temperature and the degree of lattice perfection but is otherwise largely independent of pressure. In contrast, electron conduction, whether by holes in the valence band or by free electrons in the conduction band, varies as some fractional power of p_{O2}, eqn (14.20) (14.21): this conduction passes through a minimum at a pressure p_{min}, hole conduction predominating at high pressures and free electron conduction at low. This minimum usually occurs at sub-atmospheric pressures, in the region of 10^{-14} atm (ZrO_2, ThO_2, Eu_2O_3) to 10^{-3} atm (MgO, CaO, Cu_2O, TiO_2). Other oxides of interest are NiO (ca. 10^{-8} atm) and Al_2O_3 (10^{-5} atm). As the temperature is raised there is usually a small shift in p_{min}, but a more significant change is the increased electronic conductivity, whether by e or h, relative to vacancy or interstitial diffusion. Thus, for ZrO_2–15%CaO at 1000°C, conduction is almost exclusively by oxygen anions ($t_O = 1$), with t_{Zr} and t_h both ca. 10^{-5}, for oxygen partial pressures above 10^{-10} atm; whereas, at 10^{-30} atm, electronic conduction predominates ($t_e > t_O$). Similarly, ThO_2–15%Y_2O_3 at 1000°C displays $t_h = 0.3$, $t_O = 0.7$ at 1 atm partial pressure but $t_O = 1$ at 10^{-5} atm. In general, however, it is fair to assume that electronic conduction (by e or h) is the easiest process in high-temperature oxidation or sulphidation, with anion or cation movement as the rate determining process.

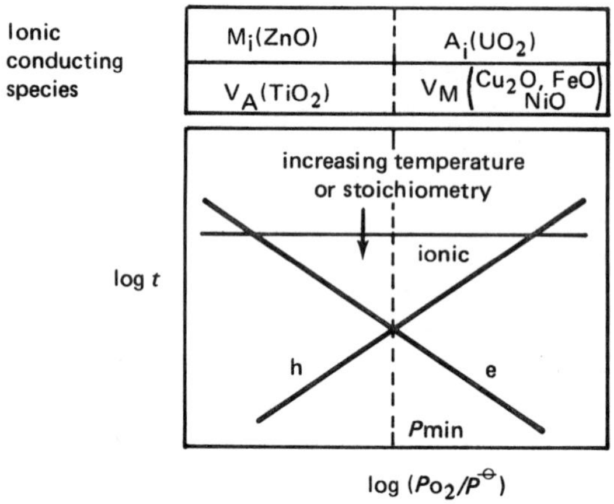

Fig. 14.2 Relative transport numbers in doped stoichiometric oxides. Note that $\Sigma t = 1$. It is assumed that intrinsic semiconduction is small.

Small alloying additions to a metal result in contamination of the oxidation product. This doping alters the stoichiometry and, with it, the population of electrons and holes. Thus, in p-type compounds, ionic conductivity (and hence oxidation rate) should increase with increasing addition of higher-valency cations and decrease with lower-valency cations; whilst metals giving rise to n-type compounds should display converse behaviour, lower oxidation rates resulting from doping with higher-valency cations and higher oxidation rates if doped with lower-valency cations. Some results are given in Table 14.3, where it may be seen that, although these expectations are generally fulfilled, there are some interesting anomalies. Thus, even two atomic percent addition of aluminium to copper or iron reduces the oxidation rate instead of increasing it and small chromium additions to iron have little effect. This is because these two alloying elements lead to the preferential formation of the stable stoichiometric oxides Al_2O_3 or Cr_2O_3 rather than solid solutions in the oxide of the substrate metal (section 15.1).

Table 14.3 Influence of small alloying additions on the parabolic rate constant k_p. Air or oxygen at 1 atm pressure.

(a) p-type oxides		
Copper (I, II) at 600°C		
2 at .%	Ag (I)	No effect
	Ni (II)	No effect
	Be (II)	× 0.01
	Mg (II)	× 0.01
2 at .%	Cr (III)	× 2
	Al (III)	× 0.01 (!)
Nickel (II) at 1000°C		
2 at .%	Li (I)	× 0.2
2 at .%	Cu (II)	Little effect
2 at .%	Cr (III)	× 8
	Mo (IV?)	× 1.5
(b) n-type oxide		
Zinc (II) at 400°C		
0.4 at .%	Li (I)	$\times 2.10^4$
1 at .%	Al (III)	× 0.01
Iron (II, III) at 900°C		
2 at .%	Ni (II)	No effect
	Cr (III)	No effect
	Al (III)	× 0.4 (!)
2 at .%	Si (IV)	No effect

The reader should also be aware that oxidation products are unlikely to possess uniform composition throughout their thickness. This parallels the behaviour of passive films at low temperatures, which are also normally characterised by varying oxygen content, for example the film on iron varies from approximately Fe_3O_4 at the metal/film interface to Fe_2O_3 at the outer oxygen-absorbed interface, p. 109. The reason for this is that the equilibrium chemical potential of oxygen must change from that associated with metal/oxide equilibrium at the innermost interface to the ambient (that is, surrounding) value at the outermost interface, Fig. 14.3. It is of course this chemical potential gradient that maintains the process of mass transport through the film. When there are several oxides stable at different oxygen partial pressures, the scale developed is complex. Thus, the oxidation of iron above about 600°C gives rise to a three-layer scale, Fig. 14.3, consisting of FeO (wüstite), Fe_3O_4 (magnetite) and Fe_2O_3. At each interface the equilibrium oxygen potential may be calculated: for example at 1000°C,

At A: $Fe + \frac{1}{2}O_2(g) = FeO$

$$\mu_O = \tfrac{1}{2}\mu_{O2} = \mu^{\ominus}_{FeO} = -171 \text{ kJ/mol} \qquad (14.24)$$

At B: $3FeO + \frac{1}{2}O_2(g) = Fe_3O_4$

$$\mu_O = \tfrac{1}{2}\mu_{O2} = \mu^{\ominus}_{Fe3O4} - 3\mu^{\ominus}_{FeO} = -166 \text{ kJ/mol} \qquad (14.25)$$

At C: $2Fe_3O_4 + \frac{1}{2}O_2(g) = 3Fe_2O_3$

$$\mu_O = \tfrac{1}{2}\mu_{O2} = 3\mu^{\ominus}_{Fe2O3} - 2\mu^{\ominus}_{Fe3O4} = -72 \text{ kJ/mol} \qquad (14.26)$$

At D: $\mu_O = \frac{1}{2}\mu_{O2} = \text{zero if } p_{O2} = 1 \text{ atm}$. (14.27)

The corresponding oxygen partial pressures are approximately 9.10^{-15}, 2.10^{-14} and 10^{-6} atm at A, B and C respectively. Copper behaves similarly, producing a duplex Cu_2O/CuO scale. As will be seen in the next chapter, the presence of an oxygen potential gradient in the metal substrate and in the oxide itself can lead to *internal oxidation.*

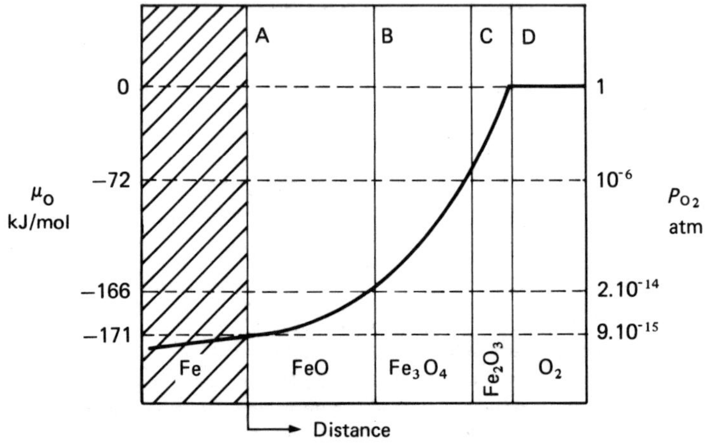

Fig. 14.3 Oxygen potential gradient through the complex scale on iron at 1000° C.

14.4 SOLID ELECTROLYTE CELLS

In section 13.1 it was explained how the free energy change accompanying the oxidation process gives rise to a driving emf

$$\mathcal{E} = -\Delta G/nF \tag{13.3}$$

whilst, from the preceding section, it is clear that this free energy change may also be expressed in terms of the change in the chemical potential of oxygen across the oxidation product. Thus, for a film consisting only of FeO, the ΔG in eqn (13.3) is $G^{\bullet}_{FeO} = \mu^{\ominus}_{FeO}$ when the oxygen partial pressure is 1 atm. The chemical potentials of oxygen at the two interfaces are $\mu^{\ominus}_{FeO}$ at the inner interface, eqn (14.24), and zero at the outer interface, eqn (14.27), so that the chemical potential difference is

$$\Delta G = \mu_O \begin{pmatrix} \text{metal/oxide} \\ \text{interface} \end{pmatrix} - \mu_O \begin{pmatrix} \text{oxide/gas} \\ \text{interface} \end{pmatrix}$$

$$= (RT/2)\ln(p_1/p_2) \tag{14.28}$$

where $p_1 = p_{O2}$ at M/MO and $p_2 = p_{O2}$ at MO/O_2. Combining eqn (13.3) (14.28) and recognising that n corresponds to the transport of divalent oxygen ions,

$$\mathcal{E} = (RT/4F)\ln(p_2/p_1) \tag{14.29}$$

This is a special example of a *concentration cell.* Its practical application is in the measurement of oxygen partial pressure in complex gas mixtures (for example combustion gases and flue gases) and of oxygen activity in liquid metals. The construction of such a cell presents some difficulty, most especially in the choice and design of the solid electrolyte, Fig. 14.4. One particular problem, which is common to the design of solid-electrolyte fuel cells, is that the electrolyte must conduct oxygen anions freely in order that there may exist an oxygen chemical potential gradient across it. Intuitively we can see that, where such conduction is not possible (that is, $t_O = 0$), no emf can be developed because the two oxygen environments are insulated from one another. In fact, it is possible to show (Note 14.5) that

$$\mathcal{E} = t_O \times (RT/4F)\ln(p_2/p_1) \ . \tag{14.30}$$

Of the few successful electrolytes, ZrO_2-CaO and ThO_2-Y_2O_3 are those most commonly employed (Note 14.6). These, as we have seen from Fig. 14.2, have $t_O \ll 1$ when the temperature becomes too high or when the oxygen partial pressure is remote from p_{min}. They are therefore successful only at relatively low temperatures and over a limited range of partial pressures. Nevertheless, they have found limited application in the monitoring of oxygen content during the refining of steel.

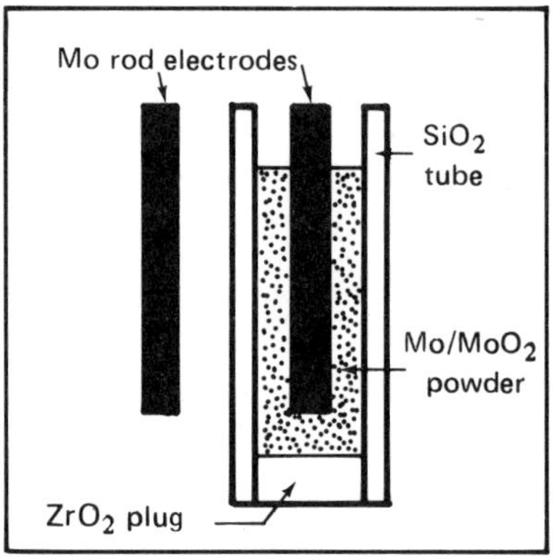

Equilibrium p_{O_2} for $Mo/MoO_2 = 8.10^{-10}$ atm at 1400°C and 3.10^{-7} atm at 1700°C.
The cell provides a direct analysis of oxygen in a BOS converter.

Fig. 14.4 Design of a typical solid-electrolyte cell for the measurement of oxygen potential. Chastant *et al., Europ. Coal Steel Comm. Report* Eur 5091 (1973). See also Fischer *et al., Arch. Eisenhüttenw.* 1976 **47** 525.

Bibliography to Chapter 14

Kofstad (1966), *High Temperature Oxidation of Metals.* Wiley.
Hauffe (1965), *Oxidation of Metals,* Plenum Press.
Kubachewski and Hopkins (1962), *Oxidation of Metals and Alloys,* Butterworth.

Notes to Chapter 14

14.1 Cabrera and Mott, *Rept. Progr. Physics* 1948 **12** 163.

14.2 The chemical potential of electrons in the lattice must be the same everywhere at equilibrium. The *standard* chemical potential of conduction electrons is usually considered to be U_c.

14.3 Extrinsic conduction is associated with a rapid change in vacancy concentration with increased addition of foreign cations. That is, the introduction of such cations ('dopants') is especially potent in establishing donor and acceptor levels.

14.4 This charge is the unbalanced positive charges of the lattice cations surrounding the vacancy. Of course, removed of an A *atom* may leave the associated electrons trapped at the vacancy, in which case V_A has no effective charge.

14.5 Wagner, *Z. physik. Chem. (B)* 1933 **21** 25 and 1936 **32** 447.

14.6 Pure zirconia undergoes a transition from a monoclinic low-temperature form to a tetragonal form at around 1100°C. The accompanying volume change means that ZrO_2 has poor resistance to thermal shock. Addition of between 10 and 20 at.% lime stabilises a higher temperature cubic form right down to room temperature. Besides being resistant to thermal shock, the ZrO_2-CaO refractory possesses a high concentration of oxygen anion vacancies. A similar situation holds for the yttria-stabilised ThO_2 refractory.

Chapter 15

Stopping High Temperature Corrosion

15.1 ALLOYING

In Table 14.3 we saw how even quite small alloying additions of aluminium and chromium led to a reduction in the rate of oxidation where oxide-conduction theories would have predicted an increase. In practice, therefore, it is necessary to take account of the fact that not all oxides are mutually soluble and, indeed, that *selective oxidation* of the most reactive constituent may occur. Such selective attack, which parallels the preferential dissolution of bimetallic couples in aqueous corrosion (section 8.4), is most frequent where there is a wide disparity in oxide stabilities. This will depend, of course, not only on the difference in standard free energies of formation (Figs 2.2 and 2.3) but upon the activities of the constituents (alloying content and oxygen partial pressure).

Consider an alloy N–B, in which B is a base alloying addition to a relatively noble metal N: for simplicity we shall assume that the appropriate oxides are NO and BO. For the oxide BO,

$$\begin{aligned}\Delta G_{BO} &= \mu_{BO} - \mu_B - \tfrac{1}{2}\mu_{O_2}\\ &= \mu^{\ominus}_{BO} - \{\mu^{\ominus}_B + RT\ln a_B + \tfrac{1}{2}\mu^{\ominus}_{O_2} + (RT/2)\ln(p_{O_2}/p^{\ominus})\}\\ &\approx G^{\bullet}_{BO} - RT\ln a_B - (RT/2)\ln(p_{O_2}/p^{\ominus}) \qquad (15.1)\end{aligned}$$

assuming that BO is insoluble in NO (so that $a_{BO} = 1$) and neglecting the entropy correction for oxygen ($\mu^{\ominus}_{O_2}$ at $T°K = \Delta H^{\ominus}_{O_2} - T\Delta S^{\ominus}_{O_2} = -0.205\,(T-298)$ kJ/mol if $\Delta C_p = 0$). That is, when the concentration of B is low ($a_B = x_B$ is small), ΔG_{BO} is unlikely to be as negative as ΔG_{NO} and only the oxide NO forms initially. As oxidation proceeds, the unreacted B accumulates at the interface until ΔG_{BO} is comparable with or less than ΔG_{NO}, at which point BO nucleates:

$$\Delta G_{BO} = \Delta G_{NO}$$

when

$$G^{\bullet}_{NO} - G^{\bullet}_{BO} = RT\ln(a_N/a_B) = RT\ln(x_N/x_B) \qquad (15.2)$$

This means that most alloys of this kind display a *subscale* of the more reactive solute, which separates the substrate and an outer scale of the more noble oxide or sulphide, Fig. 15.1(a). Typical examples are Cu-Be, Cu-Al, Fe-Cr, Fe-Al and Ni-Cr alloys. However, the subscale only forms where the alloying element is at a relatively low concentration. At higher concentrations, for which x_B exceeds the critical value in eqn (15.2), say approx. 0.2, the more stable oxide forms first and it is N that accumulates at the interface. The oxide film very often consists only of BO in such circumstances. If the BO oxide is permeable or breaks up as a result of internal stresses (the phenomenon known as 'breakaway' oxidation), then NO grows outside it, Fig. 15.1(b), and the BO layer may finally finish submerged in the oxide NO. The diffusion of B up to the interface in Fig. 15.1(b) may be represented as a concentration overpotential effect, as in eqn (13.7), with part of the driving force for B oxidation being dissipated in the diffusion process.

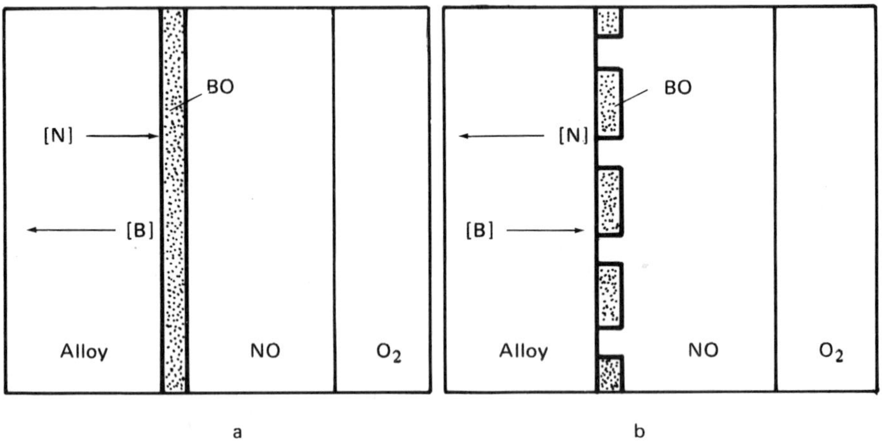

Fig. 15.1 Selective oxidation when $t_{cation} \sim 1$. (a) Low a_B: oxide NO forms before BO; (b) Moderate a_B: BO forms before NO. The BO layer may end up submerged in the main oxide NO.

This simple picture is modified by (a) any mutual solubility of NO and BO, (b) whether anions or cations are the principal ionically conducting species and (c) the diffusion rates of N and B in the alloy substrate. Mutual solubility is observed, for example, between NiO (or FeO) and Cr_2O_3, with the formation of Ni-Cr or Fe-Cr *spinel* of composition MCr_2O_4. Oxidation of Ni-Cr and Fe-Cr alloys therefore gives rise to a spinel layer through which Fe^{3+} transport ultimately leads to the growth of an outer film of Fe_2O_3. The mode of ionic conduction is important in determining the mechanical integrity of the oxidation product. If $t_M > t_O$, as in NiO and Fe_3O_4, the outward movement of cations is accomplished by the inward movement of lattice vacancies and, because these aggregate to form pores at the metal/oxide interface, the oxide itself develops porosity and the rate of oxidation slows down (Note 15.1). The presence of such pores can ultimately lead to mechanical rupture of the scale, section 14.2.

The diffusion rates of B and N in the alloy substrate *relative to that of oxygen* influence the morphology of the growing oxides. Thus, if $D_O > D_B$, the alloying constituent oxidises within the metal itself, Fig. 15.2. This phenomenon of *internal oxidation* is observed in many alloy systems, including copper- and nickel-base alloys containing chromium, aluminium, or silicon. Sometimes there is no external scale formed and, in these circumstances, the depth of the internally oxidised zone after time t is (Note 15.2)

$$\delta_{io} = (x a_O^{surface} / y a_B^{bulk})^{\frac{1}{2}} (2D_O t)^{\frac{1}{2}} \qquad (15.3)$$

for an oxide B_xO_y. The number of oxide particles formed depends on D_O/D_B and the cube of $a_O^{surface}$. Where there is also an external scale NO, the internally oxidised particles become incorporated into the scale as islands of B_xO_y in NO. In Ni-Cr alloys, for example, there develops an internally-oxidised region (Cr_2O_3 particles) and an outer scale of NiO. As oxidation proceeds further, the internally-oxidised zone moves inwards and the earlier-formed Cr_2O_3 particles become embedded in the inward-moving NiO scale, finally transforming to $NiCr_2O_4$ spinel particles.

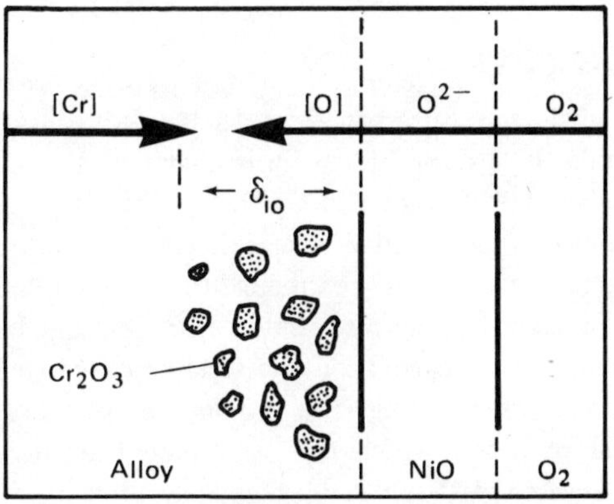

Fig. 15.2 Internal oxidation of Ni-Cr. Cr_2O_3 islands are nucleated wherever the 'solubility product' $a_{Cr}^2 . a_O^3 \geq 1/K$ for the reaction: 2 Cr(Ni) + 3 O(Ni) = Cr_2O_3(s)

Although complex scales and patterns may develop, the obvious and most important result of alloying is a reduction of the rate of oxidation of the parent metal. For practical purposes this may be expressed in terms of the **scaling temperature,** defined as that temperature below which the oxidation rate in air is less than about 0.5 mm/yr. For iron-base alloys, for example, addition of chromium progressively raises the scaling temperature from about 500°C to over 1000°C, Fig. 15.3. Further addition of nickel, besides moderating the creep properties of steels, further raises the scaling temperature until, around the 25%Cr-20%Ni composition, it reaches over 1200°C.

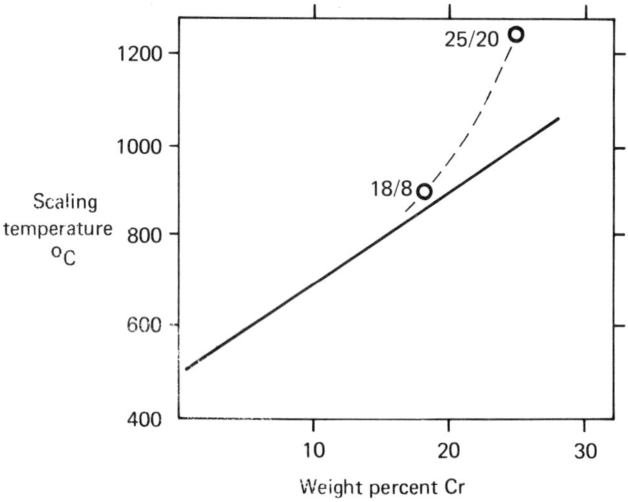

Fig. 15.3 Scaling temperature for Fe-Cr alloys in air.

15.2 ATMOSPHERE CONTROL

In a number of high-temperature processes, such as hot rolling, forging and heat treatment of metals, it is desirable to limit chemical attack, both to prevent uncontrolled dimensional changes and to ensure that alloying constituents are not selectively removed. Protective atmospheres accomplish this. Thus, for example, in *bright annealing,* heat treatment furnaces are filled with an inert gas mixture such as 'cracked' ammonia, that is nitrogen and hydrogen, enabling prolonged treatments to be carried out on steel components without the need for subsequent pickling or grinding. The problem is not simply that of lowering the oxygen partial pressure, which can be effected readily enough by using mixtures of H_2/H_2O or CO/CO_2:

$$H_2O(g) = H_2(g) + \tfrac{1}{2}O_2(g);\ \Delta G_1^\ominus$$

$$(p_{O_2}/p^\ominus)^{\frac{1}{2}} = K_1(p_{H_2O}/p_{H_2}) = (p_{H_2O}/p_{H_2})\exp(-\Delta G_1^\ominus/RT) \quad (15.4)$$

$$CO_2(g) = CO(g) + \tfrac{1}{2}O_2(g);\ \Delta G_2^\ominus$$

$$(p_{O_2}/p^\ominus)^{\frac{1}{2}} = K_2(p_{CO_2}/p_{CO}) = (p_{CO_2}/p_{CO})\exp(-\Delta G_2^\ominus/RT)\ . \quad (15.5)$$

What also needs to be prevented is *carburisation or decarburisation* of the surface layers of steels in view of the adverse changes in mechanical properties that would otherwise result (Note 15.3). The hydrogen in the first mixture can react with carbon dissolved in the steel:

$$2H_2(g) + C(Fe) = CH_4(g);\ \Delta G_3^{\ominus}$$

$$a_C = (1/K_3)\,(p^{\ominus}.\,p_{CH4}/p_{H2}^2) = (p^{\ominus}.\,p_{CH4}/p_{H2}^2)\exp(\Delta G_3^{\ominus}/RT) \quad (15.6)$$

so that decarburisation occurs if a_C is less than that required to stabilise, for example, Fe_3C in steel

$$3Fe(s) + C(Fe) = Fe_3C(s);\ \Delta G_4^{\ominus}$$

$$a_C = 1/K_4 = \exp(\Delta G_4^{\ominus}/RT) \text{ since } a_{Fe} = a_{Fe3C} = 1 \quad . \quad (15.7)$$

Similarly, an imbalance in the CO/CO_2 equilibrium can introduce carbon into the steel

$$2CO(g) = C(Fe) + CO_2(g);\ \Delta G_5^{\ominus}$$

$$a_C = K_5(p_{CO}^2/p^{\ominus}.\,p_{CO2}) = (p_{CO}^2/p^{\ominus}.\,p_{CO2})\exp(-\Delta G_5^{\ominus}/RT) \quad . \quad (15.8)$$

The depth of the carburised or decarburised layer is obviously a function of a_C, the carbon diffusivity D_C and time elapsed. For Fe_3C it is approximately

$$\delta_c = (3a_C^{\text{surface}})^{\frac{1}{2}}\,(2D_C t)^{\frac{1}{2}} \quad (15.9)$$

which closely parallels eqn (15.2) for internal oxidation (Note 15.4).

In order to predict the effect of any particular combination of gases, we may refer to the *Darken diagram*, Fig. 15.4. Like the Pourbaix diagram (Chapter 9), this is an isothermal diagram in which composition variables constitute the two axes, and domains of behaviour are separated by lines calculated on the basis of thermodynamic equilibria. In the Darken diagram, the gas composition is expressed as atom fractions of oxygen and carbon: as with the Pourbaix diagram, more highly oxidising conditions are represented by higher values of the ordinate. The atom fractions may be calculated as follows: For a gas mixture consisting of

v_{H2O} volume percent $H_2O(g)$
v_{H2} volume percent $H_2(g)$
v_{O2} volume percent $O_2(g)$
v_{CO} volume percent $CO(g)$
v_{CO2} volume percent $CO_2(g)$
and v_{CH4} volume percent $CH_4(g)$

at room temperature, the proportionate numbers of oxygen, carbon and hydrogen atoms are

$$n_O = v_{H2O} + 2v_{O2} + v_{CO} + 2v_{CO2} \text{ mol oxygen atoms}$$

$$n_C = v_{CO} + v_{CO2} + v_{CH4} \qquad \text{mol carbon atoms} \qquad (15.10)$$

$$n_H = 2v_{H2O} + 2v_{H2} + 4v_{CH4} \qquad \text{mol hydrogen atoms}$$

for which the atom fractions are

$$x_O = n_O/\Sigma n \quad \text{and} \quad x_C = n_C/\Sigma n \quad . \qquad (15.11)$$

These fractions will remain the same at all temperatures, irrespective of changes in the equilibria, eqn (15.4)-(15.8), that may occur and it is therefore possible to characterise a gas mixture by its x_O, x_C values calculated from the room temperature composition (Note 15.5). The lines in the diagram are those calculated for the equilibria

$$xM + \frac{y}{2}O_2(g) = M_xO_y; \; \Delta G_6^\ominus = yRT \ln a_O \qquad (15.12)$$

$$aM + bC = M_aC_b; \; \Delta G_7^\ominus = bRT \ln a_C \qquad (15.13)$$

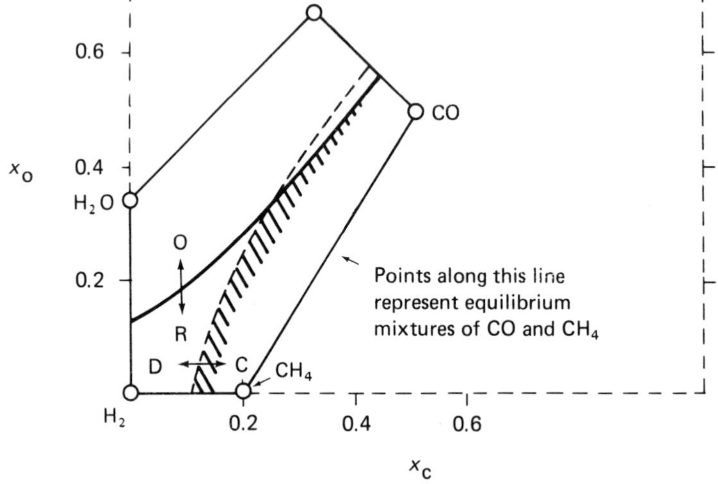

Fig. 15.4 Darken diagram for pure iron at 650°C. O = oxidising, R = reducing, D = decarburising and C = carburising. The shaded region represents those gas compositions that are suitable for bright annealing of carbon steels.

and are essentially plots of x_O (= a_O/γ_O), x_C (= a_C/γ_C) assuming that activity coefficients are unity. As indicated in the diagram, these therefore separate the domains corresponding to oxidation/reduction and carburisation/decarburisation. Bright annealing is carried out under conditions that are simultaneously reducing (region R) and very mildly carburising (region C, close to the equilibrium line) on the principle that slight carburisation may be beneficial and is certainly to be preferred to decarburisation. As may be seen from Fig. 15.5, the permissible range of bright annealing compositions varies with temperature. Because alloying elements such as chromium have different oxide and carbide stabilities from those of iron, alloy steels place further limitations on gas composition, Fig. 15.6.

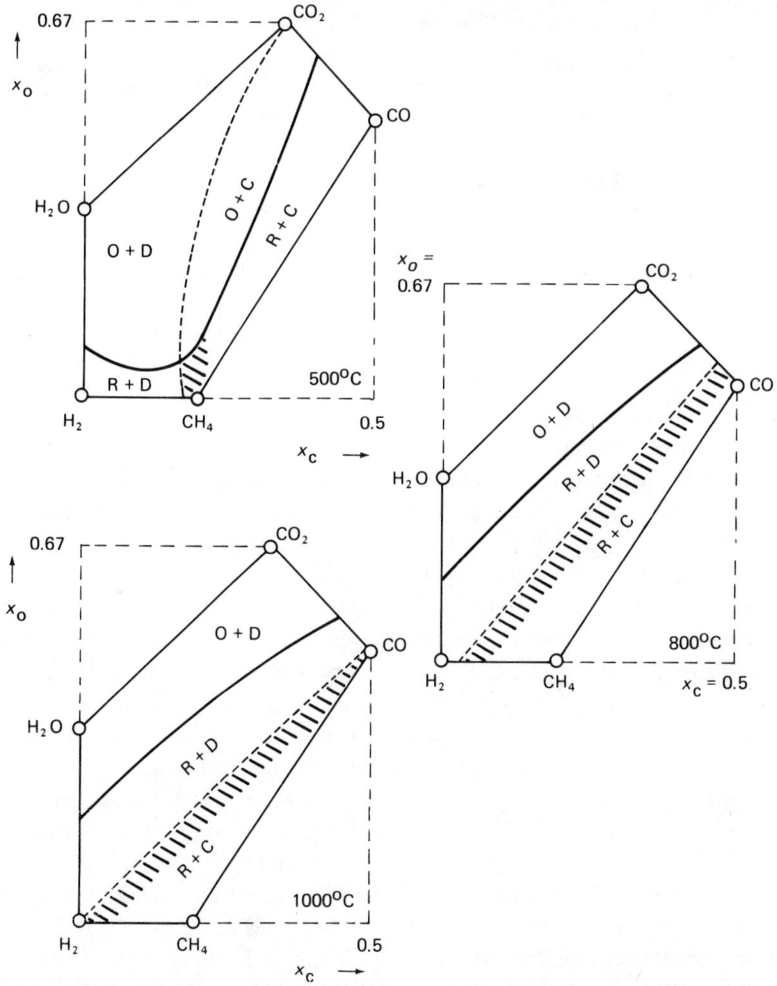

Fig. 15.5 Influence of temperature on the Darken diagram for pure iron in gas mixtures at 1 atm total pressure. The bright annealing region is again shaded.

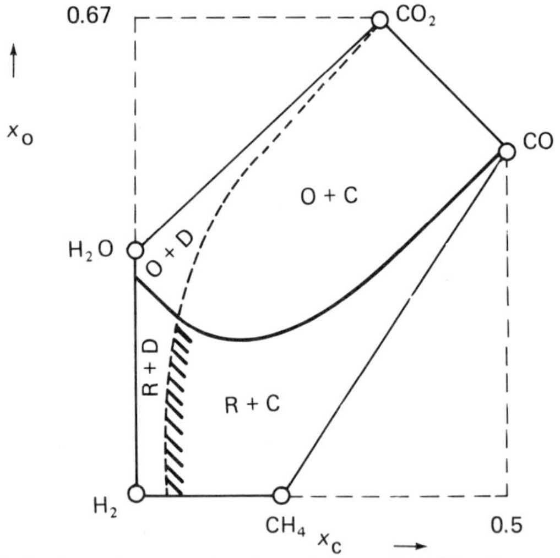

Fig. 15.6 Darken diagram for chromium at 1000°C. This applies also to high alloys of Fe-Cr and Ni-Cr, in spite of spinel formation. The bright annealing region is again shaded.

Here it may be seen that Cr_7C_3 (or $Cr_{23}C_6$) and Cr_2O_3 are so stable that there is a wide range of gas composition over which oxidation and carburisation can occur simultaneously, even at 1000°C. This disastrous combination is discussed in section 13.5.

15.3 COATINGS

The ideal coating material would be one that remains solid at high temperatures, that reacts to form an impervious film of corrosion product, and that is totally insoluble in the metal substrate. It is an unfortunate feature of the refractory metals that they are rather reactive, for example tungsten and molybdenum form gaseous or molten oxides at around 1200°C, and the scales on tantalum and niobium develop at unacceptably high rates, ca. 0.5 mm *per day,* at this temperature. One has recourse to two alternatives: either coat the metal with a refractory oxide such as alumina, Al_2O_3, or else use a reactive metal coating such as chromium or aluminium that will then transform to a protective oxide. Either way, the oxide so formed or applied must act as an efficient barrier to ionic transport, must be stable at temperature and resist thermal shock.

Refractory oxide coatings, Table 15.1, are expensive to apply and so are used only for comparatively small but critical components exposed to especially severe service conditions. They may either be applied as a slurry and subsequently sintered or else they are flame sprayed in a high temperature plasma. Successful coatings for the combustion chambers of jet engines and liquid-fuelled rockets have included heat-resistant enamels containing high concentrations of Cr_2O_3 and Al_2O_3. Rare earth oxides are also added, to confer a measure of strength and ductility.

Table 15.1 Some refractory oxide coatings
Pentecost, *High Temperature Inorganic Coatings* (Reinhold 1963).

Oxide	Melting point °C	Boiling point °C
MgO	2800	3600
ZrO_2	2720	4300
BeO	2530	3900
Cr_2O_3	2280	3000
Al_2O_3	2020	2980
SiO_2	1700	2230
ZrO_2–SiO_2	2390*	
Cr_2O_3–Al_2O_3	2050*	
MgO-Al_2O_3	1930*	

*Liquidus temperature

Metallic coatings are the most widely adopted method to improve oxidation resistance. Alloying additions of Si, Cr and/or Al are beneficial because they oxidise preferentially to create a barrier layer (section 15.1) but, unfortunately, they frequently diminish creep strength. This is especially true for the refractory metals zirconium, niobium and titanium, where the conflict between oxidation resistance and creep resistance has not yet been resolved satisfactorily. They are applied very much in the way that room-temperature coatings are applied, viz. (a) cladding, (b) electrodeposition, (c) diffusion from gas phase or pack-annealing reactions, or (d) hot dipping. However, after application, such coatings are often diffusion annealed to promote the formation of intermetallic compounds with the substrate. On subsequent service exposure, these compounds are selectively oxidised to adherent films of Al_2O_3, Cr_2O_3, etc. The long-term stability at service temperature is usually determined by interdiffusion of coating and substrate metal: where interdiffusion is sufficiently slow to allow the formation of a stable oxide film, the effectiveness of the coating is largely determined by the conductivity of the oxide.

The most common coatings are aluminium and chromium on carbon and low alloy steel components. 'Calorisation', in which steel is pack aluminised by heating in aluminium/Al_2O_3 at 950°C in the presence of a chloride catalyst, actually operates via a gas-phase reaction:

$$NH_4Cl(g) = \tfrac{1}{2}N_2(g) + 2H_2(g) + \tfrac{1}{2}Cl_2(g) \qquad (15.14)$$

$$Al(l) + \tfrac{3}{2}Cl_2(g) = AlCl_3(g) \qquad (15.15)$$

$$AlCl_3(g) = Al(Fe) + \tfrac{3}{2}Cl_2(g) \qquad (15.16)$$

where, as may be seen, the halogen is regenerated and serves to transfer aluminium to the steel surface. 'Gas chromising' is effected directly from $CrCl_3(g)$ at 550°C or else from a similar pack-annealing process to calorising. Both aluminising and chromising raise the maximum service temperature in air to about 900°C. Aluminising by direct hot dipping is also used, especially for Nimonic alloys.

Curiosities amongst metal coatings are: zinc on niobium, where a whole range of intermetallic phases ranging from NbZn to $NbZn_3$ sufficiently slow down interdiffusion to confer useful oxidation resistance up to 1050°C, and silicon on molybdenum, where the disilicide $MoSi_2$ is found to possess outstanding oxidation resistance up to almost 1700°C.

Bibliography to Chapter 15

Darken and Gurry (1953), *Physical Chemistry of Metals,* McGraw Hill.

Evans (1960), *Corrosion and Oxidation of Metals,* Arnold.

Ed. Coutsouradis (1978), *High Temperature Alloys for Gas Turbines,* Applied Science Publishers.

Institution of Metallurgists (London) (April 1978), *Surface Treatments for Protection.*

Kofstad (1966), *High Temperature Oxidation of Metals,* Wiley.

Powell (1979), 'Selection and use of wrought high nickel alloys at elevated temperatures', *Instn. Corros. Sci. Tech, Bulletin,* 77 p. 7.

Notes to Chapter 15

15.1 The rate of oxidation through porous scales is often determined by the rate at which *gaseous* oxygen can transport across the pores.

15.2 Wagner, *Z. Elektrochem.* 1959 **63** 773.

15.3 Thus, removal of carbon from iron makes it no longer hardenable by the martensite transformation. The reduction in yield stress greatly reduces fatigue resistance.

15.4 The diffusivities for carbon in α-Fe and γ-Fe are obviously different and also depend on the carbon content. The matter has been dealt with in detail by Birks and Jackson, *J. Iron Steel Inst.* 1967.

15.5 The gas mixture must be limited to a system with three active components (in this case C, H and O) at a particular total pressure. Nitrogen, where present, is ignored for the purposes of bright annealing, although some nitriding may occur. A similar Darken diagram may be used to represent the equilibria between metal oxides and sulphides and the gaseous components S, H, O (that is, H_2, SO_2, H_2S and H_2O). The axes are defined by x_O and x_S and the total diagram confined between four 'corner' gases instead of five.

Chapter 16

Some Case Histories

16.1 SHIP'S HULL

Steel boats experience frictional 'drag' due to corrosion and fouling of their hulls. This frictional effect can become very pronounced even at slow speeds and can result not only in a reduction in the maximum speed, Fig. 16.1, but also in a significant increase in fuel consumption. In an era where the cost of fossil fuels has risen rapidly, the need to conserve fuel becomes of paramount importance. For this reason and because of the need to maintain 'economic' speeds when conveying freight, it is normally necessary to resort to frequent drydocking, to

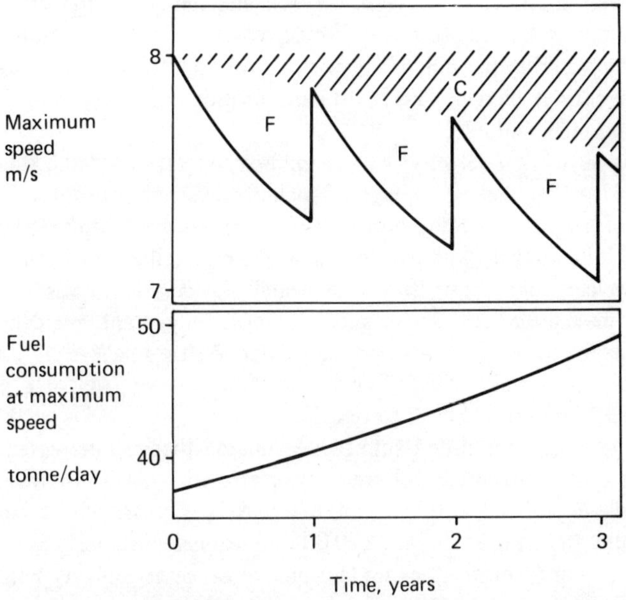

Fig. 16.1 Influence of corrosion (C) and marine fouling (F) on the performance of a steel ship drydocked annually for cleaning and painting.
Note: Nautical speed in knots is obtained by doubling the speed in m/s.

remove marine growths and restore smoothness to the hull. In fact, owing to the local roughening that results from differential aeration corrosion beneath such growths, there is a progressive deterioration, as indicated by the shaded area in Fig. 16.1 and by the increased fuel consumption at maximum ship speed.

This case history reports an experimental study begun jointly in 1970 by a number of companies in the USA and Mexico. It is based on an interim report given in 1974 and published, with several others, by the Institution of Metallurgists (Note 16.1).

It is well known that, in order to prevent marine fouling, it is necessary for the water immediately adjacent to the hull surface to be rich in copper or tin ions (p. 124). This condition may be effected by incorporating copper or tin salts into the pigment in an 'anti-fouling' paint, so that these heavy metal ions are slowly leached out to poison the infant stages of attachment and growth. An alternative is to use copper-rich alloys for the hull material, provided that again some slow corrosion is allowed to occur. This particular study examined the use of 10% nickel brass (cupronickel, Cu-10%Ni) in view of its strength, formability, weldability, corrosion resistance and fouling resistance. The corrosion rate in seawater flowing at 0.6 m/s is initially some 20 μm/yr, but this falls to 1-2 μm/yr after four years, so that the total uniform wastage in a twenty year economic life is likely to be $<$ 0.1 mm. The residual rate of 1 μm/yr ($\equiv$ 1 mA/m^2) ensures that the anti-fouling effect continues. It should be noted that the corrosion rate depends on the availability of oxygen and hence on the flow rate, rising approximately as the square root of velocity. At 8 m/s ($\equiv$ 16 knots) this means approximately treble the corrosion rate. Above 10 m/s there is the likelihood of mechanical surface damage (Fig. 10.1) and erosion-corrosion means that cupronickel is no longer suitable.

The experimental vessel was a shrimp boat operating off the Mexican coast. Because of the high cost of copper and nickel alloys, the cupronickel was used in the form of a 6 mm cladding on conventional mild steel ship's plate up to deck level. The hull interior was painted to avoid bimetallic corrosion. The results showed conclusively that, after two years' service, there was no detectable reduction in cladding thickness and, far more important, no decline in ship performance in spite of no drydocking whatsoever (normally every six months). This allows us to make the following economic assessment for a much larger vessel, say a 25 000 tonne bulk carrier.

On a normal steel-hulled ship it is estimated that the increased drag raises the fuel requirement by 3.5 tonne/day every year. At 1974 fuel prices this corresponds to some £41 000 extra fuel cost per year, whilst current 1979 prices would treble this to ca. £120 000 additional cost per year, Table 16.1. The costs arising from drydocking and hull reparation would typically be some £9000 and there would be an 'outage' time, due to some two weeks loss of service, resulting in a loss of revenue of about the same amount. Hence, the total annual savings that would result from the use of a suitable cupronickel-clad hull would be at least some £60 thousand, of which two-thirds or more is attributable to fuel savings.

Of course there is a cost penalty involved in having a more expensive hull material. Table 16.1 also lists the increased capital cost, estimated at £420 000. For the interest rates current in 1974 it may be seen that this cost could be met by annual repayments of £58 000 provided that the add-on fabrication cost (handling, shaping, welding, interior painting, etc.) did not exceed £310 000. Thus, the 'break-even' point occurs when the add-on fabrication cost of the cladding alloy is some £90 per m^2, a not unreasonable supposition. As world fuel costs increase – and when there is significant inflation – there is a clear economic advantage in using an alloy-clad hull rather than a conventional mild steel one. This advantage becomes the more obvious when the speed (and hence the frictional drag) is high. It remains to be seen whether ship manufacturers follow this compelling logic in practice.

Table 16.1 Estimated costs for 25 thousand tonne bulk carrier

(a) *Additional annual costs for normal steel hull*

		£	
Annual drydock cost		2 800	
Surface preparation	2 000		
Paint and antifouling	1 500		
Application costs	2 200		
Anode renewal	300		
		6 000	
2 weeks loss of service		9 000	
Additional fuel cost		41 000	(120 000)*
	Total £	58 800	137 800

*1979 prices: all other costs estimated for the year 1974

(b) *Additional capital cost of cupronickel hull*

	£
3500 m^2 2mm Cu-Ni cladding	110 000
Fabrication cost, £90/m^2	310 000
	£ 420 000

If repaid at 12% compound interest over 20 years, this capital loan would require an annual repayment of £58 000. This is 14% of £420 000; that is, the capital recovery factor is 14%.

16.2 SULPHURIC ACID COOLER

Sulphuric acid is most commonly manufactured by the 'contact' process, in which sulphur or sulphide ore is burnt to SO_2; this smelter gas is further oxidised to the trioxide SO_3 over a suitable catalyst and then dissolved in water:

$$S(s) + O_2(g) = SO_2(g) \tag{16.1}$$

$$SO_2(g) + \tfrac{1}{2}O_2(g) = SO_3(g) \tag{16.2}$$

$$SO_3(g) + H_2O(l) = H_2SO_4(aq) \tag{16.3}$$

The heat of solution and reaction (16.3) produces hot, strong acid (98 wt.% at nearly boiling temperature) and this has to be cooled before it can be stored or used elsewhere. This case history (Note 16.2) concerns a large Canadian factory producing some 1 million tonne/year sulphuric acid (Note 16.3).

The cooling in each of the six plants involved was effected in this instance in a number of 'cascade' units, consisting of serpentine cast-iron pipes over which fresh water cascaded and further cooled by a forced air draught. These units each occupied a ground area of 40 m^2. Although very effective, they were costly to maintain and a major source of unscheduled plant shut-down. Thus, whilst scheduled annual repairs resulted in a loss of production revenue of 6 p/tonne, unscheduled losses were:

Unscheduled repairs		2.5 p/tonne
Acid loss in spills, leaks		0.5
Paint maintenance		1
Lost production		9
	Total	13 p/tonne

This total annual loss of 19 p/tonne (£190 000) amounted to 10% of the net profit margin.

In a proposed new and larger plant, costing over £3 million, the cooler unit would be correspondingly more complex and, because of restrictions on the site, would have to be less accessible. It was estimated that unscheduled losses could rise to more than 60 p/tonne. Moreover, the cooler unit would involve considerable expense in site preparation because of the large ground area required, amounting to some £200 000. The associated pipework, pumping system and cooling tower would cost a further £100 000 or so. For these reasons it was decided to investigate an alternative heat exchanger system consisting of a tube-and-shell vertical unit, Fig. 16.2. Each of these occupied far less space (ca. 2 m^2 each), simplified the ducting and dramatically reduced the cost of site preparation.

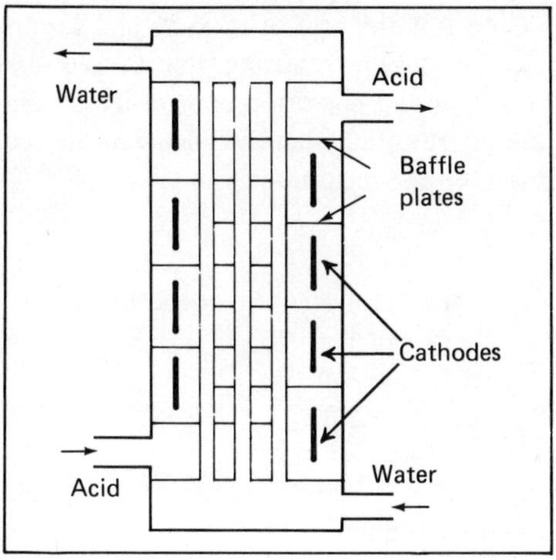

Fig. 16.2 Tube-and-shell cooler unit (schematic). Showing disposition of cathodes in the anodic protection system.

Preparatory plant trials were conducted with 316L stainless steel (low carbon 18Cr–10Ni–3Mo) units in which the acid was circulated in the tubes and fresh water in the outer shell. One fear had been that the reducing conditions engendered by hot mineral acid might lead to crevice attack at tube plates and other junctions. When, however, the material proved satisfactory, further units were designed with the acid in the outer shell and cooling water in the tubes, Fig. 16.2. These proved so successful that the fresh water was later replaced by boiler-feed water, an inspired measure that saved nearly £300 per day on pre-heating costs. However, design errors led to turbulence at the acid inlet, and this in turn caused uneven passivation and pitting corrosion on the acid side, section 10.4. These erosion/corrosion problems continued even after the expenditure of £20 000 per unit to redesign the entry configuration and slow the acid flow rate to less than 1 m/s. It was therefore decided to embark upon *anodic protection* using lead cathodes. An anodic current density of 1 A/m^2 was used during commissioning to effect initial passivation (Table 9.1 shows that this is very close to i_{crit} for an 18Cr-5Mo steel); thereafter 10 mA/m^2 was sufficient to maintain passivity throughout the acid side of the unit (that is, i_p in the same table). The advantage of this protective system is that the material requirements became less stringent. The cooling water was replaced by seawater and the steel by a nickel-base alloy which otherwise would have proved unreliable (Note 16.4).

The economics of the system are summarised in Table 16.2. This sets out the savings in capital cost, of the order of £150 000, together with the savings in running costs, amounting to an estimated £240 000 per year. It should be noted that a significant part of the capital savings is made up of a grant from the

Canadian government towards the cost of research and development. Even more important than the economic gains resulting from the redesign made possible by careful selection of material and corrosion control by anodic protection, is the business that subsequently resulted from the sale of further cooler units to other manufacturing companies in the region.

Table 16.2 Economics of new sulphuric-acid cooler units.

(a) *Capital savings*			
		£000	£
Cost of cast iron serpentine unit		220	
Savings on site preparation		300	
Government development grant		120	
			640 000
R and D expenditure		250	
Rebuilt failed units		100	
5 new cooler units		125	
Anodic protection system		10	
			485 000
	Net saving		£155 000
(b) *Annual running cost differential* for fresh water unit			
Saved shutdown losses (estimate)			£250 000 p.a.
Less Maintenance of anodic protection			8 000 p.a.
	Net saving		£242 000 p.a.

16.3 JET ENGINE COMPONENTS

In the previous two case histories the advantages accruing from corrosion protection measures are marginal, in the sense that the system is economically viable, whether a mild steel ship or a sulphuric acid factory, without resorting to the measures described. In each case, the adoption of such measures makes the system more efficient and is satisfyingly elegant in engineering terms. This final case history describes a complex structure where the use of protective measures makes the system viable: the aircraft gas turbine engine. The details relate to aspects of the development of the Conway, Spey and Dart engines manufactured by a British company and used to power a wide range of civil and military aircraft (Note 16.5).

The conditions inside a jet engine are extremely corrosive, for the materials are subjected to moist air, possibly contaminated by salt water (especially so in the case of low flying military and naval aircraft); this air is compressed before, heated adiabatically to around 600°C, it oxidises the fuel in a combustion chamber; whence, further contaminated by SO_2, hydrocarbon combustion products and various salt particles, it passes at high speed and temperatures between 1000 and 1350°C through the gas turbine. By suitable ingenious design it is possible to cool the stator vanes and turbine blades so that surface temperatures are limited to ca.1000°C, but high centrifugal stresses in the blades are unavoidable. Because of the rapid changes consequent upon start-up and shut-down, engine components are subjected to various combinations of oxidation, thermal shock and electrochemical corrosion. Careful attention must therefore be paid to design, material selection and surface coatings. The three case histories that follow relate to the surface coatings that were used for low-pressure compressor blades, high-pressure compressor discs and turbine blades.

Compressor blade failure is relatively rare, service life typically being ca. 75 000 hours. However, the blades are relatively large, and failure can produce extensive mechanical damage. For example, in the early Conway engine, the aluminium rotor blades sometimes failed as a result of intergranular corrosion pitting which led to stress concentration and cracking at the base of the fixing lugs, Fig. 16.3. Replacement of the wrecked low pressure compressor cost some £29 000, Table 16.3. In addition, ferrying the aircraft back to base, the use of a replacement aircraft and the compensation of passengers introduced further expenditure which, together with lost revenue, cost the Company some £11 000 for each failure. Because the design led to unusually high fatigue stresses in the lug area, failure resulted from the corrosion pits which hitherto had been found to be relatively harmless. The normal chromate conversion coating was clearly inadequate in these circumstances. All unpitted blades were therefore chemically cleaned and grit blasted with alumina (Al_2O_3) particles to remove any incipient corrosion, such as chloride ions trapped in the pores of the chromate film; prolongation of the blasting treatment peened the surface to improve the fatigue strength. The blades were then anodised in chromic acid to give a more impervious oxide layer than that afforded by simple chemical conversion and, finally, painted with silicone epoxy paint. The cost of this modified anticorrosion treatment was about £250 per engine. Since it extended the life of the compressor blades by at least a factor of three times, this additional cost is justified on these grounds alone. Interestingly, the author of the report commented that these additional measures would not have been undertaken had it not been for the frequent expensive failures recorded in Table 16.3.

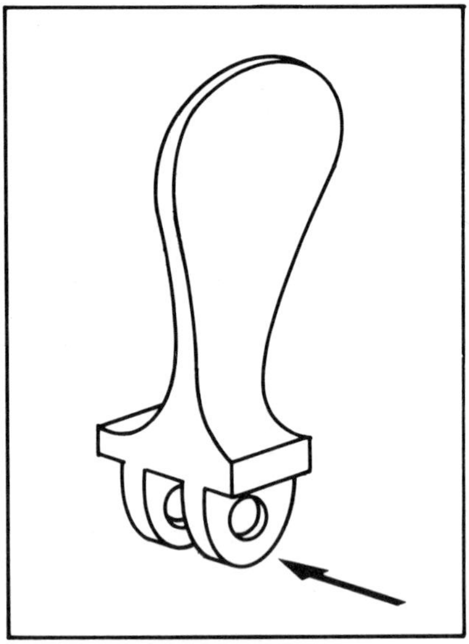

Fig. 16.3 Compressor blade in Conway engine. Fatigue failure occurred at the base of the lug (arrowed), resulting in blade release.

Table 16.3 Average expenditure resulting from eighteen compressor failures in an early design of the RR Conway engine.

	£	
Replacement of parts	20 000	
Labour cost	8 500	
Loss of revenue and additional costs	11 000	
	£39 500	per engine

The temperature in the hot (high pressure) end of the compressor reaches 500–600°C and it is therefore necessary to protect the discs on the steel rotor to which are attached the nickel-base compressor blades. These discs are usually manufactured as an integral part of the rotor itself and so, being of steel also, are especially prone to severe corrosion, especially since thermal cycling can cause condensation of chloride-saturated water and erosion can sometimes remove protective coatings locally. In the absence of any such coating, discs can become so corroded that blade loss can begin to occur after only 100 h service: whilst an effective protective coating can readily extend this period to 20 000 h.

Total replacement of the steel components of the compressor costs approximately £26 000, Table 16.4. Hence, if it is necessary on the average to replace 25% of the steel parts every 1000 h, the savings attributable to the coating amount to 0.25 × 20 × £26 000 = £130 000 per engine, less of course the very small cost of the coating itself. (It is noteworthy that the cost of a jet engine would be prohibitively high to any airline operating aircraft in which 25% parts replacement was needed every 1000 h!)

Table 16.4 Economics of steel discs in h.p. compressors

	£
Cost per engine for total replacement of steel parts	26 000
If no protective coating, cost of 25% parts replacement every 1000 h for 20 000 h life (i.e. sum saved as result of protective measures)	130 000
Less cost of coating	500
Total saving	£129 500 for an outlay of £26 500 per engine

The most effective treatments were found to be Ni-Cd electroplating, pack aluminising and sacrificial paint coatings such as aluminium-rich epoxides. The sacrificial action is essential in areas exposed directly to the erosive action of rapidly flowing air.

In the turbine region, one of the principal problems encountered is 'black plague' (section 13.5), the chloride-catalysed sulphidation that occurs in Nimonic alloys at high temperatures. Early Spey and Dart engines suffered especially from this phenomenon, many turbine blades having to be replaced at even shorter intervals than 1000 h (approximately every three months' service). Had such a replacement rate continued to the present (Note 16.6), the million blades in service would have had to be replaced, at a cost of £60 each + £45 labour, four times a year and hence totalling ca. £420 million p.a. The cost per engine would be about £50 000 p.a. It should also be noted that no engine manufacturer could supply these expensive replacement blades in sufficient quantity . . .

The solution to the sulphidation problem was found to be pack aluminising to give a 50 μm alloyed surface layer. This extended the life to well over 5000 h and in many cases to over 15 000 h. Careful engine management, with re-aluminising at intervals, has further improved matters, thereby both conserving nickel and making the engines a commercial proposition.

Notes to Chapter 16

16.1 Todd, *Economics of Corrosion Control* (Institution of Metallurgists, London 1974) p. 46; see also Thiele, *Copper nickel hulls for longer service free life* (Copper Devt. Assoc. report, 1974).

16.2 Jones, *Economics of Corrosion Control (loc. cit.)* p. 110.

16.3 Some idea of this output can be gained by appreciating that 1 million t/yr sulphuric acid can be used to make sufficient phosphate fertiliser to feed 10% of the world's population.

16.4 316L steel, although generally satisfactory in seawater, is prone to pitting under reducing conditions when there is impingement. To avoid seawater contamination of the acid (and also acid loss), Incoloy 825 (Fe-25Cr-43Ni-2Cu) was substituted, partly because of its higher pitting resistance (higher E_b) in both seawater and H_2SO_4 and no doubt partly because it passivates more readily (lower i_{crit} and i_p in acid than 316L).

16.5 Helan, *Economics of Corrosion Control (loc. cit.)* p. 118.

16.6 The report (note 16.5) was presented in 1974, and the 'present' referred to in the text means that date also.

Numerical Problems

THERMODYNAMICS

1. Calculate the enthalpy change per mole for the reactions:
   (a) $H_2 + CO_2 = H_2O + CO$ (all gaseous)
   (b) $Ni + SO_2 = NiS + O_2$
   (c) $Al_2O_3 + 3C = 2Al + 3CO$.
   Use 298K data from Table 2.1.

2. Calculate the standard enthalpy change per mole for the reactions:
   (a) $2Fe + \frac{3}{2}O_2 = Fe_2O_3$ (b) $Fe + \frac{1}{2}O_2 = FeO$
   (c) $3FeO + \frac{1}{2}O_2 = Fe_3O_4$ (d) $2Fe_3O_4 + \frac{1}{2}O_2 = 3Fe_2O_3$
   and hence demonstrate that Hess's law applies, viz.

   $3a = 6b + 2c + d.$ (Table 2.1).

3. Calculate (a) the enthalpy of NiO at 2000K and (b) the heat required to raise the temperature of 1 mole NiO from 298K to 2000K. (eqn (2.7) Tables 2.1 and 2.2).

4. Confirm the entropy changes L/T' for the melting of Al, FeO and $ZnCl_2$. (eqn (2.8) and Table 2.3).

5. Calculate the standard entropy change accompanying the reaction $2Cu + \frac{1}{2}O_2 = Cu_2O$ at 298K. Then, using the data in Table 2.2, calculate the ΔC_p correction for the entropy change at 1298K. (eqn (2.10) and Table 2.1).

6. Using the $\Delta H^\ominus$ and $S^\ominus$ data in Table 2.1, calculate the standard free energy change at 298K for the formation of 1 mole of $CuCl_2$, FeS and TiO_2 and check your answer against the tabulated value. (eqn (2.13)).

7. Repeat the Hess's law calculation of Q.2 for the free energy changes instead of the enthalpies.

8. Calculate $\Delta G^{\ominus}$ for the formation of 1 mole of Al_2O_3 at 1298K using (a) the approximation of eqn (2.13) and (b) the ΔC_p correction from Table 2.2 (eqn (2.7) (2.10)). This neglects the melting of aluminium at 933K (Table 2.3). Calculate (c) the further correction for this (eqn (2.14)) and compare your answers.

9. The Raoultian activity coefficient of silicon in molten iron at infinite dilution is 0.8. (a) If Si exhibits ideal Henrian behaviour when $x_{Si} = 0.01$, what are the Henrian and Raoultian activities of this solute at this mole fraction, eqn (2.29)(2.30) ? (b) Calculate the difference in free energy between the Henrian and Roultian standard states, eqn (2.31); (c) Using the relationship $w_{Si}/100 \approx (M_{Si}/M_{Fe})\, x_{Si}$, where M is the relative atomic mass, calculate the wt.%Si (that is, w_{Si}) corresponding to $x_{Si} = 0.01$; (d) Derive the relationship between w_{Si} and x_{Si}.

10. Sievert's law relates the solubility of a 'Henrian' gas to the partial pressure of the gas over a liquid or solid in which it is dissolved. Since most diatomic gases dissociate upon dissolving in metals, we have at equilibrium (say for hydrogen in iron)

$$H_2(g) = 2H(Fe); \quad K = a_H^2/(p_{H2}/p^{\ominus})$$

$$= (\gamma_H^{\infty} x_H)^2/(p_{H2}/p^{\ominus})$$

so that $x_H = (K/\gamma_H^{\infty})^{\frac{1}{2}}\, (p_{H2}/p^{\ominus})^{\frac{1}{2}}$
and solubility varies as the square root of the partial pressure, which is Sievert's law, p. 000. Given that $K/\gamma_H^{\infty} = 3.10^{-11}$ for hydrogen in iron, what is the proportionality constant between concentration in ppm and p_{H2} in atm?

11. Calculate the ionic activities at 298K in aqueous solutions of (a) $FeCl_2$ (b) H_2SO_4 and (c) $AlCl_3$, all at 0.1 molal concentration. (eqn (2.36) and Table 2.4).

12. Calculate the chemical potentials of the ions in Q.11 relative to that of hydrogen ion (eqn (2.38) and Table 2.5).

13. Calculate the equilibrium constants for the formation of $CuCl_2$, FeS and TiO_2 at 298K (Q.6) and express each of these in terms of an activity quotient. quotient.

14. Repeat Q.13 for a temperature of 1000K and assuming the validity of eqn (2.13).

15. Calculate the dissociation partial pressures of Cu_2O, Al_2O_3, NiS and FeS at 1000K using eqn (2.13) and Table 2.1. Check your answers against those given in Table 13.1.

16. Determine, from the Ellingham diagram (Fig. 2.1), $\Delta G^{\ominus}$ for the following carbothermic reactions at 1000°C:
(a) $FeO + C = Fe + CO$
(b) $Al_2O_3 + 3C = 2Al + 3CO$
and compare your answer with that calculated from data in Table 2.1 and eqn (2.13). (Note: degrees Celsius!)

17. Calculate $\Delta S^{\ominus}$ for the reaction $2Zn + S_2 = 2ZnS$ at 500°C and 1500°C from Fig. 2.3 and eqn (2.48). Confirm your answer using Tables 2.1 and 2.2.

CHEMISTRY AND ELECTROCHEMISTRY

18. Calcualte the pH of a 0.1 molal solution of sulphuric acid at 298K, eqn (3.8). Repeat for molalities of 0.3, 1, 3 and 10. Then recalculate allowing for the activity coefficient, (eqn (2.36)).

19. Repeat Q.18 for HCl(aq) and NaOH(aq). For each pH value, calculate the corresponding value of pOH, eqn (3.9).

20. A saturated solution of $PbCl_2$(aq) at 298K is found to possess a chloride ion activity of 0.027. Ignoring activity coefficients, what is the lead ion activity? Hence calculate the solubility product (eqn (3.12)) and compare your result with the value in Table 3.1.

21. A mixed sulphide solution contains sulphide ions at an activity of 10^{-20}. Calculate the equilibrium activities of Ag(I) and Sn(II) at saturation.

22. The rate of a reaction doubles on raising its temperature from 27°C to 37°C. Calculate (a) the (apparent) activation enthalpy for the reaction and (b) the relative rate of change on going from 37°C to 100°C, eqn (3.16) (13.5).

23. The activation enthalpy for the epoxide polymerisation reaction is some 48 kJ/mol. If it takes 24 h for an epoxide glue to set hard at 5°C, how long will it take if hardened over a radiator at 75°C?

24. Calculate the equilibrium constant for the formation of the activated complex at 1000K if $\Delta G^{\ddagger}$ is 50 kJ/mol, eqn (3.20).

25. The rate of carbon diffusion in solid α-Fe was found to be smaller by a factor of 7 on reducing the temperature from 650° to 500°C. Calculate the apparent activation enthalpy and deduce whether carbon is in interstitial or substitutional solid solution.

26. (a) Calculate the driving emf for the corrosion cells zinc-in-acid and iron-in-aerated-neutral-water, p. 75 and Tables 4.1, 4.2. Whence
(b) calculate the free energy changes for

$$Zn(s) + 2HCl(aq) = ZnCl_2(aq) + H_2(g)$$
$$Fe(s) + \tfrac{1}{2}O_2(g) + H_2O(l) = Fe(OH)_2(aq)$$

eqn (5.10). Finally (c) compare your answers with those deduced from Table 2.1. $G^{\bullet}$ for HCl(aq) is −95 kJ/mol.

27. The work done on plastically extending a metal specimen 30% at an average flow stress of 500 MN/m^2 is 0.3 × 500 MJ/m^3. Since 1 m^3 of many common metals corresponds to about 1.5×10^5 mol, this plastic work is ca. 1 kJ/mol. If 10% of this energy is stored as the elastic energy of dislocations, calculate the reduction in equilibrium single potential that is likely to result from cold work of a divalent metal, eqn (5.10).

28. Using the free energy data of Table 2.5, calculate the standard equilibrium single potentials of Ag^+/Ag, Cu^{2+}/Cu and Fe^{2+}/Fe. Compare your answers with those in Table 4.1.

29. Calculate the standard equilibrium single potentials of (a) iron/$Fe_2O_3/H^+(aq)$ and (b) lead/$PbO_2/H^+(aq)$. $G^{\bullet}_{PbO2} = -217$ kJ/mol.

30. (a) Calculate the equilibrium single potentials of Ag^+/Ag, Cu^{2+}/Cu and $Fe/Fe_2O_3/H^+$ at ionic activities of 10^{-6}.
(b) What pH does this correspond to in the third example?

31. (a) Calculate the single potential of the Zn^{2+}/Zn electrode at 298K on the standard hydrogen electrode scale for a solution containing 0.3 molal $ZnSO_4$, Tables 2.4 and 2.5.
(b) Convert your answer to the saturated calomel scale (SCE, Table 7.1).

32. Calculate the standard single potentials at 298K for
(a) copper in cyanide solution (Note: Cu(I))
(b) nickel in ammoniacal solution
(c) zinc in alkaline solution.
(Tables 2.5 or 4.1; and Table 4.3).

ELECTRODE KINETICS

33. The exchange current density for Fe^{2+}/Fe is pH-dependent in sulphate solutions with $n = 2$ in eqn (6.4). If the value at 298K and pH 7 is 10^{-4} A/m^2, calculate i_o at pH 3.

34. Calculate the anodic Tafel coefficient (b_a) at 298K for a 1-electron and a 2-electron charge-transfer process, each having a symmetry factor of 0.5, eqn (6.8).

35. Calculate the charge transfer overpotential for (a) zinc dissolution at 10 A/m^2 and (b) hydrogen evolution on zinc at 10 A/m^2. In (a) take the linear mean value of b_a and the geometric mean value of i_o, eqn (6.7).

36. Check the correspondence between A/m^2 and mm/yr for various metals, eqn (6.11).

37. Calculate the corrosion rate for a reaction involving a metal and an oxidising process whose equilibrium single potentials are separated by 0.45 V, assuming $|b_c| = 2b_a = 0.10$ V/decade and i_o for each process is equal to 10^{-1} A/m^2. What further assumption is necessary to validate the calculation?

38. Derive an analytical expression for the corrosion rate of a corrosion cell under charge-transfer control, in terms of the equilibrium single potentials and various Tafel parameters. (This is *not* eqn (7.1) (7.2)!)

39. Calculate the corrosion rate of zinc at 298K when it is displaying a corrosion potential of −0.85 V, SHE in seawater, eqn (7.2).

40. Calculate the limiting current density for cathodic deposition from a unimolal $CuSO_4$(aq) solution at 298K given that $D_{Cu2+} = 2.10^{-10}$ m^2/s and that the diffusion layer thickness is 100 μm, eqn (6.16).

41. Confirm, using the Nernst-Einstein relationship, eqn (13.11), that $D_{Cu2+} = 2.10^{-10}$ m^2/s is consistent with an ionic mobility of 1.6×10^{-8} m^2/V s for copper ions.

42. The limiting current density for nickel deposition from Ni^{2+}(aq) is 500 A/m^2 at 50°C when the solution is lightly stirred. Calculate
    (a) i_L at 60°C if $\Delta H^{\ddagger}$ is ca. 50 kJ/mol;
    (b) i_L if the temperature is raised to 65°C and the stirring rate is simultaneously increased so as to halve the diffusion layer thickness;
    (c) the concentration overpotential at 50°C when depositing at 480 A/m^2.

43. A corrosion meter, employing the Stern linear polarisation principle, records a current increment of 8 μA for a voltage increment of 3 mV, for a 10 cm^2 test coupon corroding uniformly under constant immersion conditions. Calculate the polarisation conductance and hence the corrosion rate if b_a = 0.06 V. Why is it not necessary to know b_c in this instance? (eqn (7.6) 7.7)).

44. Show graphically how the anode/cathode ratio influences the corrosion rate.

45. If the electrolyte resistance between permanently-separated anode and cathode areas on a partially immersed specimen is 0.1Ω, calculate the corrosion rate in Q. 37. (eqn (8.1)).

PASSIVATION

46. Referring to the Pourbaix diagram for iron at room temperature (Fig. 9.2), derive the equations for the lines bounding the following pairs of phase fields:

(a) Fe^{2+}/Fe^{3+} (b) Fe^{2+}/Fe_2O_3 (c) Fe_3O_4/Fe_2O_3 (d) $Fe_3O_4/Fe(OH)_3^-$.

Substitute for the various constants, using Tables 2.1, 2.5 and 4.3, and put all ionic activities equal to 10^{-6} (except that of hydrogen ion). You now have the equations actually used to construct Fig. 9.2.

47. From Table 9.1, express i_{crit} and i_p for iron-chromium alloys as a function of chromium content and hence estimate these quantities for a 3%Cr steel. Compare your answers with Fig. 9.5.

48. Determine the passive range ($E_b - E_{pp}$) for iron, Fe-13%Cr and Fe-17%Cr in 0.01, 0.1 and 1.0 molal chloride at pH 7. Note that E_{pp} for iron is pH sensitive, obeying approximately the relation $E_{pp} \approx 1.00 - 0.06\,p$H. (Tables 9.1, 9.2).

49. If the resistivity of the passive film on iron is 10^8 Ωm and the film has an average thickness of 4 nm, what is the iR drop across the film for a current density i_p = 2 A/m^2? Hence, calculate E_{pp} for iron assuming this iR drop is entirely responsible for the discrepancy between E_{pp} and the theoretical equilibrium single potential for $Fe/Fe_3O_4/H^+$. (Note that thickness, composition and resistivity are all likely to depend on pH, so that the discrepancy will also vary with conditions.)

50. The limiting current density for the reduction of unstirred nitric acid may be represented approximately by the equation

$$i_L = 15\ m^{\frac{5}{3}} \quad \text{where } m = \text{molality of } HNO_3.$$

If i_{crit} for titanium and iron are respectively 5 and 2000 A/m^2 in this acid, what strength of acid will passivate each metal?

CORROSION PREVENTION

51. A corrosion inhibitor is found to inhibit the anodic reaction only, leaving the cathodic reaction unaffected. (a) If the anodic area is reduced to 1% of the uninhibited value, calculate the reduction in corrosion rate if $b_a = 0.06$ and $b_c = -0.12$ V. (b) What is the change in corrosion potential, and (c) how would this be different if anodic and cathodic areas were inhibited equally?

52. Calculate the inter-anode separation on a cathodically protected pipeline in seawater (a) using zinc anodes when the coating is extensively damaged so that $\beta = 10^{-2}$ and (b) using magnesium anodes and substituting $E_l = -0.53$ V, SHE and $E_{corr} = -0.35$ V, SHE. (eqn (11.10) and Table 11.1).

53. (a) The corrosion potential of a buried cable rises by 10 mV when a neigbouring cathodic protection system is switched on. Calculate the proportional change in corrosion current if $b_a = +0.06$ V.
    (b) How is this conclusion affected if the presence of sulphate reducing bacteria lowers b_a to +0.02 V?

54. It is observed that the polarisation curve for oxygen reduction on iron, nickel and zinc, in an electrolyte consisting of a condensed film of moisture, is characterised by a quasi-Tafel slope of −0.33 V and passes through the point 0.00 V, SHE; 0.1 A/m^2.
    (a) Calculate the corrosion potentials of these three metals when exposed to moist air, neglecting the effect of electrolytic resistance.
    (b) A steel surface is coated with a layer of nickel. Calculate, or determine graphically, the corrosion rate of the iron exposed at pores in the coating if these constitute 1% of the surface area, neglecting the resistance of the pores.
    (c) Repeat (b) allowing for an iR drop of 0.1 V in the pores.
    (d) Repeat (b) if the nickel coating is replaced by a layer of zinc of similar porosity.
    (Table 6.1, Fig. 11.5).

STRESS CORROSION AND CORROSION FATIGUE

55. Calculate the critical flaw sizes of the following materials when stressed at 60% of the yield stress (eqn (12.25)):
    (a) Alloy steel ($\sigma_y = 1500$ MN/m^2) with $K_{Ic} = 70$ MN/m$^{\frac{3}{2}}$
    (b) Ti alloy 850 60
    (c) Al alloy 300 35

56. Repeat Q.55 for SCC conditions, given that $K_{Iscc} = 15$ MN/m$^{\frac{3}{2}}$ in each case and that linear elastic calculations are valid.

57. A maraging steel in the vacuum-melted condition possesses a fracture toughness of 85 MN/m$^{\frac{3}{2}}$. Calculate the value of K_{Iscc} when the hydrogen content is increased, by cathodic charging, from 0.05 to 2 ppm. Assume $k = 14\,000$, $\alpha = 5.10^{-5}$ in eqn (12.20).

58. The rate of SCC crack propagation in a 13%Cr steel (alloy A in Q. 54, that is, $K_{Ic} = 70$ MN/m$^{\frac{3}{2}}$ and $K_{Iscc} = 15$ MN/m$^{\frac{3}{2}}$) approximates to a parabolic function of the stress intensity:

    $$da/dt = A\{(K/K_{Iscc}) - 1\}^2 \quad \text{where } A = 10^{-8} \text{ m/s.}$$

    A component made from this steel is subjected to a constant tensile stress. It contains a semi-elliptical surface flaw of depth 0.2 mm which, under these conditions, corresponds to an initial stress intensity $K_i = 22$ MN/m$^{\frac{3}{2}}$. Calculate:
    (a) the critical flaw depth necessary to initiate SCC and
    (b) the flaw depth immediately prior to final fast fracture, assuming in each case that the flaw maintains a constant shape while propagating.
    (c) Integrate the equation to give the time to propagate the flaw by SCC from 0.1 mm depth to this final value. Eqn (12.7) (12.25) (12.26).

59. A mild steel component contains a sharp semi-elliptical surface flaw of depth 1 mm at right angles to the stress axis: the flaw shape parameter Q is 1.3. The component is subjected to a stress of 45 ± 15 MN/m^2.
    (a) Calculate the initial range of stress intensity ΔK_i due to the flaw. Hence, if the threshold intensity range ΔK_{th} is 6 MN/m$^{\frac{3}{2}}$, deduce whether or not the component will fail by fatigue.
    (b) The presence of salt water lowers ΔK_{th} to 1.5 MN/m$^{\frac{3}{2}}$. If the number of cycles to failure (for $\Delta K_i > \Delta K_{th}$) is given by

    $$N_f = \frac{(1-R)^2}{\pi Q C (\sigma_{max}\, \Delta K_i)^2} \quad \text{where } R = K_{min}/K_{max}$$

    and C (the Paris constant) is here 10^{-12} when ΔK is in MN/m$^{\frac{3}{2}}$, calculate N_f for corrosion fatigue in seawater. Hence
    (c) determine the time to failure of the component if the stress cycling frequency is 20 Hz.

HIGH-TEMPERATURE OXIDATION

60. Deduce the Pilling-Bedworth ratio from first principles. Hence calculate this ratio for Cu_2O and Al_2O_3 and compare your answer with values in Table 13.4.

61. The electrical conductivity of CoO above 1000°C satisfies eqn (14.21) for pressures above $p_{min} = 10^{-5}$ atm. If the activation enthalpy is 56 kJ/mol and the conductance is $2\Omega^{-1}m^{-1}$ at 1350°C and 10^{-4} atm oxygen, calculate the conductance at 1200°C in air at 1 atm.

62. (a) Calculate the driving emf for the oxidation of copper to Cu_2O at 1000°C and 3.10^{-4} atm oxygen.
    (b) Under these conditions the conductance κ is $100\Omega^{-1}m^{-1}$ and the transport numbers are $t_h = 1$, $t_{Cu} = 6.10^{-5}$, $t_O = 10^{-8}$. Calculate k_p in m^2/s from eqn (14.22), given that $\rho_{Cu2O} = 6200$ kg/m^3.
    (c) Convert your answer to mm/yr, assuming that oxidation continues according to the parabolic law for one year.

63. Calculate μ_O and p_{O2} at the Cu/Cu_2O and Cu_2O/CuO interfaces for the oxidation of copper at 500°C. Eqn (14.24)-(14.26).

64. (a) Calculate the oxygen activity in molten steel at 1700°C for the cell in Fig. 14.4 if $\mathcal{E}$ = 237 mV and the oxygen transport number in lime-stabilised ZrO_2 at this temperature is 0.7.
    (b) If the carbon-oxygen product, [wt.%C]×[wt.%O], is 2.10^{-3} at this temperature and assuming ideal Raoultian behaviour for oxygen, what is the equilibrium carbon content of the steel?

65. If the Mo/MoO_2 reference electrode in Q.64 were replaced by Cr/Cr_2O_3, calculate the emf for the same conditions.

66. What chromium content, expressed in atomic % and assuming ideal Raoultian behaviour, will lead to $\Delta G_{Cr2O3} = \Delta G_{NiO}$ in the oxidation of Ni-Cr alloys at 1000°C? Eqn (15.2).

67. Calculate the depth of the internally oxidised zone in a silver-1 at.%cadmium alloy after 24h at 850°C at an oxygen partial pressure of 10^{-9} atm. The particles formed are CdO. The diffusivity of oxygen in silver at this temperature is 10^{-10} m^2/s. Assume that cadmium displays ideal Henrian behaviour when dissolved in silver, with $\gamma^{\infty} = 0.5$. Eqn (15.3).

68. From the rate constant k_p expressed in (mg/cm^2)^2/h, derive the oxidation rate expressed in mm/yr, that is, the penetration after 1 year's exposure, assuming parabolic oxidation throughout the period.

69. Determine the atomic fractions, x_C and x_O, of carbon and oxygen for the following gas compositions measured at room temperature (volume %):
   (a) 70 H_2O, 20 H_2, 10 CO_2
   (b) 45 CO, 25 CO_2, 20 H_2, 10 H_2O
   (c) 45 H_2, 35 CO, 15 CH_4, 5 CO_2
   (d) 63 H_2, 25 H_2O, 12 CO.

70. Determine whether the mixtures in Q.69 will be suitable for
   (i) bright annealing carbon steels at 650°C
   (ii) bright solution-annealing iron-chromium alloys at 1000°C.

Answers to Numerical Problems

1. (a) $-243 - 111 - (0 - 394) = +41$ kJ/mol
(b) $-82 + 0 - (0 - 297) = +215$ kJ/mol
(c) $0 - 333 - (-1676 + 0) = +1343$ kJ/mol.

2. (a) -822 kJ (b) -267 kJ (c) $-1118 - (-801) = -317$ kJ
(d) $-2466 - (-2256) = -210$ kJ.
$3a = -2466$ kJ; $6b + 2c + d = -1602 - 634 - 210 = -2446$ kJ, an error of 0.8%.

3. $a + bT = 57.3 + (3.5 \times 10^{-3})(2000) = 64.3$ J/mol K.
$\int(a+bT)\mathrm{d}T = a(T_2 - T_1) + (b/2)(T_2 - T_1)(T_2 + T_1)$
$= 57.3(1702) + (1.75 \times 10^{-3})(1702)(2298) = 104.4$ kJ.

4. Al: $11000/933 = 11.8$ J/mol K (cf. 12)
FeO: $31000/1650 = 18.8$ J/mol K (cf. 19)
$ZnCl_2$: $24000/638 = 37.6$ J/mol K (cf. 38).

5. $\Delta S^{\ominus} = 101 - (66 + 102.5) = -67.5$ J/mol K.
$\Delta C_p = (59.8 - 45.6 - 12.8) + (25.9 - 12.2 - 7.6)T/10^3 + 7.2T^2/10^6 = 1.4 + 6.1T/10^2 + 7.2T^2/10^6$
$\int(\Delta C_p/T) = 1.4\ln(T_2/T_1) + 6.1(T_2 - T_1)/10^3 + 3.6(T_2 - T_1)(T_2 + T_1)$
$= 2.06 + 6.1 + 5.75 = 13.9$ J/mol K
That is, corrected $\Delta S^{\ominus} = -67.5 + 13.9 = -53.6$ J/mol K
(a correction of some 20%; such large corrections are not common).

6. $CuCl_2$: $\Delta S^{\ominus} = 108 - (33 + 223) = -148$;
$\Delta G^{\ominus} = -220 - 0.298(-148) = -176$ kJ (agrees);
FeS: $\Delta S^{\ominus} = 60 - (27 + 32) = 1$
$\Delta G^{\ominus} = -100 - 0.298(1) = -100$ kJ (agrees);
TiO_2: $\Delta S^{\ominus} = 50 - (30 + 205) = -185$
$\Delta G^{\ominus} = -912 - 0.298(-185) = -857$ kJ (cf. -853).

7. (a) -90 kJ (b) -54 kJ (c) $-146-(-162)=+16$ kJ
(d) $-270-(-292)=+22$ kJ
$6(b)+2(c)+(d)=-324+32+22=-270=3(a)$ Q.E.D.

8. (a) $2Al+\frac{3}{2}O_2=Al_2O_3$; $\Delta S^\ominus=51-56-307.5=-312.5$ J/mol K
$\Delta G^\ominus=-1676-1.298(-312.5)=-1270$ kJ/mol.
(b) $\Delta C_p=(102.9-40.0-38.3)+(25.1-27.0-22.8)T/10^3 + 2.8T^2/10^6$
$=24.6-24.7T/10^3+2.8T^2/10^6$
$\int\Delta C_p dT=24.6-(12.35\times1.596)+0.93(2.19-0.03)$
$=6.9$ kJ/mol
$\int(\Delta C_p/T)dT=24.6\ln(1298/298)-24.7+(1.4\times1.596)$
$=16.7$ J/mol K
Correction $=6.9-1.298(16.7)=-14.8$ kJ/mol and corrected $\Delta G^\ominus$ $=-1270-14.8=-1285$ kJ/mol.
(c) Since L is for reactant in this case, $L=-22$ kJ and correction is $-22\{1-(1298/933)\}=+8.6$ kJ, so final corrected $\Delta G^\ominus=-1270-14.8+8.6=-1276$ kJ/mol. That is, error in (a) is only 0.5%.

9. (a) $a=\gamma^\infty x=0.8\times0.01=0.008$; $h=x=0.01$.
(b) $\Delta G=\mu^\infty-G^\bullet=RT\ln\gamma^\infty=8.31\times298\ln0.8=-553$ J/mol.
(c) $w=(28/56)\times1=0.5\%$
(d) In 100 g of iron, $x_{Si}=w_{Si}/M_{Si}\div[\{100-w_{Si})/M_{Fe}\}+(w_{Si}/M_{Si})]$
$\approx(w_{Si}/M_{Si})/(100/M_{Fe})$ Q.E.D.

10. 1 ppm H in Fe = 1 mol H per $(10^6/56)$ mol Fe
or $x_H=(5.6\times10^{-5})c_H$
But $x_H=(3.10^{-11})^{\frac{1}{2}}(p_{H2}/p^\ominus)^{\frac{1}{2}}$
hence $c_H=0.098\,(p_{H2}/p^\ominus)^{\frac{1}{2}}$.

11. (a) Fe^{2+} : $0.1\times0.52=0.052$
Cl^- : $2\times0.1\times0.52=0.104$
(b) H^+ : $2\times0.1\times0.27=0.054$
SO_4^{2-} : $0.1\times0.27=0.027$
(c) Al^{3+} : $0.1\times0.34=0.034$
Cl^- : $3\times0.1\times0.34=0.102$.

12. (a) Fe^{2+} : $-84.9+(8.31\times0.298)\ln(0.052)=-92.2$ kJ/mol
Cl^- : $-131.1+(8.31\times0.298)\ln(0.104)=-136.7$ kJ/mol
(b) H^+ : $0.0+(8.31\times0.298)\ln(0.054)=-7.2$ kJ/mol
SO_4^{2-} : $-736.6+(8.31\times0.298)\ln(0.027)=-745.5$ kJ/mol
(c) Al^{3+} : $-483.1+(8.31\times0.298)\ln(0.034)=-491.5$ kJ/mol
Cl^- : $-131.1+(8.31\times0.298)\ln(0.102)=-136.8$ kJ/mol.

13. $K = \exp(-\Delta G^{\ominus}/RT)$
$CuCl_2$: $\exp(176/8.31{\times}0.298) = 7.3 \times 10^{30}$
FeS : $\exp(100/8.31{\times}0.298) = 3.4 \times 10^{17}$
TiO_2 : $\exp(857/8.31{\times}0.298) = 1.9 \times 10^{150}$(!)

14. $CuCl_2$: $\Delta G^{\ominus} = -220 + 148 = -72$ kJ/mol
$K = \exp(72/8.31) = 5.8 \times 10^3$, that is, less stable.
FeS : $\Delta G^{\ominus} = -100 - 1 = -101$ kJ/mol
$K = \exp(101/8.31) = 1.9 \times 10^5$
TiO_2 : $\Delta G^{\ominus} = -912 + 185 = -727$ kJ/mol
$K = \exp(727/8.31) = 9.9 \times 10^{37}$.

15. Cu_2O : $\Delta S^{\ominus} = 101 - (66 + 102.5) = -67.5$ J/mol K
$\Delta G^{\ominus} = -167 - (-67.5) = -99.5$ kJ/mol
$p_{O2} = p^{\ominus} \exp 2(-99.5/8.31) = 4.0 \times 10^{-11}$ atm (cf. $5{\times}10^{-11}$)
Al_2O_3: $\Delta S^{\ominus} = 51 - (56 + 307.5) = -312.5$ J/mol K
$\Delta G^{\ominus} = -1676 - (-312.5) = -1364$ kJ/mol
$p_{O2} = p^{\ominus} \exp(2/3)(-1364/8.31) = 3.1 \times 10^{-48}$ atm (agrees)
NiS : $\Delta S^{\ominus}$ (from S_2(g)) $= 53 - (30 + 114) = -91$ J/mol K
$\Delta G^{\ominus} = -82 - (-91) = +9$ kJ/mol
$p_{S2} = p^{\ominus} \exp 2(9/8.31) = 8.7$ atm (cf. 1.6 atm)
FeS : $\Delta S^{\ominus} = 60 - (27 + 114) = -81$ J/mol K
$\Delta G^{\ominus} = -100 - (-81) = -19$ kJ/mol
$p_{S2} = p^{\ominus} \exp 2(-19/8.31) = 10^{-2}$ atm (cf. $5{\times}10^{-3}$).

16. (a) $\Delta S^{\ominus} = 27 + 198 - (54 + 6) = 165$ J/mol K
$\Delta H^{\ominus} = 0 - 111 - (-267 + 0) = 156$ kJ/mol
$\Delta G^{\ominus} = 156 - 1.273(165) = -54$ kJ/mol
From Ellingham diagram, separation of 2FeO and 2CO lines at 1000°C is −75 kJ, giving $\Delta G^{\ominus}$ for reaction = −75/2 = −37.5 kJ/mol. The error arises from omitting the ΔC_p correction.
(b) $\Delta S^{\ominus} = 56 + 594 - (51 + 18) = 581$ J/mol K
$\Delta H^{\ominus} = +3019$ kJ/mol (Q.1(a))
$\Delta G^{\ominus} = 1343 - 1.273(581) = +603$ kJ/mol
From Ellingham diagram, separation of $\frac{2}{3}Al_2O_3$ and 2CO lines at 1000°C is +399 kJ, giving $\Delta G^{\ominus}$ for reaction = (3/2)×399 = +598 kJ/mol. An 8 kJ/mol error results from neglecting the melting of aluminium and again there is a ΔC_p correction.

17. Slopes at 500 and 1500°C = 190 and 330 kJ per 1000°C for 2ZnS, hence $\Delta S^{\ominus}$(500°C) = −190 J/mol K and $\Delta S^{\ominus}$(1500°C) = −330 J/mol K. From $S^{\ominus}$(298K) and ΔC_p data we obtain

$\Delta S^{\ominus}(298\text{K}) = 116 - (84 + 228) = -196$ J/mol K
$\Delta C_p = (107 - 44.4 - 32.6) + (8.0 - 22.6 - 3.7)T/10^3$
$- (8\times10^5)/T^2 = 30.0 - 18.3T/10^3 - (8.10^5)T^2$ J/mol K

(a) $\int(\Delta C_p/T)\mathrm{d}T$ at 500°C = 30 ln(773/298) − 0.0183(773 − 298) + $(4\times10^5)\{(1/773)^3 - (1/298)^3\}$ = 19.9 J/mol K.
Additionally, Zn melts at 420°C: $\Delta S^{\ominus} = -2L/693 = -20$ J/mol K so that $\Delta S^{\ominus}(773\text{K}) = -196 + 19.9 - 20 = -196$ J/mol K, a disagreement by 3%.

(b) $\int(\Delta C_p/T)\mathrm{d}T$ at 1500°C = 30 ln(1773/298) − 0.0183(1773–298) + $(4\times10^5)\{(1/1773)^3 - (1/298)^3\}$ = 26.5 J/mol K.
Additionally, Zn boils at 907°C: $\Delta S^{\ominus} = -2L/1180 = -195$ J/mol K so that $\Delta S^{\ominus}(1773\text{K}) = -196 + 26.5 - 195 = -364$ J/mol K, a disagreement by 10%.
The errors lie in the assumption that $\Delta H^{\ominus}$ is invariant with temperature, that is, the lines in the diagram are not in fact straight.

18. At 0.1, 0.3, 1, 3 and 10 molal, $m_{H+}/m^{\ominus}$ = 0.2, 0.6, 2, 6 and 20. Whence pH from eqn (3.8) = 0.7, 0.2, −0.3, −0.8 and −1.3. Allowing for $f_{\pm}$, h_{H+} = 0.054, 0.108, 0.26, 0.84 and 11.2 and true pH = 1.3, 1.0, 0.6, 0.1 and −1.0.

19. (a) Activities in HCl: h_{H+} = 0.08, 0.23, 0.81, 3.96, 104 so that
pH = 1.1, 0.6, 0.1, −0.6 and −2.0
pOH = 12.9, 13.4, 13.9, 14.4 and 16.0.
(b) Activities in NaOH: h_{OH-} = 0.08, 0.21, 0.68, 2.34 and 32.3
pOH = 1.1, 0.7, 0.2, −0.4 and −1.5, whence
pH = 12.9, 13.3, 13.8, 14.4 and 15.5.
As a check, observe how pH falls with increasing acid concentration and rises with increasing alkali.

20. If m_{Cl-} = 0.027 mol/kg, m_{Pb2+} = 0.0135 mol/kg whence $K_s = 0.0135 \times (0.027)^2 = 9.8 \times 10^{-6}$ (cf. 10^{-5}).

21. K_s for $Ag_2S = 10^{-49}$, so $h_{Ag+} = (10^{-49}/10^{-20})^{\frac{1}{2}} = 3.2 \times 10^{-15}$
$SnS = 10^{-26}$, so $h_{Sn2+} = 10^{-49}/10^{-20} = 10^{-29}$.

22. (a) $\ln(r_{310}/r_{300}) = -(\Delta H^{\ddagger}/R)\{(1/310)-(1/300)\}$
whence $\Delta H^{\ddagger} = (8.31 \times 300 \times 310 \ln 2)/10 = 53.6$ kJ/mol.

(b) $$\ln(r_{373}/r_{310}) = \frac{53600 \times 63}{8.31\times373\times310} = 3.51$$

whence increase in rate is 34-fold.

23. $\ln(r_{348}/r_{278}) = (48000 \times 70)/(8.31 \times 348 \times 278) = 4.18$
corresponding to a 65-fold increase in rate, so that hardening time = 24 h/65 = 22 minutes.

24. $K^{\ddagger} = \exp(-\Delta G^{\ddagger}/RT) = \exp(-50/8.31) = 2.4 \times 10^{-3}$.

25. $\Delta H^{\ddagger} = (8.31 \times 923 \times 773 \ln 7)/150 = 77$ kJ/mol.
From Table 3.2, this indicates that the process is interstitial diffusion (of carbon in α-iron).

26. (a) Zn in acid:
At $h_{Zn2+} = 10^{-6}$, $E_{Zn} = -0.76 + 0.03(-6) = -0.94$ V, SHE.
$\mathcal{E} = E_H - E_{Zn} = 0.00 - (-0.94) = 0.94$ V at pH 0.
Fe in aerated water:
At $h_{Fe2+} = 10^{-6}$, $E_{Fe} = -0.44 + 0.03(-6) = -0.62$ V, SHE.
$\mathcal{E} = E_{O2} - E_{Fe} = 0.80 - (-0.62) = 1.42$ V at pH 7.
(b) Zn/HCl: $n = 2$, so $\Delta G = -2\times96.5\times0.94 = -181$ kJ/mol.
Fe/O_2: $n = 2$, so $\Delta G = -2\times96.5\times1.42 = -274$ kJ/mol.
(c) Standard free energy change for Zn/HCl is
$\Delta G^{\ominus} = 369 + 0 - (0 - 190) = -179$ kJ/mol for $ZnCl_2$(s).
This agreement with (b) is fortuitous since $ZnCl_2$ is dissolved in non-standard conditions. Thus, the reaction is in fact $Zn(s) + 2H^+(aq;h{=}1) = Zn^{2+}(aq;h{=}10^{-6}) + H_2(g)$ so that, using μ^m data from Table 2.5,
$\Delta G = -147.2 + (8.31\times0.298)\ln 10^{-6} + 0 - (0 + 0)$
$= -181$ kJ/mol (agrees).
For Fe/O_2, $\Delta G^{\ominus} = -244 - (0 + 0 - 237) = -7$ kJ/mol for FeO(s); this becomes -250 kJ/mol if $Fe(OH)_2$(s) is used, illustrating the danger of 'trying the nearest compound'. However, recognising that the $Fe(OH)_2$ is dissolved and so using μ^m data: $G^{\bullet}_{Fe(OH)2(aq)} = -84.9 - 314.4 = -399$ kJ/mol and $\Delta G^{\ominus} = -399 + 237 = -162$ kJ/mol. Correcting for the Fe^{2+} and OH^- activities then gives agreement with (b).

27. $\Delta E = -\Delta(\Delta G)/nF = -0.1/2\times96.5 = -0.5$ mV. This miniscule difference in the driving emf of the corrosion cell is not of itself sufficient to cause stress-corrosion effects. Experimentally observed values of 40 mV or more are entirely due to rupture of surface films.

28. (a) $Ag^+ + e = Ag$: $\Delta G^{\ominus} = -(+77.1)$, $E^{\ominus} = +77.1/96.5 = 0.80$ V, SHE (cf.0.80 V in Table)
(b) $Cu^{2+} + 2e = Cu$: $E^{\ominus} = +66.6/2\times96.5 = 0.35$ V, SHE (agrees)
(c) $Fe^{2+} + 2e = Fe$: $E^{\ominus} = -84.9/2\times96.5 = -0.44$ V, SHE (agrees).

29. $Fe_2O_3 + 6H^+ + 6e = 2Fe + 3H_2O$;
$\Delta G^\ominus = 0 - 711 - (-741 + 0) = +30$ kJ/mol
$E^\ominus = -30/6{\times}96.5 = -0.05$ V, SHE.
$PbO_2 + 4H^+ + 4e = Pb + 2H_2O$;
$\Delta G^\ominus = 0 - 474 - (-217 + 0) = -257$ kJ/mol
$E^\ominus = +257/4{\times}96.5 = +0.67$ V, SHE.

30. Using $E^\ominus$ values from Q. 28, 29,
(a) $E_{Ag} = 0.80 + 0.06 \log(10^{-6}) = 0.44$ V, SHE
$E_{Cu} = 0.35 + 0.03 \log(10^{-6}) = 0.17$ V, SHE
$E_{Fe203} = -0.05 + 0.01 \log(1/10^{-6})^6 = 0.31$ V, SHE.
(b) $pH = -\log h_{H+} = 6.0$.

31. (a) $E^\ominus = -147.2/2{\times}96.5 = -0.76$ V, SHE; $h_{Zn+} = 0.3 \times 0.08 = 0.024$
$E = -0.76 + 0.03 \log(0.024) = -0.81$ V, SHE.
(b) $E_{SCE} = E_{SHE} - 0.25 = -1.06$ V, SHE (When in doubt, on convert- reference scales, draw two parallel vertical lines to represent the two scales, marking in 0.0 V and the reference electrode voltage on the SHE scale, with the latter opposite the 0.0 V mark on the reference scale.)

32. (a) $E^\ominus_{aq} = +50.4/96.5 = +0.52$ V, SHE for Cu(I),
$E^\ominus_{complex} = E^\ominus_{aq} - 1.66 = -1.14$ V, SHE.
(b) $E^\ominus_{aq} = -0.23$ V, SHE for Ni(II),
$E^\ominus_{complex} = -0.23 - 0.25 = -0.48$ V, SHE.
(c) $E^\ominus_{aq} = -0.76$ V, SHE for Zn(II),
$E^\ominus_{complex} = -0.76 - 0.46 = -1.12$ V, SHE.
The results of (a) (c) illustrate how it is possible to co-deposit Cu and Zn, as α-brass solid solution, from an alkaline cyanide solution of Cu(I) and Zn(II).

33. $i_o(pH3)/i_o(pH7) = \{(h_{OH-} \text{ at } pH3)/h_{OH-} \text{ at } pH7)\}^2$
whence required $i_o = 10^{-4}(10^{-11}/10^{-7})^2 = 10^{-12}$ A/m^2.

34. $b_a = 2.303{\times}8.31{\times}298/0.5{\times}z{\times}96500 = 0.118/z$
For $z = 1$, $b_a = 0.12$ V (V/decade); for $z = 2$, $b_a = 0.06$ V.

35. (a) η_a for Zn $= 0.045 \log(10/10^{-2}) = 0.135$ V.
(b) η_c for HER on Zn $= -0.12 \log(10/10^{-7}) = -0.96$ V. Note that, since $\mathcal{E}$ for Zn in HCl is ca. 0.94 V (Q.26), then the sum of the overpotentials ≈ 0.94 V. This indicates that, in this instance, $\eta_c = 0.80$ V or i_o for HER is close to $10^{-5.8}$ A/m^2.

36. $r/i = 3.2\times10^{10}\, M/\rho\, F = 3.3\times10^{5}(M/\rho)$
For Fe, $10^{6}M/\rho = 3.5$ whence $r/i = 1.2$

Ni	3.3	1.1
Al	3.3	1.1
Cu	3.5	1.2

For most other metals, especially the light and heavy ones, the equality fails. Thus, the r/i ratios are:
Zn 1.5, Pt 1.5, Ti 1.7; U 2.1, Mg 2.3, Sn 2.7, Pb 3.0, Ag 3.4; Hg 4.8.

37. If $\mathcal{E} = \eta_a + |\eta_c| = 0.45$ V and writing corrosion c.d. = i,
$0.45 = 0.05 \log(i/10^{-1}) + 0.10 \log(i/10^{-1}) = 0.15 \log(i/10^{-1})$
whence $i = 10^{-1} \times 10^{3} = 100$ A/m^2.
This assumes charge transfer control and zero resistance.

38. Putting corrosion c.d. = i and exchange c.d. of A and C as i_A, i_C:
$\mathcal{E} = E_C - E_A = b_a \log(i/i_A) + |b_c| \log(i/i_C)$
$= (b_a + |b_c|)\log i - b_a \log i_A - |b_c| \log i_C$
and $\log i = (E_C - E_A + b_a \log i_A + |b_c| \log i_C)/(b_a + |b_c|)$.
Note that the corrosion potential $E = E_A + b_a \log i$ as eqn(7.1).

39. From Q.26, $E_{Zn} = -0.94$ V, SHE so that
$-0.85 = -0.94 + 0.045 \log(i/10^{-2})$
whence $i = 1$ A/m$^2 \equiv 1.5$ mm/yr (from Q.36).

40. 1 mol/kg $\equiv 10^3$ mol/m^3
$i_L = 2\times96500\times10^{3}\times(2.10^{-10})/10^{-4} = 386$ A/m^2.

41. $u_{Cu2+} = 2\times96500\times2.10^{-10}/8.31\times298 = 1.56 \times 10^{-8}$ Q.E.D.

Units are $\dfrac{(\text{C/mol})\,(\text{m}^2/\text{s})}{(\text{J/mol K})\,(\text{K})} = \dfrac{(\text{m}^2/\text{s})}{(\text{V})}$

42. As with Q.22, 23, (a) becomes
$\ln(i_{333}/i_{323}) = 50000\times10/8.31\times333\times323 = 0.56 = \ln(1.75)$
whence i_L at 333K = 500 × 1.75 = 875 A/m^2.
(b) Similarly, $\ln(i_{343}/i_{323}) = 50000\times20/8.31\times343\times323 = 1.09$
$= \ln(2.96)$
i_L at 343K = 500 × 2.96 if same δ. If δ is halved, i_L is doubled so answer is 2 × 500 × 2.96 = 2.96 kA/m^2.
(c) Since $n = 2$, $\eta^C = (8.31\times298/2\times96500) \ln[1 - (480/500)]$
$= 0.0128 \ln(0.04) = -41$ mV.

43. Since for corrosion in aerated water $|b_c| \gg b_a$, eqn(7.7) may be used.
$\Delta i = 8\times10^{-6}/10\times10^{-4} = 8$ mA/m².
$K_{corr} = 0.008/0.003 = 2.67\ \Omega m^2$ and $i_{corr} = 0.06\times2.67/2.303$
$= 0.07$ A/m² (mm/yr).

44. The appropriate diagram is Fig. 9.7. However, greater insight (and an analytical expression) is given by plotting on a log-linear basis:

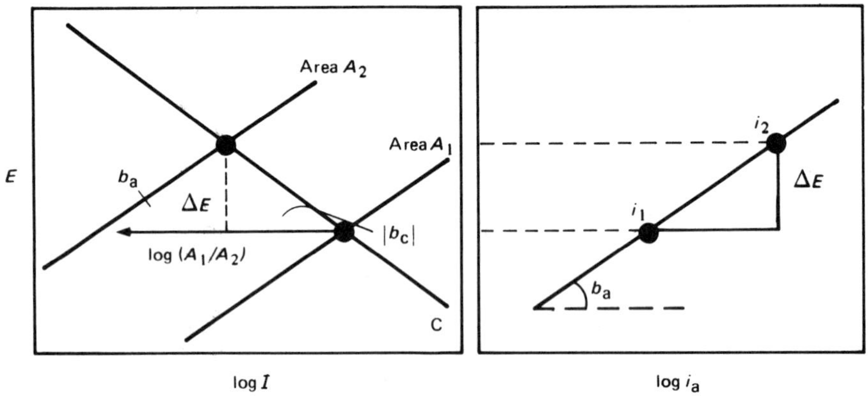

The LH diagram shows that $\log(A_1/A_2) = (\Delta E/b_a) + (\Delta E/|b_c|)$
whence $E = \{b_a|b_c|/(b_b + |b_c|)\}\log(A_1/A_2)$
In RH diagram, $\log(i_2/i_1) = E/b_a = \{|b_c|/(b_a + |b_c|)\}\log(A_1/A_2)$.
For $|b_c| = 2b_a = 0.12$ V, $i_2/i_1 = (A_2/A_1)^{-\frac{2}{3}}$.

45. $\mathcal{E} = 0.45 = \eta_a + |\eta_c| + iR = 0.15\log(i/10^{-1}) + 0.1i$
i must be < 4.5 (from RH term) and trial gives the solution as 2.4 A/m².
(cf.100 A/m² in absence of R)

46. (a) $Fe^{3+} + e = Fe^{2+}$; $\Delta G^{\ominus} = -84.9 - (-10.6) = -74.3$ kJ/mol,
$E^{\ominus} = +74.3/96.5 = 0.77$ V, SHE.
$E = 0.77 + 0.06\log(10^{-6}/10^{-6}) = 0.77$ V, SHE,
which, being independent of pH, is a horizontal line.
(b) $Fe_2O_3 + 6H^+ + 2e = 2Fe^{2+} + 3H_2O$; (Check: 2Fe(II) are oxidised to 2Fe(III), hence 2e)
$\Delta G^{\ominus} = -169.8 - 711 - (-741 + 0) = -139$ kJ/mol,
$E^{\ominus} = 139/2\times96.5 = 0.72$ V, SHE.
$E = 0.72 + 0.03\log(a_{Fe2O3}\cdot h^6_{H+}/h^2_{Fe2+}\cdot a_{H2O})$
$= 0.72 - 0.18\,p\text{H} - 0.06\log(10^{-6})$ since Fe_2O_3 and H_2O essentially pure,
$= 1.08 - 0.18\,p\text{H}$ V, SHE
which is a line of slope -0.18 V/pH.

(c) $3Fe_2O_3 + 2H^+ + 2e = 2Fe_3O_4 + H_2O$; (Note: Fe_3O_4 is a spinel $FeO.Fe_2O_3$ so that here again 2Fe(II) are oxidised to 2Fe(III)) $\Delta G^\ominus = -2030 - 237 - (-2223 + 0) = -44$ kJ/mol,
$E^\ominus = +44/2 \times 96.5 = 0.23$ V, SHE.
$E = 0.23 + 0.03 \log(a^3_{Fe2O3} . h^2_{H+} / a^2_{Fe3O4} . a_{H2O})$
$= 0.023 - 0.06\,pH$ V, SHE
which is a line of slope -0.06 V/pH.

(d) $Fe_3O_4 + 5H_2O + 2e = 3Fe(OH)_3^- + H^+$;
To calculate $\Delta G^\ominus$ we need to know μ^m for $Fe(OH_3^-$.
Table 4.3 shows $-pK_n$ for trihydroxyl Fe(II) = 8, that is,
$\Delta G^\ominus$ for $Fe^{2+} + 3OH^- = Fe(OH)_3^-$ is $-RT \ln K_n$
$= -(8.31 \times 298)\ln(10^8) = -45.6$ kJ/mol, so that
$\mu^m_{Fe(OH)3} - (-84.9 - 471.6) = -45.6$ and $\mu^m_{Fe(OH)3} = -602$ kJ/mol.
$\Delta G^\ominus$ for the Fe_3O_4 eqn $= -1806 + 0 - (-1015 - 1185) = +394$ kJ/mol,
$E^\ominus = -394/2 \times 96.5 = -2.04$ V, SHE.
$E = -2.04 + 0.03 \log(a_{Fe3O4} . a^5_{H2O} / h^3_{Fe(OH)3} . h_{H+})$
$= -2.04 + 0.03\,pH - 0.09 \log(10^{-6})$
$= -1.50 + 0.03\,pH$ V, SHE
which is a line of slope +0.03 V/pH.

47. $\log i_{crit} = 4.0 - 0.08(Cr)$ where (Cr) = wt.% Cr in Fe.
$\log i_p = 0.3 - 0.12(Cr)$
(in passing, it is interesting to see how the passive film c.d. is so much more sensitive to chromium content than is the critical passivating c.d.)
whence, for 3%Cr steel, $i_{crit} = 10^{3.76} = 5.8$ kA/m² (cf.3–4 kA/m²)
$i_p = 10^{-0.06} = 0.9$ A/m² (cf.1.5–2 A/m²).

48. E_{pp} for Fe at pH7 = 1.00 − 0.42 = 0.58 V, SHE.
E_b for Fe-13Cr and Fe-17Cr in 0.01 m chloride is not known.
However, (risky) extrapolation of the Table 9.2 data gives approx. +0.76 and +0.82 V, SHE respectively.
Fe: $E_b - E_{pp} = 0.45 - 0.58 < 0$ (0.01*m*); $0.22 - 0.58 < 0$ (0.1*m*);
$0.02 - 0.58 < 0$ (1.0*m*). That is, iron pits or is non-passive in all three solutions.
Fe-13Cr(= Fe-14Cr): $E_b - E_{pp} \approx 0.76 - (-0.10) \sim 0.9$ V (0.01*m*);
$0.32 - (-0.10) = 0.42$ V (0.1*m*);
$0.14 - (-0.10) = 0.24$ V (1.0*m*).
Fe-17Cr(= Fe-18Cr): $E_b - E_{pp} \approx 0.82 - (-0.15) \sim 1.0$ V (0.01*m*);
$0.36 - (-0.15) = 0.51$ V (0.1*m*);
$0.20 - (-0.15) = 0.35$ V (1.0*m*).
Note how the high-Cr alloys of iron are usefully passive over a range of oxidising conditions, even in moderately strong chloride solutions.

49. $R = \rho x$ (ρ = resistivity, x = thickness)
so iR drop $= i_p \rho x = 2 \times 10^8 \times 4.10^{-9} = 0.8$ V.
$Fe_3O_4 + 8H^+ + 8e = 3Fe + 4H_2O$; $\Delta G^\ominus = 0 - 948 - (-1015 + 0)$
$= 67$ kJ/mol,
$E^\ominus = -67/8 \times 96.5 = -0.09$ V, SHE $= E$ at pH 0.
Hence predicted single potential is $-0.09 + 0.8 = 0.71$ V, SHE.
Experimental value is 0.7 − 1.0 V, probably owing to adsorbed oxygen layer.

50. Passivation occurs when $i_L \geqslant i_{crit}$.
Ti: $5 = 15m^{\frac{5}{3}}$ whence $m = 0.52$ mol/kg.
Fe: $2000 = 15m^{\frac{5}{3}}$, $m = 18.8$ mol/kg.

51. (a)

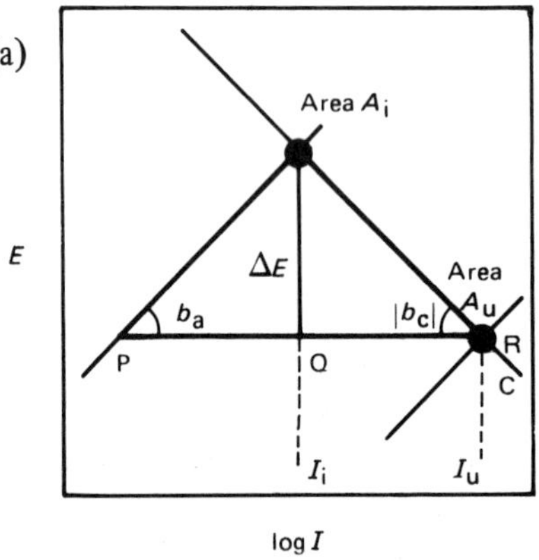

Let uninhibited and inhibited anode areas be A_u, A_i and corresponding corrosion *currents* be I_u, I_i.
In the triangle,
PR = PQ + QR
PR $= \log(A_u/A_i)$; QR $= \log(I_u/I_i)$
$= \Delta E/|b_c|$;
PQ $= \Delta E/b_a = (|b_c|/b_a)\log(I_u/I_i)$.
Therefore $\log(A_u/A_i) =$
$\{1 + (|b_c|/b_a)\}\log(I_u/I_i)$

$\log(100) = 3\log(I_u/I_i)$ and $I_u/I_i = 4.64$,
that is, I is reduced to $1/4.64 = 22\%$ of its uninhibited value.

(b) $\Delta E = |b_c|\log(I_u/I_i) = 0.12 \times 2/3 = +80$ mV.
(c) E is unchanged from uninhibited value.

52. (a) From eqn (11.10), when $\beta = 10^{-3}$, $l = 300$ m
so, for $\beta = 10^{-2}$, $l = 300 \times (10^{-3}/10^{-2})^{\frac{1}{2}}$
$= 95$ m
whence anode separation $= 2l = 190$ m (cf.600 m)
(b) Substituting potential values, with E_{dp} for Mg $= -1.40$ V, SHE,
logarithm terms for Zn: $\ln\{1 - (0.32/0.50)\} = -1.02$
Mg: $\ln\{1 - (0.87/1.05)\} = -1.76$
so spacing increased in ratio 1.76/1.02
that is, $190 \times (1.76/1.02) = 330$ m.
In practice a safety allowance compensates for the possible loss of half the anodes, so that spacing is halved or even less.

53. (a) $0.01 = 0.06 \log(i_{new}/i_{initial})$
whence $i_{new}/i_{initial} = \text{antilog } 0.167 = 1.47$
that is, rate increased by 47%.
(b) $i_{new}/i_{initial}$ is now antilog $0.5 = 3.16$ so rate just over 2x than in (a).

54. Treating i_o and E_{eq} of cathode reaction as 0.1 A/m² and 0.00 V, SHE, with Tafel slope −0.33 V, solve graphically (by plotting E *vs.* $\log i$) or analytically, for example eqn. in answer to Q. 38.
(a) Fe: Equilibrium E at 10^{-6} activity = −0.62 V, SHE.
$\log i = (E_C - E_A + b_a \log i_A + |b_c| \log i_C)/(b_a + |b_c|)$
$= (1/0.39)\,(0.0 - (-0.62) + 0.06 \log(10^{-4.5}) + 0.33 \log(0.1))$
$= 0.05$ (that is, $i = 1.1$ A/m²)
and, from eqn (7.1), $E_{corr} = -0.62 + 0.06 \log(10^{0.05}/10^{-4.5})$
$= -0.35$ V, SHE.
Ni: $E = -0.23 + 0.03 \log(10^{-6}) = -0.41$ V, SHE
Assume kinetics (i_o and b_a) as for iron, viz. $10^{-4.5}$ and 0.06.
Then $\log i = (0.41 - 0.27 - 0.33)/0.39 = -0.49$ ($i = 0.33$ A/m²)
$E_{corr} = -0.41 + 0.06 \log(10^{-0.49}/10^{-4.5})$
$= -0.17$ V, SHE.
Zn: $E = -0.94$ V, SHE (Q.26(a))
$\log i = (0.94 - 0.09 - 0.33)/0.375 = 1.39$ ($i = 24$ A/m²)
$E_{corr} = -0.94 + 0.045 \log(10^{1.39}/10^{-2}) = -0.79$ V, SHE.
(b) Surface is effectively Ni, so $E_{corr} = -0.17$ V, SHE.
Hence corrosion rate of Fe substrate given by
$-0.17 = -0.62 + 0.06 \log(i/10^{-4.5})$
$i = 1$ kA/m² (≡ 1 *metre* per year!)
(c) If $iR = 0.1$ V, E_{corr} at base of pores = −0.27 V, SHE
that is, $-0.27 = -0.62 + 0.06 \log(i/10^{-4.5})$
$i = 22$ A/m²
that is, the iron substrate corrodes 22/1.1 = 20 times faster than would uncoated iron and some 70 times faster than the nickel coating.
(d) Surface is effectively Zn so $E_{corr} = -0.79$ V, SHE. This is below E_{eq} for Fe, so iron is cathodically protected.

55. (a) $a_c = 0.25(K_{Ic}/\sigma)^2 = 0.25(K_{Ic}/0.6\sigma_y)^2 = 0.69(K_{Ic}/\sigma_y)^2$.
$= 1.5$ mm
(b) 3.4 mm (c) 9.4 mm.

56. Replace K_{Ic} in Q.55 by $K_{Iscc} = 15$ in each case, viz.
(a) 69 μm (b) 215 μm (c) 1.7 mm.

57. Young's modulus of Fe = 210 GN/m^2.
From eqn (12.20),
$K_{Iscc}^2 = K_{Ic}^2 - 4\alpha kRTE \ln(c/c_o)$
$= (7.23\times10^{15}) - (4\times5.10^{-5}\times1.4\times10^4\times8.31\times298\times2.1\times10^{11}) \ln(2/0.05)$
$= (7.23\times10^{15}) - (5.37\times10^{15})$
whence $K_{Iscc} = 43$ MN/m$^{\frac{3}{2}}$.

58. From eqn (12.7), $K = 1.12\sigma(\pi a/Q)^{\frac{1}{2}}$ whence it follows that, for constant σ and Q, $K \propto (a)^{\frac{1}{2}}$.
(a) $a_{scc} = a_i(K_{Iscc}/K_i)^2 = 0.2\times(15/22)^2 = 0.093$ mm.
(b) $a_c = 0.2\times(70/22)^2 = 2.02$ mm.
(c) Required equation most conveniently expressed in terms of $\alpha = K_i/K_{Ic}$ and $\beta = K_{Iscc}/K_{Ic}$ as follows:

$$t = \frac{2a_i}{A}\left(\frac{\beta}{\alpha}\right)^2 \left(\frac{\beta(1-\alpha)}{(\alpha-\beta)(1-\beta)} + \ln\frac{1-\beta}{\alpha-\beta}\right)$$

In this instance $\alpha = 22/70 = 0.314$, $\beta = 15/70 = 0.214$ and

$$t = (2.10^8\times0.0002)(0.214/0.314)^2\left(\frac{0.214\times0.686}{0.100\times0.786} + \ln(0.786/0.100)\right)$$

$$= 7.31\times10^4 \text{ s} = 20 \text{ h}.$$

Neglecting any induction period, 20 hours is therefore the life of the component under these conditions.

59. (a) $\Delta K = 1.12(\Delta\sigma)(\pi a/Q)^{\frac{1}{2}} = 1.12\times30\times(\pi\times0.001/1.3)^{\frac{1}{2}}$
$= 1.65$ MN/m$^{\frac{3}{2}}$.
This is $< \Delta K_{th}$, hence no fatigue failure.
(b) $R = K_{min}/K_{max} = 30/60 = 0.5$; $\sigma_{max} = 60$ MN/m$^{\frac{3}{2}}$;
$N_f = (1-0.5)^2/\pi\times1.3\times10^{-12}\times(60\times1.65)^2 = 6.25\times10^6$ cycles.
(c) $t_f = N_f/\text{frequency} = (6.25/20)\times10^6 = 3.13\times10^5$ s = 87 h.

60. 1 mol metal P occupies volume M_P/ρ_P (M = relative mol.mass)
(ρ = density)

On conversion to oxide $P_x.O_y$, $(1/x)$mol occupies $\dfrac{xM_P + 16y}{x\,\rho_{PxOy}}$

$$\text{whence } r_{PB} = \frac{M_P + 16(y/x)\,\rho_P}{\rho_{PxOy}\quad M_P} = \frac{\rho_P}{\rho_{PxOy}}\{1 + (16/M_P)(y/x)\}$$

Substituting values,
Cu_2O: $r = (9/6.2)\{1 + (16/63.5)(1/2)\} = 1.63$ (cf. 1.6)
Al_2O_3: $r = (2.7/4.0)\{1 + (16/27)(3/2)\} = 1.28$ (cf. 1.3).

61. $\kappa = \text{constant} \times p^{\frac{1}{4}} \exp(-Q/RT)$
whence $\ln(\kappa_1/\kappa_2) = (\frac{1}{4})\ln(p_1/p_2) + (Q/R)\{(T_1-T_2)/T_1T_2\} = 0.25 \ln(0.2/10^{-4})$
$+ (56000/8.31)(150/1473\times1623) = 2.32$
So $\kappa_1 = 10.21\ \kappa_2 = 20\Omega^{-1}\text{m}^{-1}$.

62. (a) From Table 2.1 for Cu_2O,
$\Delta H^\ominus(298\text{K}) = -167$ kJ/mol, $\Delta S^\ominus(298\text{K}) = -67.5$ J/mol K.
whence, neglecting ΔC_p correction,
$\Delta G^\ominus(1273\text{K}) = -167 + (1.273\times67.5) = -81.1$ kJ/mol
so that $\mathcal{E} = 81.1/1\times96.5 = 0.84$ V.
(b) $Cu_2O = 0.143$ kg/mol
$k_p = 2\times0.84\times0.143\times100\times1\times(6.10^{-5})/1\times96500\times6200 = 2.4\times10^{-12}$.
Units are m^2/s. Value agrees with Table 13.3.
(c) 1 yr $= 3.1\times10^7$ s.
$y^2(m^2) = 2.4\times10^{-12}\times3.1\times10^7 = 7.4\times10^{-5}$
whence $y = 8.6$ mm and average rate is 8.6 mm/yr.
(Note: This is the volume of the *oxide*. See Q.68).

63. At Cu/Cu_2O: $\Delta H^\ominus$, $\Delta S^\ominus$ from Q.62.
$\mu_O = \mu^\ominus_{Cu2O} = -167 + (0.773\times67.5) = -114.8$ kJ/mol
$= (RT/2)\ln(p_{O2}/p^\ominus) = (8.31\times0.773/2)\ln(p_{O2}/p^\ominus)$
and $p_{O2} = 3.10^{-16}$ atm.
At Cu_2O/CuO: $Cu_2O + \frac{1}{2}O_2 = 2CuO$: $\mu_O = 2\mu^\ominus_{CuO} - \mu^\ominus_{Cu2O}$
$\Delta H^\ominus_{CuO} = -155$ kJ/mol; $\Delta S^\ominus_{CuO} = 44 - 33 - 102.5 = -91.5$ J/mol K and
$\mu^\ominus_{CuO} = -155 + (0.773\times91.5) = -84.3$ kJ/mol.
Hence $\mu_O = -(2\times84.3) + 114.8 = -53.8$ kJ/mol
$= (8.31\times0.773/2)\ln(p_{O2}/p^\ominus)$
and $p_{O2} = 5.3\times10^{-8}$ atm.

64. (a) $0.237 = (0.7\times8.31\times1973/4\times96500)\ln(a_O/3\times10^{-7})$
or $a_O = 3.10^{-7}\exp(0.237/2.97\times10^{-2}) = 8.8\times10^{-4}$.
(b) This equals x_O, that is, 8.8×10^{-4} mol O per 0.056 kg Fe.
Hence 1.57×10^{-3} mol O (= 0.025 g) per 100 g Fe; wt.% oxygen = 0.025%
and so wt.%C $= 2.10^{-3}/0.025 = 0.08\%$.

65. For Cr/Cr_2O_3 at 1973K, $2Cr + \frac{3}{2}O_2 = Cr_2O_3$. Thermodynamic data not given in Table 2.1. Ellingham diagram (Fig. 2.2) gives $\frac{2}{3}\mu^\ominus_{Cr2O3} = -395$ kJ/mol O_2;
hence $\frac{3}{2}\mu_{O2} = (1.5RT)\ln(p_{O2}/p^\ominus)$
$= \mu^\ominus_{Cr2O3}$
and $p_{O2} = \exp(1.5 \times -395)/(1.5\times8.31\times1.973) = 3.9\times10^{-11}$ atm.

Since reference oxygen level in Q.64 is 3.10^{-7} atm, emf is increased to 0.237 $\times \ln(3.10^{-7}/3.9\times10^{-11}) = 2.12$ V.
In practice, the decreased oxygen activity also reduces t_O so that the emf is not strictly proportional to log p_{O2} or a_O.

66. It is easy to show that, at equilibrium,
$G^{\bullet}_{NiO} - \frac{1}{3}G^{\bullet}_{Cr2O3} = RT\ln(a_{Ni}/a^{\frac{2}{3}}_{Cr})$
At 1000°C, the Ellingham diagram gives $\frac{2}{3}G^{\bullet}_{Cr2O3}$ = −520 kJ/mol O_2 and $2G^{\bullet}_{NiO}$ = −255 kJ/mol O_2, so LHS = −0.5(255 − 520) = 133 kJ from which $x^{\frac{2}{3}}_{Cr}/x_{Ni} = \exp(-133/8.31\times1.273) = 3.5\times10^{-6}$
and $x_{Cr} = 6.5\times10^{-9}$
This very low 'break even' value means that, for all practical values of chromium content, Cr_2O_3 forms preferentially, Fig. 15.1(b).

67. For CdO, $x = y = 1$. $a_{Cd} = \gamma^{\infty} x_{Cd} = 0.5\times10^{-2} = 5.10^{-3}$
$a_O = (p_{O2}/p^{\ominus})^{\frac{1}{2}} = 10^{-4.5} = 3.2\times10^{-5}$.
Substituting in eqn (15.3),
$\delta^2 = (3.2\times10^{-5}/5.10^{-3})(2\times10^{-10}\times86400) = 1.1\times10^{-6}\ m^2$
and δ = 1.05 mm. In view of the approximations involved, at best only two significant figures are valid.

68. For $y^2 = k_p t$, k_p is the value of y^2 (here in mg/cm² squared) after 1 hour. Hence $y_2/y_1 = (t_2/t_1)^{\frac{1}{2}} = 8800^{\frac{1}{2}} = 93.8$ and wt.gain is 93.8 × $\sqrt{k_p}$ mg/cm² after 1 yr.
If ρ g/cm³ is density of oxide, $y_2 = (0.938/\rho)\sqrt{k_p}$ mm oxide per yr. Penetration rate of metal is $r^{-\frac{1}{3}}$ times this (mm/yr).

69.

	n_H	n_C	n_O	Σn	x_C	x_O
(a)	180	10	90	280	0.04	0.32
(b)	60	70	105	235	0.30	0.45
(c)	150	55	45	250	0.22	0.18
(d)	176	12	37	225	0.05	0.16

For example, in (a)
n_H = (2×70) + (2×20) = 180 arbitrary units for moles H
n_C = 1×10 = 10
n_O = (1×70) + (2×10) = 90
Σn = 180 + 10 + 90 = 280; x_C = 10/280, x_O = 90/280.

As stated in the text, these atom fractions are valid for all temperatures and pressures and so represent specific points in the Darken diagram (below).

70.

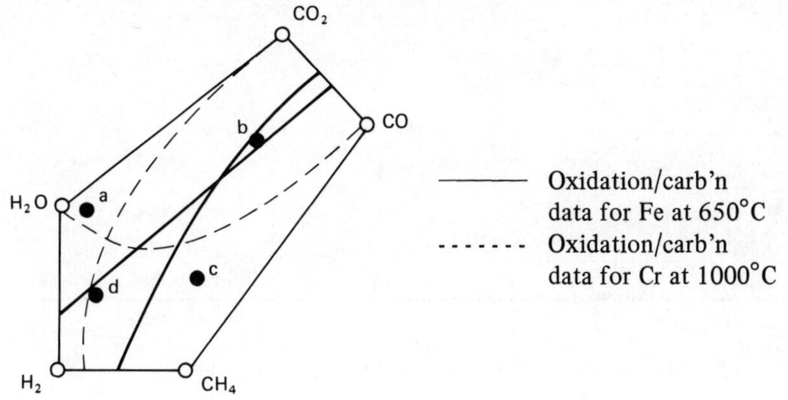

(i) (a) O + D, (b) O + C, (c) R + C approximately in the bright annealing range but a little too carburising,
(d) R + D.

(ii) (a) O + D, (b) O + C, that is, dusting liable to occur!
(c) R + C, (d) R + on borderline between D/C hence suitable for solution treatment without surface attack.

Appendix

BRITISH STANDARD SPECIFICATIONS

(a) General

BS	1133 (1966)	Sect. 6: Temporary protection of metal surfaces against corrosion during transport and storage
	4232 (1967)	Surface finish of blast-cleaned steel for painting
	4479 (1969)	Recommendations for the design of metal articles that are to be coated
	4959 (1974)	Recommendations for corrosion and scale prevention in engine cooling systems
	5493 (1977)	Protective coating of iron and steel structures against corrosion (formerly CP 2008)
CP	231 (1966)	Painting of buildings
	1021 (1973)	Cathodic protection
	3003 (1970)	Lining of vessels and equipment
	3012 (1972)	Cleaning and preparation of metal surfaces
	3189 (1973)	Phosphate treatment of iron and steel
DD	24 (1973)	Recommendations for methods of protection against corrosion on light section steel used in building
PD	6484 (1979)	Corrosion at bimetallic contacts
DEF	STAN 03-2	Cleaning and preparation of metal surfaces

(b) Materials and Testing

BS	1070 (1973)	Black paint (tar based)
	1391 (1952)	Performance tests for protective schemes used in the protection of light gauge steel and wrought iron against corrosion
	1427 (1962)	Routine control methods of testing water used in industry (see also B.S. 2690)
	1822 (1952)	Nickel clad steel plate
	2451	Chilled iron shot and grit

	2521 / 2523 (1966)	Lead based priming paints
	2524 (1966)	Red-oxide linseed-oil priming paint
	2920 (1973)	Cold reduced tinplate and black plate
	3698 (1964)	Calcium plumbate priming paints
	3740 (1964)	Steel plate clad with corrosion resisting steel
	3745 (1976)	Evaluation of results of accelerated corrosion test on metallic coatings
	3900	Methods of test for paints (Paint application, large scale brushing test, film thickness)
BS	4164	Coal-tar based hot applied coating materials for protecting iron and steel
	4652 (1971)	Metallic zinc-rich priming paint
	5411	Methods of test for metallic and related coatings (thickness)
	5466	Methods of corrosion testing of metallic coatings (salt spray, acetic acid salt spray and copper accelerated salt spray tests)

(c) **Coatings**

BS	443 (1969)	Galvanised coatings on wire
	729 (1971)	Hot dip galvanised coatings on iron and steel articles
	1224 (1970)	Electroplated coatings of nickel and chromium
	1615 (1972)	Anodic oxidation coatings on aluminium
	1706 (1960)	Electroplated coatings of cadmium and zinc on iron and steel
	1872 (1964)	Electroplated coatings of tin
	2015 (1965)	Glossary of paint terms
	2569	Sprayed metal coatings:
	(1964)	Part 1: Protection of iron and steel by aluminium and zinc against atmospheric corrosion
	(1965)	Part 2: Protection of iron and steel against corrosion oxidation at elevated temperatures
	2989 (1975)	Hot dip zinc coated steel sheet and coil
	3083 (1959)	Hot dip galvanised corrugated steel sheet
	3189 (1973)	Phosphate treatment of iron and steel
	3382 (1961-6)	Electroplated coatings on threaded components
	3597 (1963)	Electroplated coatings of tin-nickel alloy
	3830 (1973)	Vitreous enamelled steel building components
	3987 (1964)	Anodic oxide coatings on wrought aluminium for external architectural purposes
	4641 (1970)	Electroplated coatings of chromium for engineering purposes

	4758 (1971)	Electroplated coatings of nickel for engineering purposes
	4921 (1973)	Sherardised coatings on iron and steel articles
	5599 (1978)	Hard anodic oxide coatings on aluminium for engineering purposes
DTD	903D to 905A	Zinc, cadmium and (heavy) nickel plating
DEF	130	Chromate passivation of cadmium and zinc surfaces
	151	Anodizing of aluminium and aluminium alloys
	STAN 03-5	Electroless nickel coating of metals

SOME OTHER EUROPEAN STANDARDS

(a) **West German**

DIN	50010 (1961)	Corrosion testing under climatic conditions
	50907 (1952)	Resistance to marine climate and seawater
	50908 (1957)	Stress corrosion of light alloys
	50940 8.52	Testing of corrosion inhibitors for iron
	55928 6.59	Protective coatings for steel structures

(b) **Swedish**

SIS	055900 (1967)	Rust grades for steel surfaces and preparation grades prior to protective coating

SOME AMERICAN STANDARDS

AWWA	C203 (1978)	Coal tar enamel
SSPC	SPI-63 to 9-63	Surface preparation of steel
NACE	RP-01-69	Control of external corrosion on underground or submerged metal pipes
	RP-01-72	Surface preparation of steel by water blasting prior to coating
	RP-01-73	Collection and identification of corrosion products
	RP-01-75	Control of internal corrosion in steel pipelines
	RP-02-72	Direct calculation of economic appraisals of corrosion control measures
	RP-03-72	Method for lining lease production tanks with coal tar epoxy
	RP-05-72	Design etc of impressed current deep groundbeds
	TM-01-75	Visual standard for surfaces of new steel

International Standards Organisation (ISO) Standards are available from the British Standards Institution (2 Park Street, London W1Y 4AA).

A more complete list of standards is available in the *Corrosion Prevention Directory* (HMSO 1975), prepared by the Department of Industry Corrosion Committee and the Institution of Corrosion Science and Technology (14 Belgrave Square, London SW1X 8PS).

S.I. CONVERSION TABLE

(a) Base units

Metre	m
Kilogram	kg
Second	s
Ampere	A
Kelvin	K
Mole	mol

(b) Decimal prefixes

10^{-1}	deci	d	10	deca	da
10^{-2}	centi	c	10^{2}	hecto	h
10^{-3}	milli	m	10^{3}	kilo	k
10^{-6}	micro	μ	10^{6}	mega	M
10^{-9}	nano	n	10^{9}	giga	G
10^{-12}	pico	p	10^{12}	tera	T

(c) Conversion factors

1 kg = 2.205 lb; 1 metric tonne (10^3 kg, 1 t) = 0.984 ton;
1 m = 39.37 in = 3.281 ft
hence 1 A/m^2 = 10^{-2} A/dm^2 = 9.3×10^{-2} A/ft^2
and 1 g/cm^3 = 10^3 kg/m^3 = 1 t/m^3 = 62.44 lb/ft^3
1 joule (J) = 0.239 calorie (cal) = 10^7 erg = 6.24×10^{18} eV
hence 1 J/mol = 1.036×10^{-5} eV/atom
1 N/m^2 (sometimes expressed as 1 Pascal, 1 Pa) = 9.87×10^{-6} atm = 10^{-5} bar = 10 dyn/cm^2 = 1.45×10^{-4} lbf/in^2
hence 1 MN/m^2 (note that 1 meganewton/m^2 = 1 newton/mm^2) = 0.102 kgf/mm^2 = 0.145 ksi = 6.47×10^{-2} tonf/in^2
1 mm/yr = 0.040 IPY(in/yr) = 27.38ρ MDD(mg/dm^2 day)
(ρ = density in t/m^3 or g/cm^3)

Index